THE WORLD'S GREAT BOMBERS

THE WORLD'S GREAT BOMBERS

CHRIS CHANT

This edition published by Barnes & Noble, Inc.,
by arrangement with Amber Books Ltd
2000 Barnes & Noble Books

M 10 9 8 7 6 5 4 3 2 1

ISBN: 0-7607-2012-6

Editorial and design by
Amber Books Ltd
Bradley's Close
74–77 White Lion Street
London N1 9PF

Project Editor: Charles Catton
Editor: David Norman
Design: Graham Curd
Picture Research: TRH Pictures

Printed in Italy

Picture Credits

Aerospace Publishing Ltd: 10-11 (IWM), 12 (RAF Museum), 26, 40, 55, 56, 58, 63, 86, 172.
Hugh W. Cowin: 51.
TRH Pictures: 6-7, 8-9, 14-15 (IWM), 16-17, 18, 22 (US Department of Defence), 23, 24, 28-29 (RAF Museum), 30, 32 (IWM), 36, 38, 42-43, 44 (British Aerospace), 48, 49 (RAF Museum), 52-53, 54, 57, 61, 65, 66, 69, 72, 73, 74 (RAF Museum), 75, 78-79, 80, 82, 84-85, 89, 91, 96-97, 100, 102, 103 (RAF Museum), 106-107, 109, 110 (IWM), 111, 113, 114 (Dornier), 115, 118, 120 (IWM), 122 (US Air Force), 123, 126, 128-129, 131, 132 (IWM), 133 (RAF Museum), 137 (US Air Force), 138 (IWM), 140-141 (Rockwell International), 142, 144, 145 (General Dynamics), 150, 151 (US Air Force), 153, 154, 155 (US Air Force), 157 (US Department of Defence / US Air Force), 158, 160, 163, 165 (Arthur Gibson), 166, 167 (J. Widdowson), 170 (Tim Senior), 173 (US Air Force), 174 (Northrop-Grumman).

Artwork Credits

All artworks provided by **Aerospace Publishing Ltd**.

CONTENTS

CHAPTER 1
WORLD WAR I

The first major conflict of the twentieth century saw the primitive bombers of the early war years develop into specialised long-range multi-engined platforms capable of dropping bombs on the enemy's own territory.

The first bomber to be used operationally in World War I was the Avro Type 504. It remains one of the classic aircraft of all time for its docile yet tractable handling characteristics, longevity in development and service, and sizeable production run.

The Type 504 prototype made its first flight in September 1913, but a number of changes had to be made before the definitive design made its first flight during October 1914. The 'Avro', as it was known, was intended to meet military and civil needs. The first order was placed in the summer of 1913 by the War Office, which contracted for an initial 12 aircraft for the Royal Flying Corps. The Admiralty also ordered one machine for the Royal Naval Air Service (the RFC and RNAS were later amalgamated to create the Royal Air Force, which was founded on the first day of April 1918).

These aircraft were delivered between July and September 1913 at the beginning of a programme that saw the delivery of 8340 aircraft, including 3696 from Avro and 4644 from other contractors, before the end of World War I.

A Type 504 was the first British aeroplane to be shot down in World War I, on 22 August 1914, when a machine of the RFC's No 5 Squadron was lost to ground fire over Belgium. The Type 504 saw large-scale use over the Western Front up to the end of 1914 in the hands of RFC units. It was more adventurously used, although in much smaller numbers, by the RNAS for missions such as the classic bombing raid on the Zeppelin airship sheds at Friedrichshafen on Lake Constance in southern Germany during November 1914. For this raid, the aircraft each carried four 20 lb (9.1 kg) bombs and succeeded in destroying the gas production plant attached to the Zeppelin plant. The same type of armament was used for RNAS raids on the German submarine bases at Ostende and Antwerp (the latter resulting in the destruction of two U-boats) and for RFC attacks in the air on German airships, which required the Avros to form up above and slightly ahead of the giant hydrogen-filled ships before the bombs were released.

It was clear from a time late in 1914 that the Type 504's combination of good handling and indifferent performance suited the machine more for the training role than the operational task, and from this time onward most aircraft were delivered as trainers with dual controls.

LEFT: Though taken for propaganda purposes, this photograph serves to illustrate the rudimentary nature of bomb-aiming and bomb-delivery in the early part of World War I.

THE FIRST FRENCH DESIGN

Perhaps the closest French counterpart to the Type 504 was the Farman HF.20, which was the first Farman production aeroplane to reveal design influences from both the Farman brothers, Henry (sometimes rendered Henri) and Maurice. The HF.20 was developed in 1913 by Henry Farman from his F.16 with a measure of input from his brother's MF.11 'Shorthorn'. The HF.20 was a sesquiplane of fabric-covered wooden construction. The two-seat aircraft was powered by an 80-hp (59.6-kW) Gnome 7 rotary piston engine, driving a two-bladed wooden propeller.

The HF.20 proved itself an adequate if not exceptional flying machine in terms of its basic performance and flying characteristics, but was drastically underpowered for the carriage of any bomb load. Even so, the HF.20 was in service with the Belgian, British and French air services by the time of the outbreak of World War I in August 1914. Limited attempts were made to use it in the bomber role before the type was

relegated to the reconnaissance task and, from 1915, almost exclusively to the training role.

The HF.21 was an attempt to create a version of the HF.20 with better performance. The Gnome engine was replaced by a Le Rhône rotary of the same notional 80-hp (59.6-kW) rating and an increased upper wing span was fitted, but HF.21 performance was in fact poorer. The HF.22 was a further disappointing HF.20 derivative. The HF.27 was the most successful of the HF.20 series. In essence, it was a revised HF.21 with a steel airframe, new landing gear (a pair of nosewheels under the forward part of the central nacelle), an equal-span wing cellule and one Salmson (Canton-Unnè) radial piston engine rated at 140 or 160 hp (104 or 119 kW). The HF.27 could lift a 500-lb (227-kg) bomb load, and the type was used by the British in the Aegean, Africa and Mesopotamia.

Production of the HF.20 series exceeded 3300 aircraft, the vast majority used as primary flying trainers. Aircraft were built in Belgium, France, Italy, Russia and the UK, with at least eight types of powerplant.

THE VOISIN TYPE L

The Farman HF.20 was partnered in French service by the Voisin Type L (Types 1 and 2). Known as the Type 1913 or Type 13.5m after the year of its first flight or its wing span in metres, the Type L was the most important product of the Voisin company in the first stage of World War I. Despite its flimsy appearance, the aeroplane was in fact extremely robust as a result of its fabric-covered steel structure.

The structural core of the aeroplane was the short central nacelle that carried, from front to rear, the observer/gunner, the pilot, the fuel and oil tanks. A Gnome rotary engine was installed in an exposed position, droving a two-bladed wooden pusher propeller. About 70 Type Ls were produced for the French army air service, in which the type was operated by V.14 and V.21 Escadrilles (Squadrons), and more were delivered to the Imperial Russian air service. The aircraft were generally used for artillery observation up to November 1914, when most of the surviving aircraft were adapted as bombers with provision for light bombs carried on the sides of the central nacelle. The two variants were the Type 1 with one Gnome 7A rotary engine rated at 70 hp (52.2 kW) and the Type 2 with the uprated 80-hp (59.6-kW) Le Rhône 9C.

■ABOVE: The Avro Type 504B was typical of the type of general-purpose aircraft used early in World War I for tasks such as bombing, and the interception of Zeppelin airships.

The Type L was partnered and then largely supplanted in Voisin-equipped units by the Voisin Types LA and LB (Types 3 and 4). First flown in February 1914 and later allocated the service designation Type 3B.2, the Type LA was an improved version of the Type L, with an unequal-span wing cellule, inversely tapered ailerons and a powerplant of one

Salmson (Canton-Unnè) 9M radial piston engine cooled by two block radiators. The robust basic model was developed into successively more capable warplanes with heavier armament and more powerful engines. A Salmson (Canton-Unnè) 9M water-cooled radial piston engine was fitted, droving a two-bladed wooden pusher propeller.

A batch of these aircraft was awaiting export to Russia at the time of the outbreak of World War I in August 1914, and Gabriel Voisin immediately offered the aircraft to the French authorities, going so far as to arm six of them with 8-mm (0.315-in) Hotchkiss machine guns paid for by himself. It was in one of these armed aircraft that Caporal Quènault, the gunner of a Type LA of the V.24 Squadron flown by Lieutenant Joseph Frantz, made aviation and military history when he achieved the world's first air-to-air victory on 5 October 1914, by shooting down an Aviatik B I unarmed reconnaissance aeroplane with 47 rounds from his Hotchkiss machine gun.

Later aircraft were completed to the Type LA.S (Surèlevè, or raised) standard, with a slightly modified powerplant installation in which the engine was mounted at an angle so that its thrust line was tilted down. Many of the aircraft were later adapted as Type 3D.2 trainers.

The Type LA was built in larger numbers than any other Voisin type, some 800 being delivered to the French army's Aviation Militaire for general-purpose roles (mostly artillery spotting and battlefield reconnaissance) up to September 1915, when the type was reallocated to the night bombing task. A small number of aircraft equipped as three-float seaplanes were operated by the French naval air service, and others were exported to Russia (where the type was also built under licence), Belgium (enough aircraft for one squadron) and the UK.

The Type 3B.2 was the primary equipment of the French Aviation Militaire's first strategic bomber force, when VB.1, VB.2 and VB.3 squadrons were grouped into the 1er Groupe de Bombardement (1st Bomber Group) during 1918. The unit had 18 aircraft, and was later complemented by GB 2, GB 3 and GB 4 in a programme of strategic daylight attacks on targets behind the German lines, such as railroad junctions, troop concentrations and industrial targets including poison gas factories. By September 1915, these raids had achieved some useful results, especially when using later aircraft with chutes to release bombs of up to 132 lb (60 kg) size, but the increasing loss rate suffered in the summer of 1915 then led to a discontinuation of the campaign.

In Italy, 112 Type LA aircraft were built under licence by the Societé Italiana

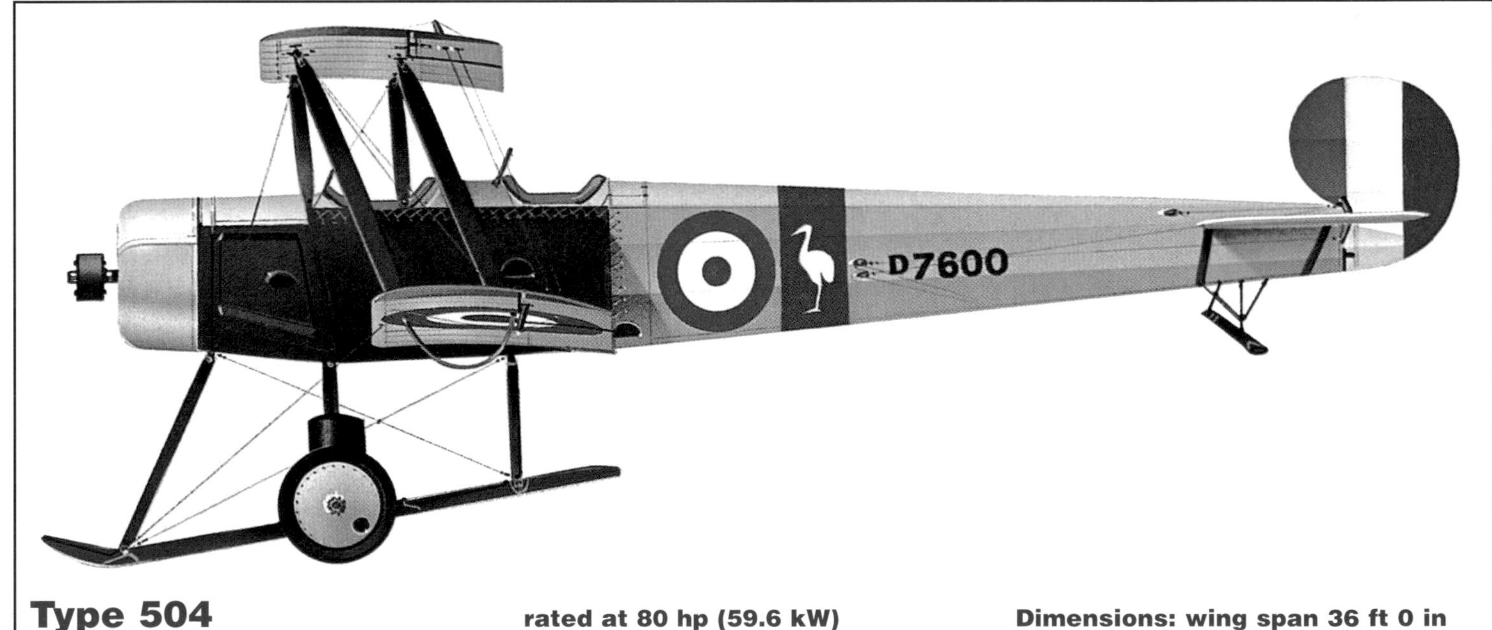

Type 504

Type: Avro Type 504 two-seat general-purpose warplane
Country of origin: United Kingdom
Powerplant: one Clerget, Gnome or Le Rhone rotary piston engine rated at 80 hp (59.6 kW)
Performance: maximum level speed 'clean' 82 mph (132 km/h) at sea level
Weights: empty 924 lb (419 kg); maximum take-off 1574 lb (714 kg)
Dimensions: wing span 36 ft 0 in (10.97 m); length 29 ft 5 in (8.97 m); height 10 ft 5 in (3.175 m); wing area 320.00 sq ft (29.73 m^2)
Armament: none

Transaerea in 1915 and 1916 for the Italian air service, which operated five squadriglie (squadrons) of the type, with an assortment of Fiat, Isotta-Fraschini and Renault engines. The most common was the Isotta-Fraschini V.4B in-line piston engine rated at 190 hp (142 kW).

Later known as the Type 4Ca.2, with 200 aircraft built after a first flight in March 1915, the Type LB was a development of the Type LA (Type 3), with a staggered wing, a modified nacelle, additional bracing and, most importantly of all, considerably more powerful armament in the form of a 37-mm (1.46-in) Hotchkiss cannon or, in just a few aircraft, a 47-mm (1.85-in) Hotchkiss cannon in the front of the nacelle. The avions canon (cannon-armed aircraft) were of little use in air combat, as the weight of the cannon degraded performance and agility to a significant degree, but proved moderately effective in the ground-attack role.

RUSSIAN DEVELOPMENTS

The Zavod A. A. Anatra (A. A. Anatra Works) was established in 1913 and during World War I was one of the five largest manufacturers of aircraft in Russia. Its plants at Sevastopol and Simferopol in the Ukraine were producing 80 aircraft per month in 1917, before the second revolution of the year that ushered in the Bolshevik regime which created the USSR out of Imperial Russia. The company concentrated on the licensed production of French aircraft, most notably designs of the Nieuport and Voisin organisations. In 1915, Anatra was building the Voisin Type 5 bomber, otherwise known as the Type LA.S, that was also being produced by the Duks, Lebedev and Shchetinin works. To improve this obsolescent type's performance, Anatra commissioned Lieutenant V. Ivanov to design an upgraded version, resulting in the VI (Voisin-Ivanov) which was in fact little altered from the original Type 5 except in detail, to reduce some drag.

Ivanov succeeded in improving speed by 13 mph (21 km/h) and reducing the time needed to reach 6560 ft (2000 m) by

Voisin Type 1B.2

Type: two-seat general-purpose warplane and light bomber
Country of origin: France
Powerplant: one 70-hp (52.2-kW) Gnome 7A rotary piston engine
Performance: maximum level speed 'clean' 59 mph (95 km/h) at sea level
Weights: empty 1820 lb (825 kg); maximum take-off 2425 lb (1100 kg)
Dimensions: wing span 44 ft 3 in (13.50 m); length 34 ft 5.33 in (10.50 m); height 9 ft 6 in (2.90 m);
Armament: one 8-mm (0.315-in) rifle or carbine, plus up to 132 lb (60 kg) of bombs

LEFT: Epitomising the first generation of true bombers in World War I were the French Voisin Types VIII and IX two-seaters able to carry some 660 lb (300 kg) of bombs.

5 minutes. However, lateral control was distinctly poor, the controls in general were not very effective and, as it had not been strengthened despite the aircraft's increased weight, the landing gear was prone to failure.

Anatra received an order for 139 examples of the VI to be delivered between March 1915 and March 1916, but the last of these was completed only in the middle of 1918. The type was notably unpopular with Russian aircrews, and this dislike continued even after 1917, when Ivanov introduced improvements that cured most of the VI's major problems apart from the weakness of the landing gear.

FURTHER FRENCH PROGRESS

The years up to the outbreak of World War I had witnessed a steady stream of increasingly-capable Breguet biplanes. The most important of these aircraft was the Type III, which was adopted for military service by France and the UK in a number of variants. In the early months of World War I, Breguet himself served as a military pilot, mainly with Squadron BR.17 equipped largely with the U.3, and soon came to the realisation that the aircraft of the period lacked the structural strength and engine power for anything but the reconnaissance role, and then only in the absence of the need for energetic manoeuvring.

Breguet designed the Type IV, otherwise known by the military designation BU3. It was pusher aircraft, because the French general staff had specified that all new two-seat military aircraft should be built this way to provide the observer in the front seat with an uninterrupted field of vision and a good field of fire for his 8-mm (0.315-in) Hotchkiss machine gun. As a pusher design, the aircraft was thus a French 'B type', and the U3 portion of the designation indicated that it was powered by the 160-hp (119-kW) variant of the Salmson (Canton-Unnè) water-cooled radial piston engine.

The BU3 prototype was under construction at the time that the German advance into northeast France, late in the summer of 1914, threatened the Breguet plant at Douai, and the prototype was therefore trucked to Villacoublay outside Paris for completion. Completed late in October or early in November 1914, the BU3 prototype was rushed into service. The prototype was demonstrated by Louis Breguet himself. It was a substantial three-bay biplane with a quadricycle main landing gear arrangement and a large central nacelle carrying the crew of two, with the radial piston engine at its rear. As it was an avion de combat (warplane), the BU3 had

a partially armoured nacelle, but the observer/gunner was located in the rear seat and had therefore to stand up before he could fire his machine gun over the pilot's head. An element of the French army air service believed that the BU3 should be revised without armour, for production and service as a two-seat fighter, but sense prevailed and the BU3 was ordered into production as a bomber.

The initial variant of the BU3 built by Michelin was the BUM – a Category B aeroplane with a Salmson (Canton-Unnè) engine, built by Michelin. The type had a number of changes as a result of initial experience with the BU3, and was built for service in the Bombardement deux-place (two-seat bomber) category as the BrM2B.2, with the Salmson (Canton-Unnè) engine rated at 200 hp (149 kW). The BLM was the definitive version of the BU3 built by Michelin, and entered service as the BrM4B.2 with the uprated powerplant of one Renault 12Fb Vee piston engine rated at 220 hp (164 kW). As a result of this engine's greater length, the fuel tankage was relocated to a pair of streamlined tanks installed between the wings immediately above the intersection of the flying and landing wires in the two innermost bays.

The BLC was the light bomber and escort fighter counterpart of the BUC (escort version of the BU3), and as such was analogous to the BrM4 in relation to the BrM2. The type was therefore powered by the Renault 12Fb Vee piston engine rated at 220 hp (164 kW) and supplied with 121.5 US gal (101.2 Imp gal; 460 litres) of fuel in two tanks

ABOVE: The Short Type 184 floatplane was designed for the torpedo bomber role, but was indifferent in this task, and often used as a conventional bomber.

carried in the innermost wing bays, A later alteration was the replacement of the earlier models' long-chord ailerons by shorter-chord units that extended rearward only as far as the trailing edge of the wing panels proper.

The Breguet de Chasse was the variant of the BUC for British service with the Royal Naval Air Service, which received 17 of the type. The main change effected in the alteration of the BUC into the Breguet de Chasse was the replacement of the 2M7 radial engine by a Sunbeam Mohawk Vee piston engine or, in a couple of cases, the Rolls-Royce Falcon Vee engine.

NEW ORGANISATION

In the spring of 1916, the French air force decided to categorise its aircraft into five types, which were Category A for army co-operation aircraft, Category B for fighters (or fighting scouts as they were known at the time), Category C for three-seat avions de combat (multi-role warplanes), Category D for avions canon (cannon-armed aircraft) and Category E for bombers. The weapon chosen for the Category D aircraft was the 37 mm (1.46 in) Hotchkiss cannon, and machines with this primary weapon were divided into two subcategories: Category D.1 encompassed the aircraft with a short-barrel version of the cannon and intended mainly for the air combat role, while Category D.2 covered aircraft with the long-barrel version of this weapon and intended mainly for attacks on German observation and gunnery-spotting balloons, trains and batteries of artillery (with particular emphasis placed on anti-aircraft artillery).

THE BREGUET TYPE V

Breguet had already decided to produce a warplane designed mainly for the escort role, but which could double in the light bomber role with a payload of 20 small bombs, and this accorded well with what was soon to become the Category C specification. The prototype of this new Type V design appeared late in 1915, armed with a single short-barrel 37-mm cannon operated by the observer/gunner in the front seat. In order to meet different French operational criteria, it was soon revisedto carry a rearward-firing Lewis gun located above the centre section of the upper wing, with two rearward-sloping lengths of tubing provided for the gunner to rest against as he stood in the front cockpit to operate the rearward-firing weapon.

The Type V was powered by the Renault 12Fb Vee piston engine rated at 220 hp (164 kW). It passed its acceptance trials in April 1916 and entered limited production and service as the Bre.5Ca.2 – the 'Ca' portion of the designation indicating that it was a Canon (cannon-armed) aeroplane. The Bre.5Ca.2 never equipped a full squadron, but was instead allocated in flight strength to bomber squadrons whose other flights would be escorted by the new type. Some later aircraft were completed with the Renault 12Fbx or Fcx engine rated at 250 hp (186 kW). While the French used the Bre.5 mainly as an escort, the Royal Naval Air Service's 3rd Wing (in the form of No 5 Squadron based at Coudekerque) used 35 as bombers.

As the Type V was entering production and service as the Bre.5, there were fears that supplies of the Renault 12 engine might be inadequate. Breguet accordingly produced a revised Type VI powered by the Salmson (Canton-Unnè) A9 water-cooled radial piston engine rated at 225 hp (168 kW) and driving the pusher propeller via an extension shaft. Type VI entered service as the Bre.6B.2 two-seat bomber and Bre.6Ca.2 escort fighter with a 37-mm (1.46 in) cannon.

As the Bre.5 series was phased out of service in favour of the Breguet Bre.14, the surviving aircraft were not discarded, but instead revised for nocturnal bombing operations as the Bre.12B.2, with a twin-wheel nose unit like that of the BrM4B.2. A few other aircraft were built to a similar standard as Bre.12Ca.2 night fighters, with the 37-mm cannon adapted to carry a searchlight on its starboard side and an array of eight landing lights under the lower wing.

BRITISH EXPERIMENTS

In July 1914, the month preceding the outbreak of World War I, Squadron Commander A. M. Longmore of the Royal Naval Air Service successfully released a 14 in (356 mm) torpedo, weighing some 900 lb (408 kg), from an airborne aeroplane, in this instance a Short floatplane powered by a 160 hp (119 kW) Gnome rotary piston engine. This is thought to have been the first successful air-launch of a torpedo, although Longmore has a rival in Capitano Alessandro Guidoni of Italy. At some date in mid-1914, Guidoni achieved a similar feat, using a dummy torpedo weighing 827 lb (375 kg), and the Pateras Pescara experimental monoplane. Guidoni had undertaken his first experiments on the air-launching of torpedoes in 1912, dropping weights from a Farman biplane.

In 1913, the British achieved a significant interim step in lifting a 14 in (356 mm) torpedo into the air under a large Sopwith Type C floatplane powered by a Salmson (Canton-Unnè) engine rated at 200 hp (149 kW). However, Longmore's success was instrumental in the process of assuring the British military establishment in general, and Captain Murray Sueter, Director of the Air Department in the Admiralty, in particular, that the air-launched torpedo could rapidly be developed as a potent weapon of war.

Shortly after the start of World War I, the Short Brothers company of Rochester in Kent introduced its Type 166 floatplane, which could be fitted with torpedo-dropping equipment, but the Air Department felt that a larger and more powerfully engined type was needed for effective torpedo bomber use. Sueter dealt directly with Horace Short, eldest of the three Short brothers, about the matter (and also with the Sopwith and Wight companies) and early in 1915 there appeared the prototype of a twin-float seaplane with long-span wings which became the Type 184. This was a direct derivative of Short's contender for the 1913 Circuit of Britain seaplane race, with a more powerful engine to improve the type's payload-lifting capability.

Before even the first prototype had flown, the Admiralty contracted for 10 more aircraft of what would later be known as the pre-production batch, together with 10 examples each of the rival Sopwith Type 860 and Wright Type 840. By this time, the Admiralty was satisfied that the Type 184 was the machine it wanted and ordered it into full production in numbers too great for Short alone to fulfil at its two Kent factories. Thus an initial 75 aircraft were contracted from Short, with another 30 from Saunders at Cowes in the Isle of Wight, and batches of 12 aircraft each from a number of other manufacturers with no previous experience in aircraft manufacture. In January 1916, the Admiralty issued a second round of orders, including the somewhat different Type 184 Type B standard. This had a revised two-bay wing cellule with increased interplane gap, an increased upper wingspan with tip extensions supported by kingpost-and-cable bracing, and the span of the lower wing (now not fitted with ailerons) reduced by trimming the outer wing panels and adding rounded tips. Despite the fact that the Type 194 Type B had considerable better climb and ceiling, only 10 examples of the type were built.

FIRST OPERATIONS

Even as this process of initial mass production was being started, the two prototypes were proving the capabilities of the type. The two machines were embarked on the Isle of Man packet steamer *Ben-my-Chree,* which had been converted as a seaplane carrier, and in June 1915 arrived at the Greek island of Mitylene off the coast of hostile Turkey. The targets most desired by the British pilots were the German battlecruiser SMS *Goeben* and its light cruiser escort

Short Type 184
Type: ship-borne and shore-based torpedo and level bomber
Country of origin: UK
Powerplant: one 260-hp (194-kW) Sunbeam Maori I piston engine
Performance: maximum level speed 88.5 mph (142.5 km/h) at 2000 ft (610 m) service ceiling 9000 ft (2745 m)
Weights: empty 3703 lb (1680 kg); maximum take-off 5363 lb (2433 kg)
Dimensions: wing span 63 ft 6.25 in (19.36 m); length 40 ft 7.5 in (12.38 m); height 13 ft 6 in (4.1 m)
Armament: one 0.303 in (7.7 mm) Lewis machine gun, plus up to 810 lb (367 kg) of stores

SMS *Breslau*. However, it was with smaller fry that the aircraft scored their first and indeed only successes, starting on 12 August with a hit from 350 yds (320 m) on a 5000-ton Turkish freighter that had been immobilised a few days earlier by a torpedo hit from the British submarine HMS *E-14*. Within the week, the two Type 184s had scored hits on two other Turkish ships, in one instance the Type 184 launching its torpedo on the water after it had been compelled to land after suffering engine problems.

These successes were not allowed to disguise the fact that the Type 184, in its current form, was a very limited weapon that could lift off from the sea only if there was a slight chop to break the surface friction between the water and the smooth undersurfaces of the pontoon floats, and then only if the type was flown as a single-seater with reduced fuel. Another problem in hotter climes was the tendency of the radiator water to boil during the Type 184's long take-off run.

It was therefore decided that the Type 184 was not ideally suited to the torpedo

■ **LEFT: The pilot and observer/gunner of the RAF's No. 112 Squadron watch an armourer install a bomb's fuse on a Royal Aircraft Factory F.E.2b at St Omer, France, in July 1918.**

bomber role, and further development and use of the type was therefore centred on its level bombing capability (with German submarines as the main targets), and on its gunnery spotting capability, especially in association with Royal Navy Monitor warships.

Material changes introduced in later batches of production aircraft included the addition of a 0.303-in Lewis trainable machine gun with three 97-round ammunition drums in the rear cockpit, and the replacement of the arched cross-members between the pontoon floats by flat cross-members, with no provision for the carriage of a torpedo.

A number of the aircraft were adapted as Type 184 Type D single-seaters, the original forward cockpit being faired over to provide accommodation for nine 65 lb (29.5 kg) bombs carried vertically. No information has survived on any Type 184 Type C variant.

The Type 184 was issued to the RNAS units operating around the coast of the UK for anti-submarine and coastal reconnaissance work, although small numbers were also used by the seaplane carriers attached to the Grand Fleet and other elements of the Royal Navy's surface strength. It was a Type 184 from the seaplane carrier HMS *Engadine* that achieved the only British reconnaissance flight in the climactic Battle of Jutland (May 1916), although this flight was curtailed by a broken fuel pipe shortly after the crew had used radio equipment to report their discovery of 13 German warships, in the form of 3 cruisers and 10 destroyers, of the High Seas Fleet.

UPRATING THE 184'S ENGINES

The Type 184 was retained in production right to the end of World War I, despite its obsolescence for all but the anti-submarine role from a time early in 1917, and of orders placed for 1090 aircraft, all but 145 were completed. As production continued, several different and more powerful engines were installed: these units included the Sunbeam Gurkha rated at 240 hp (179 kW), the Renault rated at 240 hp (179 kW) and distinguishable by its upward-ejecting exhaust, the Sunbeam Maori I and II rated at 260 hp (194 kW), and the Sunbeam Maori III rated at 275 hp (205 kW) and identifiable by its two vertical exhausts.

Some of the later aircraft had the improved engine installation devised at the Royal Naval Air Station at Dover, with a frontal radiator that much improved the pilot's forward fields of vision. This Dover Type 184, which was intended mainly for service at the stations on the coast of the choppy English Channel, also had larger pontoon floats as well as longer and more streamlined underwing stabilising floats.

The Type 184 remained in limited British service after World War I for mine-spotting patrols, and modest numbers of the type were exported.

ALBATROS AIRCRAFT

In 1916, the German aircraft manufacturer Albatros flew the sole prototype of its G II medium bomber. It had a plywood-covered wooden fuselage and fabric-covered wooden flying surfaces, including a tail unit with standard Albatros shaping. The most unusual feature was the thick section of the upper and lower surfaces of the single-bay unequal-span biplane wing cellule: this section was designed for maximum lift, and was clearly intended to allow carriage of the heaviest possible bomb load. Other features of the design were the tailskid landing gear with a main unit of the through-axle type and a supplementary nose unit of the through-axle type, the X-type interplane struts whose rigidity removed the need for incidence bracing wires, and the powerplant of two Benz Bz.III in-line piston engines each rated at 150 hp (112 kW) and located in very neat naccelles above the lower wing to drive two-blade pusher propellers fitted with spinners.

The same basic concept was adopted for the G III that followed later in 1916. The fuselage had open positions for the crew of three. The production total and operational career of the G III are uncertain. It is known only that the type was used in limited numbers on the Macedonian front, where the maximum number of aircraft operational at any one time was about 10. It seems unlikely that any use was made of the G III after the third quarter of 1917.

Although it was best known for its floatplanes, Friedrichshafen was also persuaded by Theodor Kober, its chief engineer, to embark on the design of a series of large bombers. The first of these, which appeared in 1915, was the G I four-bay biplane with a biplane tail unit, a crew of three, and a powerplant of two Benz Bz.III in-line piston engines each rated at 150 hp (112 kW), driving a two-blade pusher propeller.

The G I was not ordered into production, but a better fate awaited the G II, which appeared in the first half of 1916 as a development of the G I. It used a three-bay wing cellule, monoplane tail unit, defensive armament of two 7.92 mm (0.312-in) LMG 14 Parabellum trainable machine guns (single weapon in the open nose and dorsal positions), offensive armament of 1000 kg (2205 lb) of bombs, powerplant of two Benz Bz.IV in-line piston engines each rated at 200 hp (149 kW), driving a two-blade pusher propeller with a neat spinner.

The G III – a development of the G II with outer wing panels derived from those of the G I – partnered the Gotha G V as the main strength of the German Bombengeschwadern (bomber groups) on the Western Front from early in 1917 to the end of World War I in November 1918. The G III was a four-bay biplane of mixed metal and wood construction. The G IIIa was a simple derivative of the G III, with slightly less raked wing tips and a compound tail with biplane horizontal surfaces and twin vertical surfaces. The G III and G IIIa were built by the parent company and also under licence by Daimler Motorengesellschaft Werke (245 G III and G IIIa bombers) and Hanseatische Flugzeug-Werke (93 G III and G IIIa bombers). The G III and G IIIa saw extensive use on the Western Front, which was their sole operational area. The types' greatest asset was their ability to cover long ranges with a sizeable bomb load, and the aircraft were therefore often used to bomb Paris, and were probably also involved in the bomber offensive against England.

HEINKEL'S FIRST DESIGNS

The first twin-engined aeroplane by Ernst Heinkel, chief designer of the Hansa-Brandenburg company, was the ZM of 1915. This was a bomber prototype of angular line and was typical of its period in being a fabric-covered wooden machine based on a rectangular-section fuselage, with a standard tail unit and an equal-span biplane wing cellule of the four-bay type, with ailerons hinged to the rear units of the outermost two sets of interplane struts. The powerplant comprised a pair of Maybach in-line piston engines each rated at 160 hp (119 kW) and driving a two-blade wooden pusher propeller. The engines were installed in mid-gap between the upper and lower wings within the innermost sets of interplane struts. The crew comprised three men, including the two gunners who operated the single 0.312 in (7.92 mm) Parabellum machine guns in the nose and dorsal positions. The bomb load was 551 lb (250 kg), and was carried externally to the aircraft.

No production of the ZM was undertaken, but from its basic design Heinkel evolved a more advanced type known as the GF. This was also an equal-span biplane of wooden construction, but covered with a combination of plywood and fabric. The GF first flew in 1915, and did not interest the Imperial German army air service. However, Hansa-Brandenburg already had a strong connection with the Austro-Hungarian air force through the fact that its founder, Camillo Castiglione, was an Austro-Hungarian citizen, and this latter decided to operate the type in the form of the G I licence-built by Ufag, otherwise rendered as UFAG, as its full name was the Ungarische Flugzeugfabrik A.G.. It featured an Austro-Hungarian gun armament and a pair of Austro-Hungarian engines. Estimates for the number of G I aircraft built by Ufag varies between three and perhaps 15, the latter appearing the more likely option, in a series with a revised tail unit and a shortened nose, the latter in an effort to improve the pilot's forward field of vision. A few aircraft were fitted with a 20 mm (0.787 in) Becker cannon in place of the nose-mounted 0.315 in (8 mm) Schwarzlose trainable machine gun in order to provide a surer defence against

RIGHT: With aircraft such as the Albatros G III, the concept of the bomber began to take true shape, although the type was still too small for more than a limited bomb load.

Italian fighters, but even so the G I was not successful even when operating with fighter escort.

NEW RUSSIAN AIRCRAFT

After learning to fly in France during 1909-10, Vladimir Lebedev established his own aircraft manufacturing company in 1912 near St Petersburg called the PTA (Petersburg Aviation Company). It later became Lebedev and another facility was added at Taganrog in 1917. A third facility to be set up at Penze was cancelled when the Bolshevik Revolution of November 1917 started the process of dissolving Tsarist Russia into the USSR and disengaging from World War I. The Lebedev facilities made the company one of the five major Russian aircraft manufacturers of World War I, and this allowed it to deliver about 30 aircraft per month in 1916, rising to 75 per month in 1917, as the new factories came on stream. The initial products of the Lebedev plants were mainly designs of foreign origin, most notably Deperdussin, Farman, Morane-Saulnier, Nieuport and Voisin aircraft from France, and Sopwith aircraft from the UK.

One of the most advanced types produced by Lebedev in the first part of World War I was the Sopwith Tabloid, which was manufactured as the Lebed' VII. Other aircraft included the Lebed' VIII and Lebed' IX, modelled respectively on the Albatros B II and on LVG design practices.

In 1915, the company's design team, with Ribokov as deputy to Shkulnik, combined features of the Lebed' VIII with elements of an Albatros (probably a B II) captured at some stage from the Germans, in a new Russian design optimised for the reconnaissance role with light bombing capability.

This new design was the Lebed' XI, which was a two-bay biplane of wire-braced wooden construction with a span of 47 ft 6.75 in (14.50 m). The powerplant of one Salmson (Canton-Unnè) radial piston engine was used in a small batch of 10 aircraft (including a small number of LM I twin-float seaplane derivatives) that were intended mainly for service trials, but which in fact saw a measure of operational service.

The type was generally liked by service pilots, who nonetheless saw the major failing of the type as being its large

ABOVE: The Friedrichshafen FF 45 entered service as the G III, and was a very reliable type that served with great success in the hands of Kampfgeschwadern 1, 2 and 4.

wing area, resulting in a tendency to 'float' during landings. This led to the introduction of a variant with reduced span, the Lebed' XII, with a wing cellule trimmed by 4 ft 5.15 in (1.35 m). This revised version first flew in prototype form during December 1915. In April 1916, the company received an order for 225 examples of the Lebed' XII production model. The first of these flew in August 1916, and the type entered service in October 1916 with the Salmson (Canton-Unnè) 9P radial engine rated at 150 hp (112 kW). Operational experience proved the Lebed' XII to be less than popular with its crews. Its wings had a tendency to flex, and the poor positioning of the centre of gravity (especially when carrying bombs) made recovery from a dive extremely difficult. The engine exhausts were also too close to the cockpit, and the Shkulnik bomb racks and gun mounting for the observer/gunner's weapon were inefficient and later replaced by Kolpakov equipment.

In the summer of 1917, after some 80 Lebed' XII warplanes had been delivered, the production standard switched to the Lebed' XIIbis, with a powerplant of one Hispano-Suiza 8 Vee piston engine rated at 140 hp (104 kW). Some 214 out of the ordered 225 Lebed' XII aircraft were delivered, and the survivors of this force remained in service, mainly as trainers with the trainee and instructor in the forward and rear cockpits respectively, until the early 1920s.

FRENCH IMPROVEMENTS

First flown late in 1915, the Voisin Type LA.S was an improved version of the Type LA (Type 3), with basically the same airframe revised for a powerplant of one Salmson (Canton-Unne) 9D radial piston engine rated at 150 hp (112 kW), and featuring strengthened landing gear and a larger cut-out on the centre-line of the upper wing's trailing edge. As such, the Type LA.S, known in service as the Type 5B.2, was an unequal-span biplane of fabric-covered steel tube construction. The Type 5B.2 was used only by the French Aviation Militaire, which was also the operator of the Type 6B.2 subvariant, that differed only in its use of a 155 hp (116 kW) version of the Salmson (Canton-Unne) 9D engine. Production of the two variants totalled about 450 aircraft, and these were used mainly in the night bombing role, as mass daylight attacks with the Types 3 and 4 had resulted in heavy losses and the termination of this initial French strategic bombing campaign in September 1915.

THE AIRCO D.H.4

Generally accepted as the finest single-engined bomber to have seen large-scale service in World War I, the Airco D.H.4 was a classic aeroplane by any standards and certainly one of the finest design achievements of Captain Geoffrey de Havilland, chief designer of the Aircraft Manufacturing Co. Ltd. The D.H.4 resulted from an official requirement for a high-performance bomber, and was the first British aeroplane designed specifically for this role.

The intended powerplant was a Beardmore in-line piston engine, developed from an earlier unit rated at 120 hp (89.5 kW), and at the time this improved engine entered production in March 1916, its power had risen to 160 hp (119 kW) for take-off, later increased to 192 hp (143 kW). As work on the D.H.4 proceeded, however, the highly talented engine designer, Frank Halford, secured permission to undertake a radical development of the engine to give a minimum of 200 hp (149 kW). Securing the co-operation of Sir William Beardmore and T. C. Pullinger, Halford designed the improved engine as an enlarged version of the standard Beardmore unit, with a number of features inspired by the Hispano-Suiza engines that Halford had seen in France during 1915. The basic six-cylinder in-line configuration was retained, with larger cylinders, but major changes were made to the basic construction. The new BHP (Beardmore-Halford-Pullinger) engine first ran in June 1916 at a rating of 236 hp (176 kW) and, despite a number of teething problems, offered good reliability from the beginning of its life. The engine was immediately selected for the D.H.4 and ordered into production by the Siddeley-Deasy Motor Car Co. Ltd. (precursor of the celebrated engine manufacturer, Armstrong Siddeley) and then by Galloway Engineering Co. Ltd.

As the BHP engine was approaching completion, de Havilland had been finalising the design of the D.H.4 and supervising the construction of the prototype. The whole package had the appearance of 'rightness' that so often betokens a truly thoroughbred aeroplane. The new aeroplane was of wooden construction, covered mainly with fabric. The D.H.4 prototype made its first flight in August 1916 with a powerplant of one BHP engine rated at 230 hp (171.5 kW), and quickly revealed good performance and very good handling characteristics. The D.H.4 was immediately ordered into large-scale production, but problems with quantity production of the BHP engine – which was not available until mid-1917 – meant that an alternative engine had to be found. Fortunately, a suitable one was available in the form of the Rolls-Royce Vee engine, which entered production as the Mk III (later receiving the name Eagle) with a rating of 250 hp (186 kW) for take-off. As a Vee unit, this engine was wider but lower than the BHP, which allowed a revision of the upper cowling to improve the pilot's forward and downward fields of vision.

GOOD PERFORMANCE

In this form the D.H.4 found universal favour, especially from pilots who enthused about the new type's excellent handling characteristics and very good performance. It had an unprecedented speed range, from a stalling speed of only 45 mph (72.5 km/h) to a maximum of 119 mph (191.5 km/h) which was increased significantly in later models with higher-powered engines. The low-speed docility allowed safe operations from the short and indifferent airfields of the time, and at the upper range of the D.H.4's flight envelope, its performance above a height of 15,000 ft (4570 m) was generally superior to that of contemporary fighters.

The one major criticism of the type was the location of the main fuel tank between the two cockpits: this meant that the two crew members could only communicate by means of a Gosport speaking tube, which was a major hindrance to effective tactical flying, and that fire directed at the central part of the fuselage generally hit the tank and ignited the fuel even if it did not injure or kill the crew members directly.

The D.H.4 was also fitted with a number of other engine types, including the RAF 3a in-line unit rated at 200 hp (149 kW), the BHP and very similar Siddeley Puma in-line units each rated at 230 hp (171.5 kW), the Fiat A.12 in-line unit rated at 260 hp (194 kW), the Rolls-Royce Mk II Vee unit rated at 275 hp (205 kW) and later upgraded into the Eagle VI rated at 322 hp (240 kW), the Rolls-Royce Mk III Vee unit rated at 275 hp (205 kW) and later upgraded into the Eagle VII rated at 325 hp (242 kW), and the Rolls-Royce Eagle VIII rated at 375 hp (280 kW)

The use of these different engines generally affected the appearance of the nose in accordance with the type of radiator and each engine's configuration as an in-line or Vee unit, but the length and height of the aircraft were also altered, together with its performance.

British orders for the D.H.4 totalled some 1700 aircraft. The importance of the type is attested by its survival in large numbers right to the end of World War I, and its very widespread operational employment by six RFC and three RNAS squadrons on the Western Front, six RNAS squadrons employed on coastal patrol and home defence, two RFC squadrons in Mesopotamia, one squadron over Macedonia, six RNAS squadrons

Airco (de Havilland) D.H.4

Type: two-seat light bomber
Country of origin: UK
Powerplant: one 375-hp (280-kW) Rolls-Royce Eagle VIII Vee piston engine
Performance: max level speed 'clean' 143 mph (230 km/h); max range 435 miles (700 km)
Weights: empty 2387 lb (1083 kg); max take-off 3932 lb (1784 kg)
Dimensions: wing span 42 ft 4.625 in (12.92 m); length 30 ft 8 in (9.35 m); height 10 ft 5 in (3.175 m)
Armament: One 0.303 in (7.7 mm) Vickers plus one or two 0.303 in (7.7 mm) Lewis machine guns, and up to 460 lb (209 kg) of stores

over the Aegean, four RNAS squadrons over the Adriatic, and large numbers of training establishments.

The D.H.4 was phased out of British service in the period following the Armistice that ended World War I in November 1918, but small numbers of aircraft were passed to Australia, Canada, New Zealand and South Africa for help in the creation of these countries' own air forces. Other aircraft were sold to the Greek and Spanish air forces, and at least one captured aeroplane was operated by the Soviet air force. A modest number of surplus aircraft also reached the civil market.

THE US ENTERS THE WAR

When it entered World War I in April 1917, the USA found that it lacked virtually every instrument of modern war in numbers large enough to equip the huge forces it needed to create at great speed. France and the UK promised large quantities of matèriel of the heavier type, such as artillery, as well as quantities of lighter equipment, such as machine guns and warplanes, but the USA also laid plans for a huge growth in its own production capability and initially selected a number of the best Allied warplanes for licensed production. One of the types selected for this process was the D.H.4, which had only recently entered service and was already displaying excellent capabilities over the Western Front. In May 1917, within the context of an initial procurement programme for 7375 aircraft, the Department of War ordered a first tranche of 1700 D.H.4 aircraft, generally known by the revised designation DH-4 in its American licence-built version.

The D.H.4 was approved by the Americans, as its engine bay could accommodate a large new piston engine, developed as part of the American war effort. The engine was designed in June 1917 by Jesse Vincent of the Packard automobile company and E. J. Hall of the Hall-Scott aero engine company, and first ran in the following month. It was a substantial Vee piston-engine whose width was kept to a minimum by the selection of a 45° rather than 60° angle between the two cylinder banks. It was planned that the engine should be produced in 4-, 6-, 8- and 12-cylinder models according to the power required, but virtually all of the 20,748 engines produced (nearly all of them before November 1918) by a consortium of automobile manufacturers were of the Liberty 12 model with 12 cylinders.

Orders for the DH-4 eventually totalled 10,000 aircraft, to be produced by the Dayton-Wright Aeroplane Co (5000 machines), the Fisher Body Corporation (4000 machines) and the Standard Aircraft Corporation (1000 machines). The Liberty 12 engine was first flown in a D.H.4 imported from the UK, and was ultimately rated at 395 hp (294.5 kW). The first DH-4 off the production line was delivered by Dayton-Wright in February 1918, and such was the pace of the American production programme that 3227 aircraft had been delivered by the time of the Armistice. At that time, outstanding contracts for 7502 aircraft

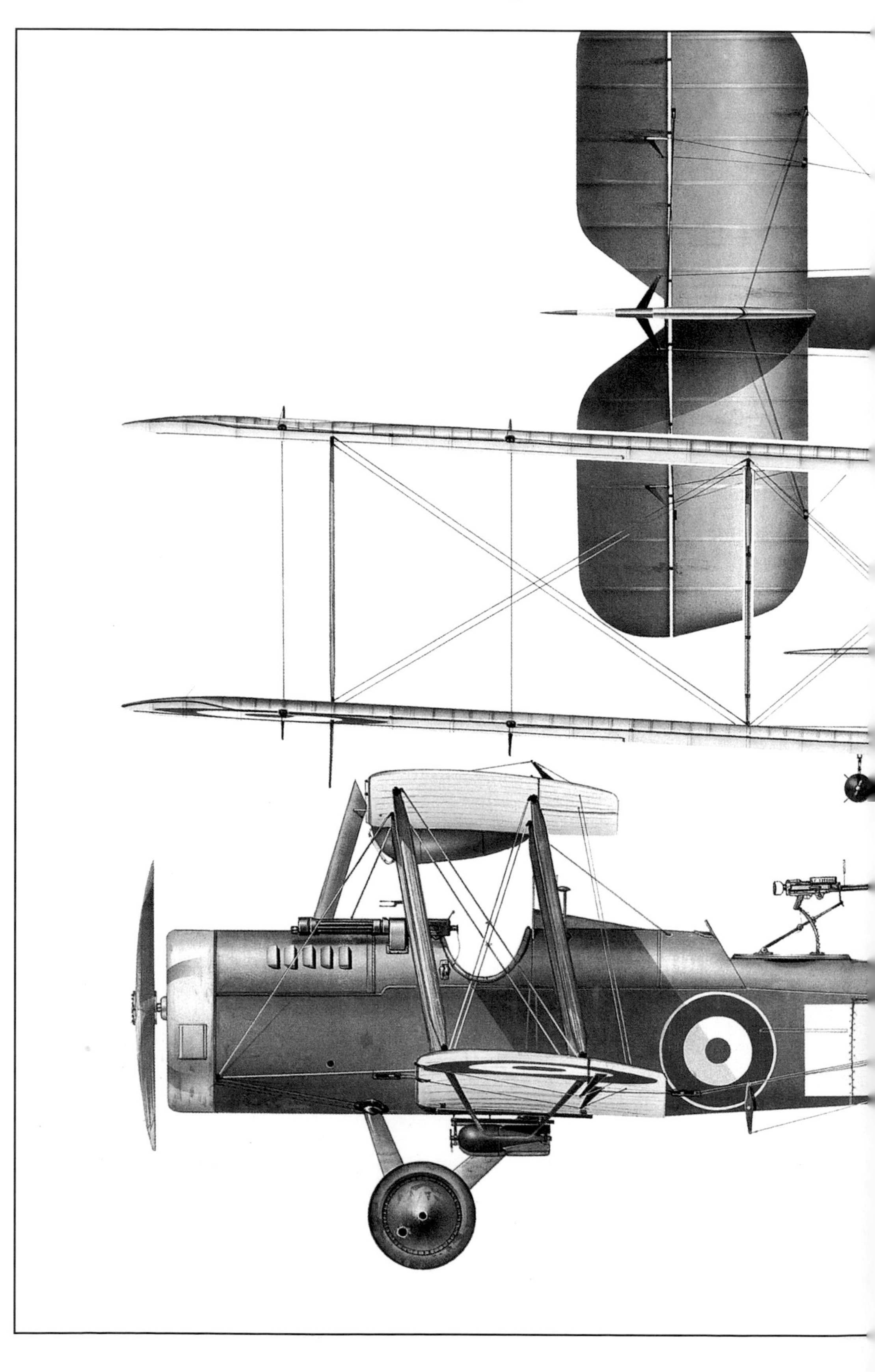

were cancelled, although many aircraft already under construction were completed to end US production at a grand total of delivery of 4844 aircraft. Some 3070 DH-4 aircraft were sent overseas from the USA before the Armistice of November 1918, in the form of 1885 complete aircraft and 1185 unassembled aircraft that reached French ports, and of the latter, 1025 were assembled. Of this total of 2910 aircraft, 1025 entered American service from May 1918 with 12 squadrons and elements of the US Naval Northern Bombing Group.

In October 1918, the Engineering Division of the Bureau of Aircraft Production, inspired by the Airco D.H.9 series, introduced the DH-4B standard, with the position of the pilot and main fuel tank exchanged so that the pilot and gunner were located close together. The opportunity was also taken to relocate the main landing gear unit slightly farther forward to reduce the DH-4's tendency to nose over during the landing run, and to extend the plywood covering of the fuselage's forward section right

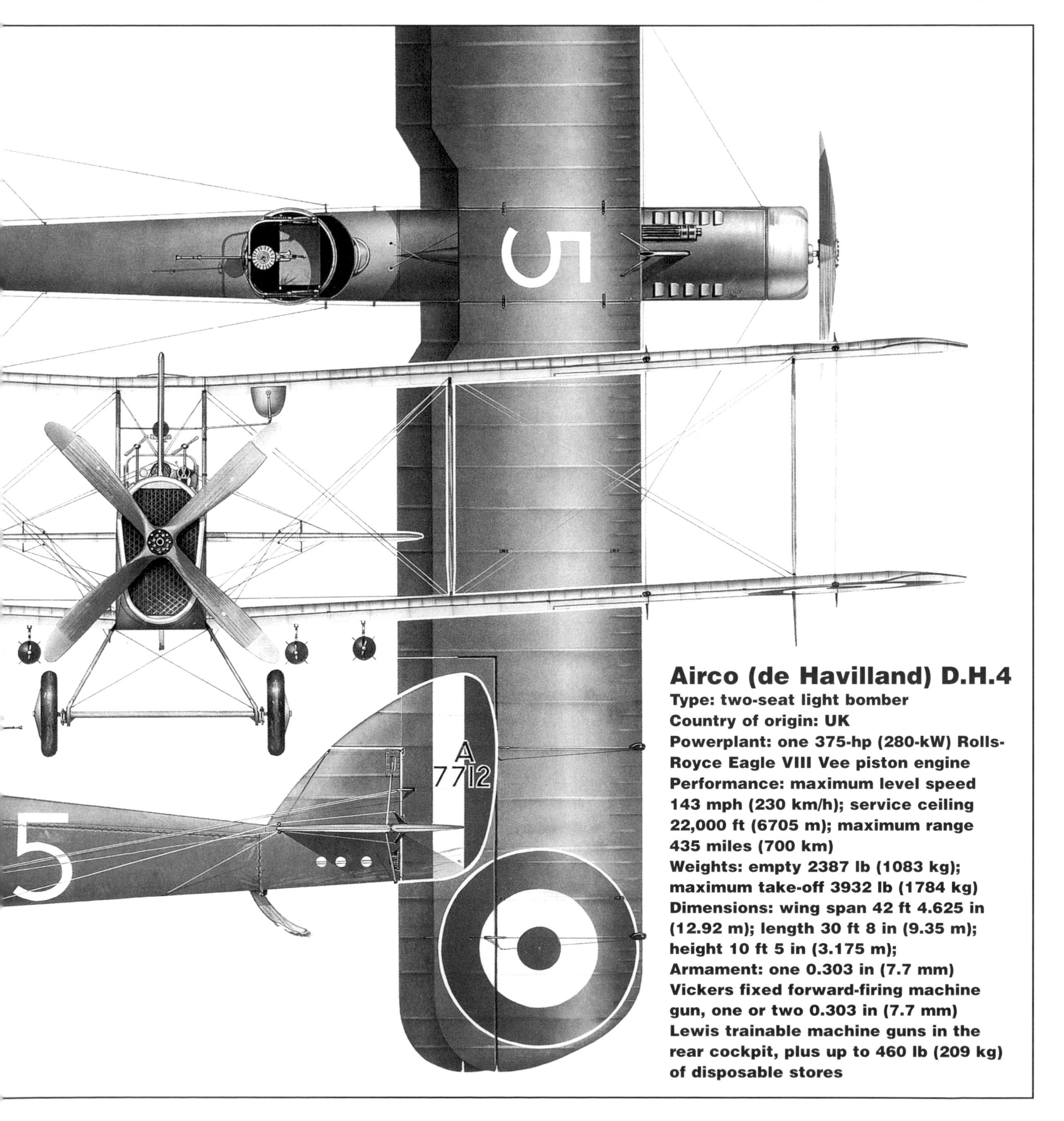

Airco (de Havilland) D.H.4
Type: two-seat light bomber
Country of origin: UK
Powerplant: one 375-hp (280-kW) Rolls-Royce Eagle VIII Vee piston engine
Performance: maximum level speed 143 mph (230 km/h); service ceiling 22,000 ft (6705 m); maximum range 435 miles (700 km)
Weights: empty 2387 lb (1083 kg); maximum take-off 3932 lb (1784 kg)
Dimensions: wing span 42 ft 4.625 in (12.92 m); length 30 ft 8 in (9.35 m); height 10 ft 5 in (3.175 m);
Armament: one 0.303 in (7.7 mm) Vickers fixed forward-firing machine gun, one or two 0.303 in (7.7 mm) Lewis trainable machine guns in the rear cockpit, plus up to 460 lb (209 kg) of disposable stores

back to the tail. No aircraft were built to this standard, but between 1919 and 1923, large numbers of existing machines were converted to this standard.

ITALIAN BOMBERS

Alongside Russia, Italy was the only country to have designed and built a multi-engined bomber type in the period before World War I. The Ca 30/31 was drawn up in 1913 as the Caproni 260 hp (the Ca 30 series designation was applied retrospectively after World War I). The Caproni 260 hp (Ca 31) prototype made its maiden flight in October 1914 while Italy was still neutral, powered by three Gnome rotary piston engines. It was a substantial three-bay biplane of completely orthodox fabric-covered wooden construction, but it was highly unusual in the disposition of its engines. The aeroplane used a twin-boom layout, and the three engines were installed in tandem in the central nacelle. The rearmost engine was a 100 hp (74.6 kW) unit driving a pusher propeller at the rear of the nacelle, and the other two were 80 hp (59.6 kW) units driving tractor propellers located at the front of the two booms by means of a differential transmission arrangement.

In other respects, the Ca 30 family established the basic pattern followed in the next generations of Caproni bombers. Its tail unit (carried at the rear ends of the two rectangular-section booms) comprised a single horizontal surface with a fixed tailplane and moving elevator and multiple vertical surfaces in the form of two all-moving rudders, while the landing gear was of the fixed tailskid type, with a skid under each of the booms, a four-wheel main unit with two wheels on the ends of each short axle carried below the boom by a wire-braced Vee-strut arrangement, and a smaller twin-wheel nose unit under the forward part of the central nacelle to prevent the aeroplane from nosing over in the course of operations onto and off the rough airfields of the time.

The Ca 31 was flyable but hardly practical, and it was soon realised that the differential gearing required to drive the two tractor propellers was weighty, liable to failure and the cause of considerable loss of power. The Ca 30 concept was therefore adapted in the new Caproni 300 hp prototype (designated Ca 32 after World War I). All three of its Gnome engines were rated at 100 hp (74.6 kW) and the two tractor units were installed at the front of the two booms to provide direct drive for the two tractor propellers. At one stage in the flight trials, the central Gnome rotary was replaced by a Curtiss OX-5 Vee piston engine rated at 90 hp (67.1 kW). Other changes effected at this stage were a revised central nacelle with a nose that was more rounded in plan view, a horizontal tail surface that was not so exaggerated in trapezoidal shape, the two all-moving rudders increased in area and supplemented by a strut-braced central fin of the same shape, a flat rather than dihedralled lower wing, and improved inter-wing bracing.

ABOVE: The Airco (de Havilland) D.H.4 was a British-designed day bomber that was then adopted for massive licensed production in the USA as the DH-4 with a Liberty engine.

THE CA 1 ENTERS SERVICE

The Italian air force saw the virtues of the revised type, of which two prototypes were built, and ordered it into production (company designation Ca 32) for service as the Ca 1 with the revised powerplant of three Fiat A.10 in-line piston engines, each rated at 100 hp (74.6 kW). Some 160 of the aircraft were delivered between August 1915 and December 1916. By late spring of 1916, Ca 1s were in service with the seven squadrons of the IVo Gruppo (4th Group) based at Aviano (five squadrons) and Comina (two squadrons), and with the single squadron of the 3rd Group based at Verona.

The Ca 2 model, of which only nine were delivered over the same period (with the contemporary company designation Ca 350 hp), was a simple evolution of the Ca 1, with the central Fiat A.10 engine replaced by an Isotta-Fraschini V.4B in-line piston engine rated at 150 hp (112 kW). In common with the Ca 1, the Ca 2 was stable and pleasant to fly, and also offered a useful range with an effective bomb load. As they were built in comparatively large numbers, the Ca 1 and Ca 2 allowed the creation of the Italian air force's strategic bomber arm, but it soon became clear that greater capabilities, especially in terms of performance and payload, would result from the adoption of a higher-rated powerplant for the aircraft.

The Ca 3 was the uprated version of the Ca 2 which was tested in prototype form late in 1916 and entered production with the company designation Caproni 450 hp (later Ca 33) for a total of 298 Italian aircraft, delivered between February 1917 and 1919. The type was basically the Ca 2, with the two outboard Fiat A.10 engines replaced by a pair of Isotta-Fraschini V.4B engines so that the powerplant was now three of these 150 hp (112 kW) units. These aircraft served mainly with the Italian air force as a heavy bomber, but the Italian navy also made limited use of the type as a torpedo bomber, and modest numbers of the basic bomber were also supplied to France, where another 83 generally similar aircraft were built under licence by Robert Esnault-Pelterie, with the designation Caproni-Esnault-Pelterie.

The Ca 3 mod (modificato, or modified) variant was known to Caproni as the Ca 36 (sometimes Ca 36M), and was an improved and structurally simplified version of the Ca 3. Deliveries between 1923 and 1927 totalled 153 aircraft to a standard that had the same dimensions as the Ca 3, but differed in details such as its uprated powerplant of three V.4B engines, each delivering 190 hp (142 kW). The Ca 3 mod bombers saw some operational service in the first stages of the military effort undertaken by Benito Mussolini's Fascist regime to 'restore Italy's lost colonies'.

THE CAPRONI CA 5

By 1917, Caproni had come to the sensible conclusion that while its Ca 3 biplane and Ca 4 triplane bombers offered considerable capabilities in terms of payload/range performance and ease of handling in the air, they lacked adequate outright performance for successful penetration of enemy airspace defended by modern fighters. The Caproni design team decided that while one possible answer was the creation of day and night bombers with basically the same performance as current types, but considerably improved defensive armament, another option was the creation of a more modern bomber with a high-rated powerplant for performance that would be improved so much that avoidance of interception became a realistic possibility.

This paved the way for the biplane bomber initially known to the manufacturer as the Caproni 600 hp, but after the end of World War I (1914-18) known as the Ca 44 series, and to the Italian air force as the Ca 5. In overall conceptual terms, the Caproni 600 hp was an updated Caproni 450 hp (Ca 3) with an uprated powerplant, a wing cellule of greater span and area, a revised central nacelle that could carry some of the bomb load as well as the crew, and a revised main landing gear arrangement.

The Ca 5 was therefore a substantial four-bay, unstaggered, equal-span biplane made largely of wood and covered mainly with fabric. The core of the airframe was the circular-section central nacelle, which carried, from front to rear, the bombardier/nose gunner armed with a single 0.256 in (6.5 mm) Revelli trainable machine gun, the pilot and co-pilot seated side-by-side in an open cockpit, the fuel tanks, the rear gunner in an open cockpit, and the central engine. This last drove a two-blade wooden propeller of the pusher type, and was surmounted by a tubular steel 'pulpit' into which the rear gunner climbed for combat; fitted with protective metal mesh over its rear surfaces, this 'pulpit' gave the gunner an all-round line of fire in the upper hemisphere with his single 0.256 in (6.5 mm) Revelli trainable machine gun.

The Caproni 600 hp prototype first flew in the second half of 1917 with a powerplant of three Fiat A.12 in-line piston engines, each rated at 200 hp (149 kW), but later replaced by three improved A.12 engines, each rated at 250 hp (186 kW). The success of the type in the course of its official evaluation is attested by the placement of large-scale orders not only with Italian manufacturers (an original total of 3900 later reduced to 3650 aircraft, of which one-third was earmarked for French service), but also with two French manufacturers (for a total of 150 or more aircraft), and with two American manufacturers (for a total of 1500 aircraft to be used by the US Air Service). The intervention of the Armistice that ended World War I in November 1918, led to the radical curtailment of these orders, and in fact no French aircraft were completed, and American production totalled just three aircraft (two Ca 44 machines by Standard and one Ca 46 machine by Fisher). Even so, Ca 5 bombers of Italian manufacture were used operationally by the French and Americans, as well as by the Italians.

The type known to the Italian air force as the Ca 5 was in fact produced in three subvariants, known to the manufacturer in its wartime and post-war designation systems as the Caproni 600 hp or 600/900 hp (Ca 44), Caproni 750 hp or 600/750 hp (Ca 45) and Caproni 900/1200 hp (Ca 46). Production of these models totalled 659 aircraft (552 by Caproni, 102 by Breda and five by Miani e Silvestri) in the period between 1918 and 1921.

The Ca 44 was powered by three A.12 or A.12bis engines rated at 250 or 300 hp (186 or 224 kW) respectively, and was the major production model in 1917. The

BELOW: The world's first four-engined bomber was a Russian type, the Sikorsky Ilya Muromets, designed before World War I and produced in only modest numbers.

■ **ABOVE: General Cadorna, commander-in-chief of the Italian army in World War I, is seen before undertaking a flight in a Caproni Ca 3, a pioneering Italian heavy bomber type.**

Ca 44 was further developed into the Ca 45, which was the variant selected by France, with a more pointed central nacelle and the revised powerplant of three Isotta-Fraschini V.6 in-line piston engines, each rated at 250 hp (186 kW) for an empty weight of 6614 lb (3000 kg), maximum take-off weight of 11,464 lb (5200 kg), maximum level speed of 93 mph (150 km/h) at sea level, climb to 3280 ft (1000 m) in 6 minutes 15 seconds, and service ceiling of 13,780 ft (4200 m). The Ca 46 was a further development along the same basic lines for production and service in 1918, with the maximum bomb load reduced to 1190 lb (540 kg), the range reduced and the powerplant altered to three Liberty 12 Vee piston engines, each rated at 360 hp (268.5 kW).

Known after the end of World War 1 as the Ca 47, the I.Ca was the seaplane conversion of the Ca 44, of which 10 were produced by Piaggio and a small number more by Bastianelli. The conversion involved the replacement of the standard wheeled landing gear by a side-by-side pair of single-step floats, resulting in an increase in length to 43 ft 3.67 in (13.20 m) and height to 16 ft 4.85 in (5.00 m).

THE GERMAN GOTHA

Gotha's first essay in the Grosskampfflugzeug (large aircraft, or bomber) field was the construction of the ill-fated G I biplane designed by Oskar Ursinus, editor of the magazine Flugsport, with a powerplant of two Mercedes D.III in-line piston engines, each rated at 160 hp (119 kW) and installed in nacelles on the upper surface of the lower wing, and a fuselage attached to the underside of the upper wing. The powerplant installation allowed the engines to be placed as close together as possible, thereby reducing asymmetric thrust problems in the event of an engine failure, while the position of the two or three crew members above the upper wing provided excellent upper-hemisphere fields of vision and fire. Several examples of the G I were produced in landplane form during 1915, and in 1916 there appeared a single UWD derivative with twin-float alighting gear. However, structural integrity was poor, performance was inadequate, handling difficult, and the crew positions extremely dangerous in the event of a nose-over on landing.

With the problems of the G I evident, Gotha secured permission for its own chief engineer, Ing Hans Burckhardt, to design a totally new aeroplane, designed specifically for the carriage of a 661 lb (300 kg) bomb load over a tactically useful range. From this start, Burckhardt produced a basic design that possessed such development potential that variants of this basic theme were still in fruitful production and service right to the end of World War I (1914–18) in November 1918. Such was the importance that the Gotha bombers came to have in Germany's strategic bombing campaign, moreover, that from 1917 Allied soldiers and civilians generally referred to all German bombers as 'Gothas'.

The three primary factors exercising Burckhardt's mind as he laid out the G II were high speed in the air, which was provided by keeping the wing span and thus area to a minimum; protection for the bombardier/gunner in the open nose position, which was provided by the incorporation of auxiliary nosewheel units to prevent any realistic possibility of a nose-over on landing; and simplicity of transport on railroad flatcars, which was provided by the manufacture of the G III in three primary sections (outer wings, forward and central fuselage with wing centre sections and engine nacelles, and rear fuselage and tail unit) that could each be carried on a single flatcar, so that an entire bomber could be delivered on three flatcars.

Completed in the early part of April 1916, the G II prototype was based on a wooden structure covered with fabric, except the forward part of the fuselage, which was skinned with plywood.

Flight trials revealed that the G II prototype possessed good handling and more than adequate performance in general terms, and only three problems. These last were inadequate directional stability, which was provided by the addition of a triangular fin; lack of adequate climb performance with the maximum bomb load, which was rectified by the adoption of a wing cellule of greater span and area incorporating aerodynamically-balanced ailerons and an additional pair of interplane struts in the outboard ends; and the tendency of the aeroplane to career along the landing strip with inadequate deceleration, which was solved by revising the landing gear to the fixed tailskid type. This last correction involved the removal of the two forward axles and the relocation of the remaining two axles to a position farther forward and thus ahead of the aeroplane's centre of gravity position, which allowed the tail to settle onto a draggy tailskid after landing.

GOTHA G II

These changes were incorporated into a second aeroplane, which was the G II production prototype completed in April 1916, and while this machine was successfully completing its service trials the manufacturer was building the first production batch of ten aircraft. The first of these aircraft was completed late in the same month, and the type was released for service use in September 1916. The details of the G II included a powerplant of two Mercedes D.IV in-line piston engines, each rated at 220 hp (164 kW) for take-off, span of 77 ft 9.1 in (23.70 m) with an area of 963.40 sq ft (89.50 m^2), length of 40 ft 0.33 in (12.20 m), height of 12 ft 9.5 in (3.90 m), empty weight of 4806 lb (2180 kg), maximum take-off weight of 7033 lb (3190 kg), maximum level speed of 84 mph (135 km/h) at optimum altitude, and endurance of 2 hours 0 minutes.

The G II was potentially a very capable warplane by the standards of its day, but the type was produced only in small numbers for limited service up to the spring of 1917 as a result of a problem with the Mercedes D.IV engine, which was an eight-cylinder in-line unit that suffered from severe crankshaft vibration, resulting in frequent failures.

The engine selected as replacement for the Mercedes D.IV was the same company's D.IVa, which incorporated a number of measures to reduce crankshaft vibration and had also been uprated to 260 hp (194 kW). This was installed in the G II to create the G III which was type-tested successfully in April 1916 with other changes that included a strengthened fuselage and the addition of a ventral position, allowing the rear gunner to adopt a prone position in the lower fuselage so that he could use a third 0.312 in (7.92 mm) LMG 14 Parabellum trainable machine gun to fire on any fighter seeking to engage the bomber in its previously vulnerable lower rear quadrant.

Deliveries of the 25 production aircraft began at the same time as those of the G II, and these bombers remained in first-line service up to a time in the fall of 1917. Two of the principal operators of the type were Kampfgeschwader 1 (Battle Squadron 1), based at Hudova for operations over the Balkan front, and Battle Squadron 2, based at Freiburg for operations over the Western Front. The success of these two units, especially the former which gained a number of operational-level successes, was one of the factors that persuaded the German authorities that production of the larger twin-engined bomber types should be increased to allow an expansion for the German bomber capability.

DEFENSIVE IMPROVEMENTS

Experience with the G III revealed that, even with its ventral gun, the type lacked adequate defence against rear-hemisphere attack under daylight conditions: the rear gunner lacked an adequate field of fire with his dorsal gun, and when operating his ventral gun in the prone position might suddenly have to scramble to his feet to man the dorsal gun if the attacking fighter climbed from a position below the aeroplane to a spot above it. Burkhard tried initially to improve the field of fire for the dorsal machine gun by revising the upper line of the rear fuselage into a sharp-ridged triangular shape to provide improved lateral/downward fields of fire, but this was a clumsy arrangement that did not provide any capability of firing into the dead zone below and behind the aeroplane. Burkhard's final solution was simpler and more effective: he hollowed out the lower part of the rear fuselage between the dorsal gunner's position and the tail, and provided a small triangular opening in the upper decking so that the dorsal gun could be depressed to fire through this opening through an azimuth angle of 25° and an elevation arc of 60°. This allowed the dorsal gunner to tackle fighters attacking under the tail without adopting a prone position, although this possibility was still open to him with the optional 0.312 in (7.92 mm) LMG 14 Parabellum machine gun located in the ventral position and now given a considerably enlarged field of fire. Provision was also made for a fourth 0.312 in (7.92 mm) LMG 14 Parabellum trainable machine gun on a pillar mounting, located on the forward upper decking between the pilot and the bombardier/gunner. Manned by an

Caproni Ca 3
Type: four-seat heavy bomber
Country of origin: Italy
Powerplant: three 150-hp (112-kW) Isotta-Fraschini V.4B piston engines
Performance: max level speed 87 mph (140 km/h); service ceiling 15,750 ft (4800 m); max range 280 miles (450 km)
Weights: empty 5071 lb (2300 kg); maximum take-off 8576 lb (2890 kg)
Dimensions: wing span 72 ft 10 in (22.20 m); length 35 ft 9.25 in (10.90 m); height 12 ft 1.5 in (3.70 m)
Armament: up to 0.256 in (6.5 mm) Revelli machine guns, plus up to 992 lb (450 kg) of bombs

additional crew member, this installation was seldom used as it meant the sacrifice of part of the bomb load to offset the additional weight.

These changes were introduced in the G IV bomber that otherwise differed from the G III in having a fuselage that was completely covered with plywood for additional strength, and in the addition on the outboard ends of the lower wing's trailing edge of ailerons strut-connected to those of the upper wing.

The G IV, which entered limited service in the fall of 1916 (perhaps in the form of the single interim machine with the triangular rear decking), but full service from March 1917, was the type designed to bear the brunt of the Germans' 'Türkenkreuz' (Turk's cross) bomber campaign against England. This effort had been planned from the end of 1916, when it became evident that the airship bombing campaign against England had been an exceptionally costly failure, and was to be operated by 'G' category twin-engined bombers and, when available in useful number, 'G' category four-engined bombers. The first unit to equip with the new type was Battle Squadron 3, which was later renamed Bomber Squadron 3, at its St Denis-Westrem and Gonterode bases, although British bombers subsequently forced Bomber Squadron 3 to move to Mariakerke and Oostracker; all four of these bases were in the Ghent area of German-occupied Belgium.

In November 1916, the German air force ordered 35 production examples of the G IV, increasing this total to 50 in February 1917, and the G IV was successfully type-tested in December 1916 with a view to the availability of 30 aircraft with the four (from July 1917 six) flights of Battle Squadron 1, in time for the planned start of the 'Türkenkreuz' offensive at the beginning of February 1918. Events were to prove the over-ambition of this schedule, especially as production of the G IV was severely hampered in its early stages by lack of the necessary materials and then the failure of the G IV to meet its performance requirements.

RAIDS ON ENGLAND

Early operations were directed at London, and faults discovered at this stage necessitated the replacement of the engines as a result of defective bearings in the original units, the revision of the main fuel tanks to ensure that all their capacity could be used, and the addition of a second gravity-feed fuel tank on the upper wing to ensure that there was enough fuel for attacks on London without the need for an intermediate stop in northern Belgium for the tanks to be topped off.

On 25 May 1917, some 23 G IV bombers were committed to the first of 22 raids on targets in England, and the success of these initial raids is attested by the urgent and relatively large-scale effort mounted by the British to bolster their aerial defences of south-east England, which generally lacked the fighters capable of attaining the altitude of 14,765 ft (4500 m) or more at which the G IV bombers could operate. By September 1917, the introduction of Bristol F.2 Fighter, Royal Aircraft Factory S.E.5 and Sopwith F.1 Camel fighters had improved the British defences to the point at which the Germans switched to night bombing in an effort to reduce the rate of bomber losses. The night raids lasted to May 1918, and in the course of this combined day and night campaign, the Gotha bombers of Bomber Squadron 3 dropped 186,830 lb (84,745 kg) of bombs, suffering the loss of 61 aircraft in the process (24 on operations and a further 37 in accidents, often as a result of combat damage).

By this time, two other production sources had come on stream in an effort to maintain the G IV force at reasonable strength: in December 1916, Siemens-Schuckert Werke had received an order for 80 G IV bombers, and Luft-Verkehrs-Gesellschaft was contracted at a slightly later date to deliver 100 aircraft. The first aircraft from Siemens-Schuckert and LVG successfully completed their type-tests in April and June 1917 respectively, but the aircraft from these two sources never reached the performance of the Gotha-built aircraft as a result of the fact that the IdFlieg (Inspektion der Fliegertruppen, or inspectorate of flying troops) had specified a strengthened and therefore heavier airframe for these licence-built aircraft.

The aircraft built by Siemens-Schuckert were delivered mainly to the Battle Squadrons 3 and 4, and the bomber training school at Paderborn (first batch) between July 1917 and February 1918, a second batch following between December 1917 and August 1918 mainly for the use of training units, as the G IV was rightly regarded as

BELOW: The Gotha G III was one of the most important and successful bombers operated by the Imperial German army air service in the middle part of World War I.

Gotha G IV

Type: three-seat long-range bomber
Country of origin: Germany
Powerplant: two 260-hp (194-kW) Mercedes D.IVa in-line piston engines
Performance: maximum level speed 92 mph (148 km/h); endurance 3 hours 45 minutes
Weights: empty 5254 lb (2383 kg) maximum take-off 7997 lb (3635 kg)
Dimensions: wing span 77 ft 9.25 in (23.70 m); length 38 ft 11 in (11.86 m); height 14 ft 1.25 in (4.30 m)
Armament: up to three 0.312 in (7.92 mm) LMG 14 machine guns plus 1102 lb (500 kg) of bombs

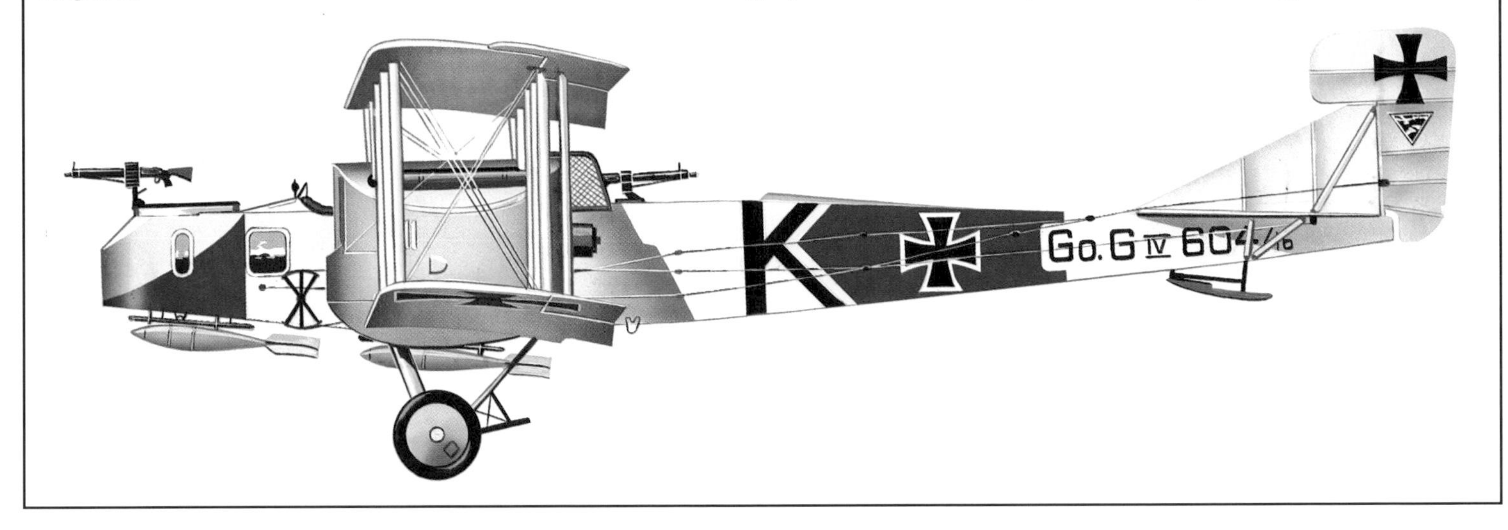

obsolescent. The aircraft of this second batch were completed to a down-rated standard, with the fuel tankage relocated to the fuselage for reduced vulnerability, the powerplant altered to two NAG C.III or Argus As.III in-line piston engines, each rated at 185 or 180 hp (138 or 134 kW) respectively, an auxiliary landing gear unit installed under the nose to reduce the number of nose-over landing accidents, and a Flettner servo-tab added to the rudder to reduce control loads.

A few of the Siemens-Schuckert aircraft were used for the development of ways in which the performance of the G IV might be improved: one machine was revised with a powerplant of two Maybach Mb.IVa in-line piston engines each rated at 245 hp (183 kW) and driving a tractor rather than pusher propeller. One was fitted with an additional set of interplane struts on each side to permit an increase in span to 81 ft 8.33 in (24.90 m) with an area of 956.94 sq ft (88.90 m^2), and another was fitted with a supercharger installation developed by Siemens.

Deliveries of the LVG-built aircraft were also made to operational units and then to training schools. From February 1918, some 30 examples of the G IV – now deemed obsolescent in German service – were transferred to the Austro-Hungarian air force. These machines were completed by Oeffag, with a defensive armament of three 0.315 in (8 mm) Schwarzlose trainable machine guns and a powerplant of two Hiero in-line piston engines, each rated at 230 hp (171.5 kW) and driving a two-blade pusher propeller.

THE GOTHA G V

With Siemens-Schuckert and LVG increasingly carrying the weight of G IV production, Burkhard was able to turn his attention from the spring of 1917 to an improved version of the G IV for production first by Gotha and then by the company's two licensees. This improved model was the G V, which incorporated the ideas not just of Burkhard, but also of operational units, most specifically Battle Squadron 3, and was based on the desirability of removing the main fuel tanks from their current position under the engines, where they could burst in crash landings, spilling their remaining contents over the hot engines with almost inevitably fatal consequences for members of the crew.

In the G V, therefore, the main fuel tankage was shifted into the central fuselage, the engines were installed in smaller and better streamlined nacelles positioned just above the lower wing on four short struts, and the bomb load was carried externally under the fuselage and lower wing. The G V was successfully type-tested in July 1917 and started to enter service with Bomber Squadron 3 in August of the same year. It had been hoped that the new bomber would offer a performance increase sufficient to permit the resumption of daylight raids on London and other English targets, but it soon became clear that in performance terms the G V was no real improvement over the G IV, the higher level speed of the prototype having been purchased at the cost of climb rate.

Full-production examples of the G V also suffered from reduced engine power, the D.IVA's notional rating of 260 hp (194 kW) having been reduced to some 245 hp (183 kW) by the need to use poorer fuel, and an increase of between 882 and 992 lb (400 and 450 kg) as a result of additional equipment and the need to use not fully seasoned timber. With dimensions and armament identical to those of the G IV, the G V had an empty weight of 6041 lb (2740 kg) and a maximum take-off weight of 8763 lb (3975 kg), and its performance details included a maximum level speed of 87 mph (140 km/h) at 11,975 ft (3650 m), climb to 9845 ft (3000 m) in 28 minutes 0 seconds, and service ceiling of 21,325 ft (6500 m), an altitude that was reached in 52 minutes 30 seconds.

These performance figures could only be attained by a bomber without armament, and it was reckoned that each one per cent increase in weight resulted in a loss of 195 to 260 ft (60 to 80 m) in service ceiling and a comparable worsening of climb performance. The effect of this fact was that while the G IV had often been able to cruise over England in its first daylight raids at altitudes in excess of 16,405 ft (5000 m), in later raids, with a greater bomb load and more fuel, it could seldom climb to a

height of more than 13,125 ft (4000 m). The more heavily laden G V, therefore, was forced to fly its first missions at heights of up to only 8200 ft (2500 m) and its later raids at a mere 5575 ft (1700 m). Both these altitudes were within the rapid climb capability of British fighters, which could thus rise and intercept before – rather than after – the bombers had delivered their warloads.

After the end of the German bomber offensive against England in May 1918, the surviving aircraft were used over the Western Front up to the end of World War I, although from June 1918, the use of the G V in this theatre was being scaled down as small numbers of improved aircraft made their appearance.

THE LATER VARIANTS

These improved variants were the G Va and G Vb, which were both fitted with a compound tail unit (biplane horizontal surfaces and twin vertical surfaces) for improved controllability in single-engined flight. With the earlier models, asymmetric thrust problems in single-engined flight had required the remaining engine to be throttled back, but in the new variants, the greater control authority of the tail unit allowed single-engined flight at full throttle. The new tail, with its smaller overall dimensions, also provided the rear gunner with improved fields of fire. Other changes effected in these variants were a shorter nose, a twin-wheel auxiliary landing gear unit under the nose, or two twin-wheel auxiliary landing gear units immediately ahead of the main units in the manner of the original G II and, on some aircraft, Flettner servo tabs on the ailerons to reduce lateral control loads.

The G Va was successfully type-tested in February 1918 and entered production in the following month for a service debut in April 1918. Production of a limited number of aircraft continued up to June 1918, when the G Va was replaced on the Gotha production line by the G Vb, with a measure of internal revision to permit the carriage of a useful load 805 lb (365 kg) heavier than had been possible with the G V and G Va. This useful load was the crew, machine guns and their ammunition, bombs and fuel which, on the basis of an empty weight of 6504 lb (2950 kg) allowed a maximum take-off weight of 10,031 lb (4550 kg), even though this meant a slight loss in maximum level speed. Production of the G Vb continued in Germany up to the end of World War I, but totalled only about 30 aircraft out of some 200 aircraft of the G V series.

■ **ABOVE: So effective was the Airco (de Havilland) D.H.9A improved version of the D.H.4, that the type was kept in service by the British until the 1930s for policing the empire.**

THE BRITISH RESPONSE

On 13 June 1917, a daylight raid on London by 18 Gotha G IV bombers caused more casualties (162 dead and 432 wounded) than all the raids previously undertaken by the German airship force, and as a direct result, Field Marshal Sir William Robertson, the Chief of the Imperial General Staff, asked for a major increase in the number of British warplanes. Only a week later, the British war cabinet decided that the strength of the Royal Flying Corps should be increased from 108 to 200 squadrons, with most of the new squadrons equipped for the bombing role as a means of taking the war to Germany. The need for new aircraft with which to equip the fresh squadrons was reflected before the end of the month by orders for an additional 700 Airco (de Havilland) D.H.4 day bombers, and, at much the same time, Field Marshal Sir Douglas Haig, commanding the British Expeditionary Force in France, was informed that development had been set in hand of an improved version of the D.H.4 with longer range so that the area of British bombing operations could be enlarged.

This last comment related to the scheme detailed to the Air Board a few days earlier for the D.H.9 as an extensively changed version of the D.H.4, with greater range as well as a maximum level speed of 112 mph (180 km/h) at 10,000 ft (3050 m). The Air Board was not minded initially to let the introduction of a new type affect deliveries of the D.H.4 but, when advised that the introduction of the new type would curtail bomber deliveries by Airco and other D.H.4 contractors for a maximum of only four weeks, it relented and ordered that the outstanding D.H.4 orders should be amended to cover the improved D.H.9.

The D.H.9 was a development of the D.H.4 mainly in its fuselage, and this meant that exactly the same wing cellule and tail unit could be used. The primary changes effected in the fuselage were the exchange of the pilot's cockpit and main fuel tank, so that the crew could communicate more effectively in tactical conditions and the threat posed to the pilot in a crash landing from movement or cracking of the fuel tank was removed, and the introduction of a more refined engine installation to reduce drag and thereby boost speed. The engine installation was based on that developed on the D.H.4 for the Fiat A.12 in-line piston engine, which was located with much of its vertical cylinder bank exposed above the nicely-shaped nose, with a radiator that could be retracted into the underside of the forward fuselage as a means of providing adequate cooling with minimum drag.

The D.H.9 prototype was a D.H.4 conversion that made its first flight in July 1917 with a powerplant of one Galloway Adriatic in-line piston engine, which was a development of the BHP engine with a higher compression ratio, rated at 230 hp (171.5 kW) and driving a two-blade wooden propeller. The flight trials of the prototype proceeded without problem, but the engine selected for the production version of the D.H.9 was the version of the standard BHP, built by Siddeley-Deasy as the Siddeley Puma, with a rating of 300 hp (224 kW). Siddeley-Deasy was currently building up to 30 BHP engines per week, but plans had already been made for it to manufacture up to 100 Pumas per month. An immediate problem, however, was the supply of aluminium cylinder blocks for the engines, of which no less than 90 per cent were defective, and resulted in an immediate down-rating of the engine to 230 hp (171.5 kW).

This fact caused considerable concern in the RFC, for it had been revealed to senior officers by Geoffrey de Havilland, designer of the D.H.4 and D.H.9, that the performance of the Puma-engined D.H.9 would now be inferior, especially in terms of speed, climb and ceiling, to that of the current D.H.4 with the Rolls-Royce Mk III (later Eagle III) Vee piston engine. Haig, at the instigation of Major General Hugh Trenchard, commanding the RFC in France, in November 1917 asked for production of the D.H.9 to be limited to the aircraft required by just 15 squadrons, as the type would be obsolete by June 1918. This sensible request came too late, however, for plans had not only been laid, but already implemented for the D.H.4 to be complemented and then supplanted by the D.H.9, and production of the D.H.9 was soon in full swing to match deliveries of the BHP engine, that soon attained 200 units per week. It was most appositely said that the D.H.9 was a 'D.H.4 which has been officially interfered with in order to be suitable for mass-production and the BHP motor'.

FIRST DELIVERIES

The first D.H.9 aircraft came off the production line late in 1917, and were powered by the BHP engine produced by Galloway or Siddeley. Early tests of these aircraft confirmed the fact that the type was a fine warplane, whose potential was lost to a poor engine: designed to carry a greater load (bombs, machine guns and ammunition, fuel, oil, water and crew) than the more powerfully engined D.H.4, the D.H.9 inevitably suffered from inferior performance in all-round terms, and was particularly disadvantaged by its inability to reach and cruise at the same height as the D.H.4. It was seldom possible for D.H.9 formations to cruise at more than 13,000 ft (3960 m), and even at that height, the strain on the engine was so great that failures were not

■ **ABOVE: The relatively gargantuan scale of the Handley Page O/100 twin-engined bomber is revealed by its juxtaposition with a Royal Aircraft Factory S.E.5a fighter.**

infrequent, the consequent reduction of numbers within the formation severely curtailing the ability of the D.H.9 bombers to provide mutual cover for each other against German fighter attack.

The D.H.9 was issued to bomber squadrons from a time early in 1918, and the first units to take the type into action were Nos 98, 206 and 211 Squadrons, which reached France in April 1918, as the Germans were making their last determined land efforts to defeat France and the UK before the large-scale arrival of fresh American formations to bolster the allied effort on the Western Front, which would inevitably eventually lead to Germany's defeat.

By this time, production of the new type was accelerating rapidly, despite the spate of aircraft lost and missions aborted as a result of engine problems. Trenchard decided in June 1918 that the type should be replaced in first-line service from August of the same year, but such was the spate of deliveries that the type was retained in service right to the end of World War I in November 1918.

Given the poor performance of the D.H.9 by contemporary standards, it was fortunate for its crews that the German fighter arm had by that stage of the war been rendered largely inactive by shortages of fuel, and the major problem therefore faced by the RAF crews was the continuing unreliability of the various engines, all derived from the original poorly-designed BHP.

Manufacture of the D.H.9 continued to a time late in 1918, and totalled 3204 aircraft, delivered by a very large production organisation. The type remained in service, largely with export customers, into the 1930s.

THE LIBERTY ENGINE

In August 1917, the US Secretary of War announced the completion of the first Liberty aero engine a mere 28 days after design on the type had been started. This was indeed a very impressive achievement, and the Secretary of War then went on to describe the capabilities of the Liberty engine in the most glowing of terms, ending with the assertion that it was 'the best aircraft engine produced in any country'.

As events were to prove, the Liberty was indeed a fine engine, but at the time of the Secretary of War's announcement, the engine had yet to fly and was also to encounter the series of teething problems that beset every engine as it is developed toward the production stage.

The first engine to fly was the Liberty 8 with eight cylinders in the Vee arrangement retained for all Liberty engines, but this initial type was soon overshadowed by the Liberty 12 with 12 cylinders. This was first tested at a rating of 314 hp (234 kW) in August 1917, but two months later had been cleared for production at a rating of 395 hp (295 kW). Plans called for production of the Liberty engine to reach 4800 per month by May 1918, but this rate was never in fact achieved and total deliveries by the end of that month were only 1100 engines out of a planned 9420, as a result in shortages of the required jigs, tools and gauges, together with the need to implement no fewer than 1022 modifications in the period between September 1917 and February 1918.

Despite this failure to meet production targets, the Liberty 12 was nonetheless a considerable achievement, and its high power rating made the type especially attractive to the British authorities, which were seeking an alternative to the Rolls-Royce Eagle whose production was falling considerably behind demand. An early Liberty 12 had been test flown in an Airco (de Havilland) D.H.4 bomber in October 1917, flight trials revealing a significant improvement in performance over the standard BHP- and Puma-engined variants of the same bomber. The British authorities therefore decided to exploit the capability supposedly offered by the very large American production programme. By the end of January 1918, the British had asked for 3000 examples of the Liberty engine, with deliveries beginning in the same month at the rate of 500 engines per month, but the first 10 engines did not arrive until March, and deliveries ended in July after the arrival of only 1050 engines.

Given the fact that the engine had been successfully test-flown in a converted D.H.4, the British decided that the anticipated steady flow of Liberty 12 engines should be used primarily to improve the disappointing D.H.9, itself a development of the D.H.4, with the main fuel tank relocated from the D.H.4's position between the pilot's and gunner's cockpits to a position forward of the pilot's cockpit, which was thus moved to the rear so that the crew of two could communicate more readily as a means of improving the type's tactical capabilities. Airco was too heavily involved in the design of the D.H.10 Amiens twin-engined bomber to undertake the redesign required to turn the D.H.9 into the Liberty-engined D.H.9A, and the task was therefore entrusted to the Westland Aircraft Works of Petters Ltd at Yeovil in Somerset. This company had been fully involved in the D.H.4 and D.H.9 programmes, and was therefore already well versed in the basic design of the Airco aeroplane.

THE DH.9A

The D.H.9A that emerged from this process bore a stronger superficial resemblance to the D.H.4 than to the D.H.9, as it had a frontal radiator and therefore the same type of nose contours as the D.H.4 in combination with the main fuel tank, pilot and gunner positions of the D.H.9 and a somewhat revised airframe with wire cross-bracing in the fuselage in place of the D.H.9's plywood cross partitions, as a means of improving its strength and therefore its ability to carry the heavier engine. Also the biplane wing cellule was of greater span and chord for greater area and therefore better rate of climb and ceiling. The D.H.9 was a thoroughly orthodox two-bay biplane in which there were no remarkable features.

The first D.H.9A was a D.H.9 conversion that flew with a powerplant of one Eagle VIII Vee piston engine, driving a four-blade wooden propeller, to allow a start to be made on the flight test program pending delivery of the first Liberty 12 engines from the USA. This was particularly provident, for it simplified the task of adopting the Eagle VIII as the alternative powerplant for the new bomber once it had become clear that deliveries of the Liberty 12 would be too small in quantity and too late in arrival for the fast-moving D.H.9A production programme. Even so, the majority of D.H.9 aircraft were in fact powered by the Liberty 12 engine rated at 400 hp (298 kW) for differences that included an empty weight of 2770 lb (1256 kg), normal take-off weight of 4220 lb (1914 kg), maximum take-off weight of 4645 lb (2107 kg), maximum level speed of 123 mph (198 km/h) at sea level declining to 102 mph (164 km/h) at 16,500 ft (5030 m), endurance of 5 hours 15 minutes, initial climb rate of 890 ft (271 m) per minute, climb to 6500 ft (1980 m) in 6 minutes 50 seconds, and service ceiling of 19,000 ft (5790 m).

The production programme was entrusted to members of basically the same organisation that was currently building the D.H.9, and by the end of June 1918, the first 18 of an eventual 2300 aircraft had been delivered. In March 1918, Major General Hugh M. Trenchard, commanding the Royal Air Force (created in April 1918 by amalgamation of the Royal Flying Corps and Royal Naval Air Service) in France, had urged that the highest possible priority be attached to production of the D.H.9A so that the D.H.9 could be replaced in his bomber squadrons. However, in fact it was August 1918 before No 110 Squadron reached France as the first operational D.H.9A unit. On arrival in France, No 110 Squadron was allocated to the Independent Force, as the British strategic bombing force was named, and undertook its first operation in mid-September 1918.

IMPROVED PERFORMANCE

The D.H.9A was much liked for its performance, which was considerably higher than that of the D.H.9, especially at altitudes of over 13,000 ft (3960 m), but was initially distrusted for the coil ignition system used in the Liberty 12 engine. Such an ignition system was rare in British service, and it was only after the British mechanics had come to appreciate the virtues of the system, and how to maintain it properly, that the Liberty 12 engine began to come into its own and offer the type of reliability wanted by the RAF.

Up to the end of December 1918, some 885 D.H.9A aircraft had been built, but only 405 of these had been delivered to

Airco (de Havilland) D.H.9A

Type: two-seat day bomber
Country of origin: UK
Powerplant: one 375-hp (280-kW) Rolls-Royce Eagle VIII Vee piston engine
Performance: maximum level speed 125.5 mph (202 km/h); service ceiling 20,000 ft (6095 m); maximum endurance 5 hrs 15 mins
Weights: empty 2705 lb (1227 kg); max take-off 4815 lb (2184 kg)
Dimensions: wing span 45 ft 11.625 in (14.01 m); length 30 ft 3 in (9.22 m); height 11 ft 4 in (3.45 m)
Armament: one 0.303 in (7.7 mm) Vickers machine gun, plus up to 740 lb (336 kg) of bombs

the RAF up to the end of October of that year. The type served mainly over the Western Front, where it served with Nos 18, 99, 110 and 205 Squadrons, but the type was also operated in the coastal patrol role with Nos 212 and 273 Squadrons from bases near the English coast, and also by training units located at Cranwell, Fowlmere and Waddington among others. When the Allied powers intervened on the side of the White Russian forces seeking to combat the Bolshevik forces in post-revolutionary Russia, part of the British effort was vested in two D.H.9A units, namely Nos 47 and 221 Squadrons.

The D.H.9A was one of the few World War I types selected for continued British production in the period after the war, when demobilisation and financial retrenchment resulted in an extraordinarily rapid decline in the UK's military strengths, especially those of the army and the RAF. This extra production eventually totalled some 300 more aircraft delivered up to 1928 and included a small number of aircraft used mainly in the military mail role, with a powerplant of one Napier Lion W-type piston engine rated at 450 hp (335.5 kW).

OVERSEAS SERVICE

In the immediate aftermath of the war, most of the D.H.9A squadrons were allocated to the air component of the Allied occupation forces in Germany, but the squadrons were soon reduced to cadre strength and then disbanded. The sole exception to this process was No 99 Squadron, which in May 1919 was posted to northwest India as part of the RAF's three-squadron reinforcement of its current strength of only two squadrons in this vital area, where the 3rd Afghan War (1919–20) had just started.

Pilots found that in the air of India, they had to relearn their flying techniques: the take-off was long and the subsequent climb slow in the hot air of low altitude; flight at high altitude was then extremely uncomfortable as a result of the cold, and a sideslipped landing had to be avoided at all costs if the main landing gear unit was not to collapse. Engine cooling was also a problem, and in August 1920 an additional radiator was added under the nose. Other changes gradually effected to the D.H.9A force included a long-range tank under the starboard upper wing, a spare wheel attached to the port side of the forward fuselage or under the fuselage, a water bag (usually made from an animal skin), emergency rations and bed rolls.

■ABOVE: The Handley Page O/400 was a much improved development of the O/100, and was, without doubt, the most effective British heavy bomber of World War I.

The D.H.9A also served as the primary day bomber of the RAF's home-based air strength up to 1924, when it was replaced by the Fairey Fawn and later types. The D.H.9A was also used by the Auxiliary Air Force that was created in 1925, and also by a number of flying training schools. The last D.H.9A aircraft in British home-based service had been retired from first-line service by 1930.

A small number of D.H.9A bombers surplus to British requirements was sold to Spain in 1922, and these aircraft differed from their British counterparts in having their Eagle VIII engines cooled by a pair of Lamblin radiators under the fuselage, between the landing gear legs.

Given its earlier decisions to build large numbers of the D.H.4 as the DH-4 and then the D.H.9 as the USD-9, the Americans sensibly decided that the probability of World War I lasting into 1919 should be reflected in large-scale orders for the altogether more capable Liberty-engined D.H.9A, which was to be known as the USD-9A. In October 1918, Dayton-Wright built an initial four aircraft of this type, followed in the following month by five more machines, constructed by the Engineering Division of the Bureau of Aircraft Production. The main production source was to have been the Curtiss Aeroplane and Motor Co Inc, but in November 1918, its contracts for

4000 USD-9A aircraft were cancelled almost immediately after the end of hostilities. The few USD-9A aircraft were employed mainly for test work, and in February 1919, one of the aircraft became the sole USD-9B after it had been fitted with the Liberty 12A engine rated at 420 hp (313 kW) and a wing cellule of increased area.

A TRUE HEAVY BOMBER

Retrospectively allocated the company designation H.P.11 when Handley Page introduced this system in 1924, the O/100 was arguably the first truly effective heavy bomber to enter service anywhere in the world. The aircraft's original designation was based on the use of a letter to indicate the sequence of the design in alphabetical order and, in a suffix of the type added from 1911, a numeral indicating a primary feature, such as the powerplant's horsepower or the aircraft's wing span.

The technical origins of this important warplane can be found in 1913, when the Daily Mail newspaper offered a prize of £10,000 for the pilot of the first aeroplane to achieve a flight across the Atlantic Ocean. This was a very considerable prize by the standards of the day, and one of the three aircraft designed and built in the hope of winning this prize was the Handley Page L/200. This was a biplane with a crew of two, equipped with dual controls, powerplant of one Salmson (Canton-Unne) water-cooled radial piston engine rated at 200 hp (149 kW), span of 60 ft (18.29 m), and an estimated endurance of 23 hours at a speed of 80 mph (129 km/h). The L/200 was never put to the test, for the outbreak of World War I came in August 1914, when the aeroplane was still incomplete. Despite this unfortunate fact, the L/200 is of considerable importance, as it was the first type to be designed after Frederick Handley Page had come to a full appreciation of the importance that should be attached to large aircraft capable of carrying a major load of fuel and/or payload.

In December 1914, the Admiralty issued to British manufacturers its requirement for a large warplane capable of undertaking extended over-water patrols with a tactical significant bomb load. The specification called for a crew of two, twin-engined powerplant, maximum level speed of 62.5 kt (72 mph; 116 km/h), defensive armament of one 0.303 in (7.7 mm) rifle, and offensive armament of six 100 lb (45 kg) bombs. Handley Page responded with the design for a large biplane powered by two Beardmore in-line piston engines, each rated at 120 hp (89.5 kW), and this design so impressed Commodore Murray Sueter, Director of the Air Department in the Admiralty, that he asked Handley Page to expand the concept to produce a 'bloody paralyzer' of an aeroplane. With the assistance of G. R. Volkert, Handley Page revised his original design with greater overall dimensions and a powerplant of two Sunbeam in-line piston engines each rated at 150 hp (112 kW), and this model received an order for one prototype of the type that was now known to the company as the O/100, to indicate that it followed the N/80 project for a scout (fighter) with a powerplant of one Gnome rotary piston engine rated at 80 hp (59.6 kW), and had a span of 100 ft 0 in (30.48 m).

The Handley Page plant worked seven days per week to complete the prototype, which presented considerable problems, as it was by far the largest aeroplane yet attempted in the UK. No one had any practical experience of the design and construction of so large an aeroplane, and to ensure adequate structural integrity, every significant component was tested to destruction before an identical item was installed. Even so, the prototype was ready for testing less than 12 months after the receipt of the construction order. Even as the airframe manufacturer was proceeding with the O/100 prototype, Rolls-Royce was pressing ahead with the development of its Mk II Vee piston engine, that was to be vital in the future career of the O/100 and its successors. Originally planned at a rating of 200 hp (149 kW) and later named Eagle, this engine was first run in March 1915 and by August of the same year was being run at 300 hp (224 kW) at 3000 rpm, although a rating of 250 hp (186 kW) at 1600 rpm was selected for the production model to ensure reliability.

In accordance with a February 1915 amendment to the original contract (soon altered to a total of four prototypes and an initial eight production aircraft), two of these Rolls-Royce engines replaced the originally specified pair of Sunbeam engines, each engine being located in an armoured nacelle that also contained protected fuel and oil tanks. Further armour and bullet-proof glass were fitted for the protection of the three-man crew on an enclosed flightdeck in the extreme forward end of the short fuselage section, ahead of the wing cellule. It was in this form that the O/100 prototype made its first flight in December 1915. The flight trials indicated the need for a number of modifications, one of these being the removal of the flightdeck enclosure, which had collapsed during one test flight, and its replacement in the second prototype and all later aircraft with a long plywood-covered nose section that located the two pilots some 12 ft 0 in (3.66 m) farther forward than their original position. This allowed the incorporation of a nose gunner's position to complement the rear gunner, who was also aided in production aircraft with a dorsal position and secondary ventral trapdoor position for defence against fighters attacking from below and to the rear. The changes to the forward fuselage were accompanied by the deletion of virtually all the armour protection, including that of the fuel tanks in the engine nacelles.

Production of the O/100, including the four prototypes brought up to full production standard, was 46 aircraft, all completed by Handley Page rather than Mann, Egerton & Co Ltd, as had originally been planned. The last six aircraft had a powerplant of two Sunbeam Cossack Vee piston engines, each rated at 320 hp (238.5 kW), and while the first 40 aircraft should therefore have had the powerplant of two Eagle II engines as originally specified, single aircraft were used for trial installations of the Cossack and the Fiat A.12bis in-line piston engine rated at 260 hp (194 kW).

THE 0/100 IN SERVICE

These aircraft were delivered to the Royal Naval Air Service from September 1916, initially to equip a training squadron based at Manston in Kent, and then as the equipment of the squadrons of No 5 Wing based at Dunkerque on the northern French coast. Initially only three O/100 bombers were allocated to No 5 Wing in November 1916, but from April 1917, more aircraft were delivered to allow the full equipment of this wing's Nos 7 and 7A Squadrons, as well as part of No 3 Wing based at Luxeuil farther south in France, for attacks on German industrial targets. The aircraft in northern France were initially tasked with coastal anti-ship and anti-submarine patrols, but the loss of two aircraft to anti-aircraft fire suggested that the O/100 was too large and cumbersome for daylight operations, and the two RNAS squadrons were then reallocated to the nocturnal bombing role against German industrial targets, as well as the airfields used by the German bomber force raiding southern England at this time.

From October 1917, a number of the aircraft were transferred to the new 'A' Squadron forming at Manston as the nucleus for the major force that the Royal Flying Corps and RNAS (combined as the Royal Air Force in April 1918) was planning and creating for use as the Independent Force in a strategic bombing campaign against Germany's war industries. 'A' Squadron flew to Ochey in France later in October 1917 to become part of the 41st Wing, first element of the Independent Force, and in January 1918, became No 16 (Naval) Squadron or, in RAF service, No 216 Squadron for service right up to the Armistice in November.

Only one O/100 bomber was used outside the European theatre, this being a single machine allocated to the RNAS station on Mudros island in the Aegean Sea for a bombing campaign against Constantinople, the Turkish capital, now known as Istanbul. The aeroplane made only one raid on Constantinople at the beginning of its career in July 1917 before being reallocated to the patrol role for three months. On its second visit to Constantinople, undertaken at the end of September 1917, the aeroplane was forced down in the Gulf of Xeros by engine failure, and the crew was taken prisoner by Turkish forces.

THE HANDLEY PAGE O/400

Retrospectively allocated the company designation H.P.12 when Handley Page introduced this system in 1924, the O/400 was a logical development of the O/100, with the numerical suffix in its designation now indicating engine horsepower rather than the span of 100 ft 0 in (30.48 m). It was intended mainly for service with the Royal Flying Corps, which had followed the lead of the Royal Naval Air Service into the heavy bombing role after it realised the significance of the German 'Türkenkreuz' (Turk's cross) bomber offensive against the UK which started in February 1917 and began to achieve significant morale effect in the late spring and summer of that year.

Up to that time, the RFC had believed in the greater importance of the light day bomber, which offered speed rather than bomb load as its major tactical attribute, in the belief that a smaller weight of bombs delivered more accurately by day was of greater value than a larger weight of bombs delivered less accurately by night. So strong was this belief in the minds of senior RFC commanders that as late as July 1917, they decided to end all development of heavy bombers. By August of the same year, the RFC had been forced to reconsider its position in the light of the successes achieved by the Germans' Gotha bombers and revelations about the accurate bombing achieved at night by the RNAS's small O/100 force. A first step in the readoption of the heavy bomber concept for the RFC was the August 1917 placement of orders for prototypes of the Handley Page V/1500 heavy and Vickers F.B.27 Vimy medium night bombers, and then the contract for 100 initial examples of the O/400 improved version of the O/100.

The validity of this British decision was forcibly borne home from the beginning of the following month, when the Germans switched their bomber effort from day to night attacks on English targets; the raids were successful, and German losses declined. As a result, the Air Board ordered another 200 O/400 bombers and then a further 100 in response to the request of Field Marshal Sir Douglas Haig, commanding the British Expeditionary Force in France, that 25 per cent of all new bombers for the Western Front should be completed as night bombers.

The development of the O/400 was the direct result of operational experience with the O/100 by the RNAS in France, and the single most important change involved in turning the O/100 into the O/400 was the adoption of a totally revised fuel system. Whereas the O/100 carried two 120 Imp gal (545.5 litre) tanks in the engine nacelles to supplement the 130 Imp gal (591 litre) tank in the central fuselage, the O/400 had two 130 Imp gal (591 litre) tanks in the central fuselage. Each of the tanks were surmounted by a wind-driven pump that propelled the fuel directly to the engine carburettors and also into two 14 Imp gal (63.6 litre) gravity-feed tanks in the upper-wing centre section, which could supply the engines in the event of a pump failure.

This change allowed the shortening and therefore lightening of the two engine nacelles, which still carried the oil tanks for each engine and were supported by a different arrangement of struts. The only other visible changes were the adoption of a full-length interplane strut behind each engine nacelle and the movement of the central fin farther to the rear, so that its leading edge was slightly behind those of the fixed tailplanes. The powerplant intended for the O/400 was a pair of Rolls-Royce Vee piston engines in its most recent and uprated forms,

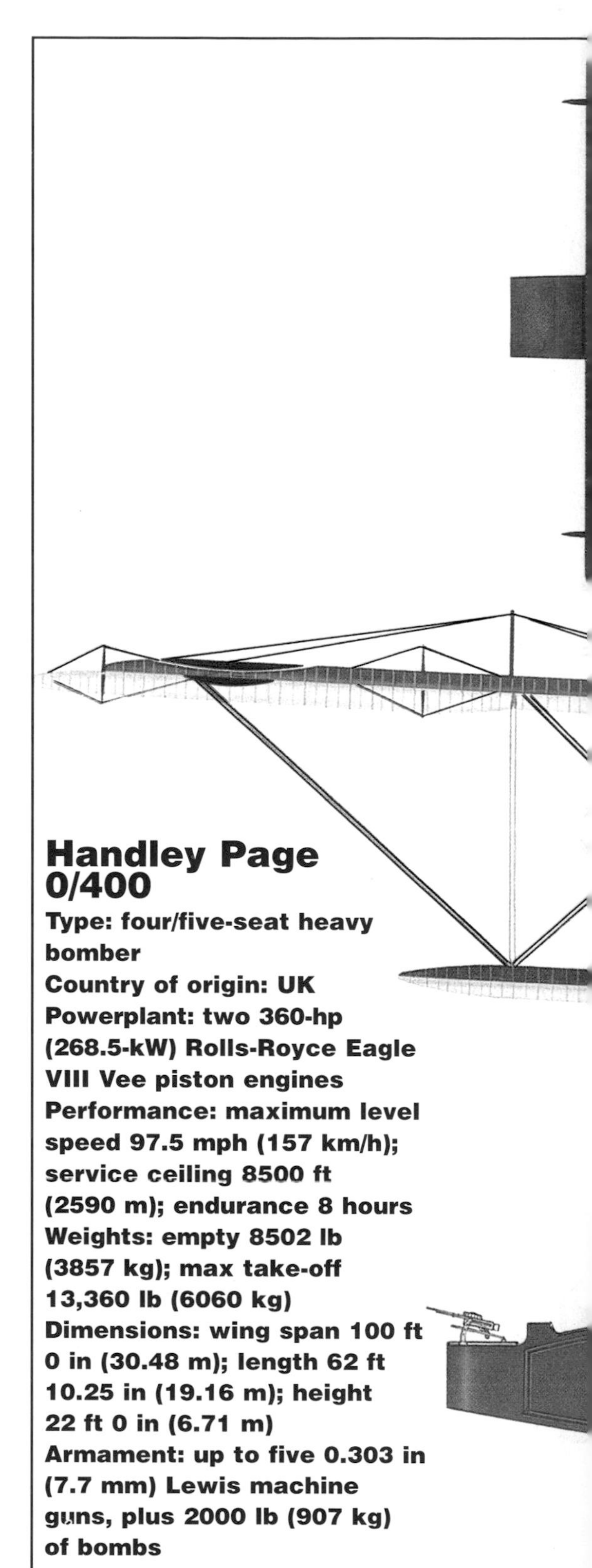

Handley Page O/400
Type: four/five-seat heavy bomber
Country of origin: UK
Powerplant: two 360-hp (268.5-kW) Rolls-Royce Eagle VIII Vee piston engines
Performance: maximum level speed 97.5 mph (157 km/h); service ceiling 8500 ft (2590 m); endurance 8 hours
Weights: empty 8502 lb (3857 kg); max take-off 13,360 lb (6060 kg)
Dimensions: wing span 100 ft 0 in (30.48 m); length 62 ft 10.25 in (19.16 m); height 22 ft 0 in (6.71 m)
Armament: up to five 0.303 in (7.7 mm) Lewis machine guns, plus 2000 lb (907 kg) of bombs

namely the Eagle IV and Eagle VIII rated at 284 and 360 hp (212 and 268.5 kW) respectively, but Eagle production was never adequate to supply demand, and other engines were evaluated: these included the Fiat A.12bis in-line piston engine rated at 260 hp (194 kW) and the Sunbeam Maori Vee piston engine rated at 275 hp (205 kW).

The O/400 inherited the basic structure of the O/100 and was therefore of perfectly conventional design and construction, with a covering of fabric over a wire-braced structure of wood. The fuselage was of rectangular section and produced in three parts, of which the primary section was the central unit, including the internal weapons bay with spring-loaded doors, and to this core the nose and tail sections were attached. The tail unit comprised biplane horizontal and triple vertical surfaces. The horizontal surfaces each included a fixed tailplane, of which the lower unit was attached to the lower longerons, and aerodynamically balanced elevator halves. The upper tailplane was

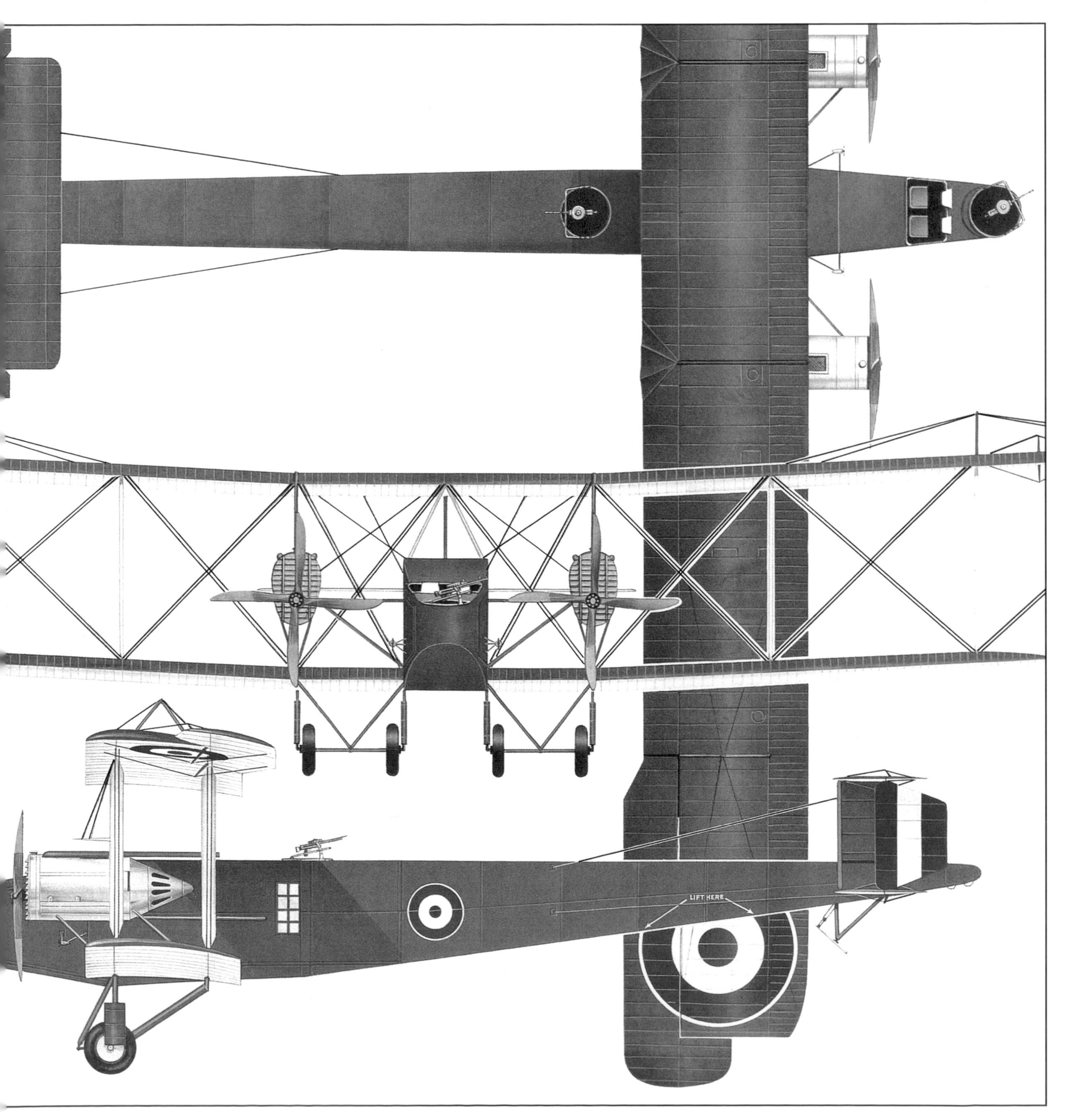

supported above the lower tailplane by an arrangement of four vertical struts flanking the central fin above the rear fuselage, and two more vertical struts forward of the pair of aerodynamically balanced rudders.

The unstaggered wing cellule was of the three-bay type, with a lower wing that was 30 ft 0 in (9.14 m) shorter than that of the upper wing. The upper and lower wings were each of constant thickness and chord, but while the lower wing was built in four sections, the longer-span upper surface was produced in five sections. The lower wing was based on two flat centre-section halves, that extended from the lower longerons and carried the two outer panels, which were each slightly dihedralled and ended in rounded tips. The upper wing was based on a flat centre section carried above the fuselage by fore-and-aft sets of inverted-Vee struts, and this carried the two slightly dihedralled outer wing panels, that were each built in two sections with the outer section, braced by an overhead kingpost-and-cable arrangement, ending in a square-cut tip whose forward edge was rounded off and whose trailing edge was occupied by the large aerodynamically balanced aileron. The outer wing panels were separated by two sets of parallel interplane struts and could be folded to the rear to reduce hangarage requirements, and the whole wing cellule was braced with the normal arrangement of flying and landing wires.

The airframe was completed by the powerplant and landing gear. The powerplant of two Eagle Vee piston engines, each driving a four-blade wooden propeller and cooled by a large frontal radiator, was installed in a pair of short nacelles, carried in the interplane gap between the outer ends of the upper- and lower-wing centre sections. Each nacelle was supported above the lower wing on a fore-and-aft pair of short Vee struts, and itself supported the outer end of the upper-wing centre section with a fore-and-aft pair of inverted Vee struts. The landing gear was of the fixed tailskid type, and each main unit comprised a two-wheel sprung axle carried at the base of two strut-braced N-type strut arrangements, extending vertically below the inboard and outboard ends of the lower-wing centre section.

PRODUCTION

Production of the O/400 was 548 aircraft out of an ordered 788 aircraft, completed by Handley Page (211 aircraft out of an order for 324 of which 113 were later cancelled), Birmingham Carriage Co (102 aircraft out of an order for 120 of which

BELOW: In the absence of the powered equipment to which we are so accustomed today, tasks such as the hand-powered refuelling of an O/400 bomber were very laborious.

18 were later cancelled), Royal Aircraft Factory (18 aircraft), Metropolitan Waggon Co Ltd (100 aircraft out of an order for 175, of which 75 were later cancelled), Clayton & Shuttleworth Ltd (46 aircraft out of an order for 50, of which 4 were later cancelled), National Aircraft Factory No 1 operated by Cubitt Ltd (70 aircraft out of an order for 100, of which 30 were later cancelled), and Harland & Wolff Ltd (one aeroplane as replacement for the pattern machine diverted to the Standard Aircraft Corporation in the USA).

INDEPENDENT FORCE

O/400 bombers did not begin to pour off the production lines until the spring of 1918, and in fact it was the middle of August 1918 before the Independent Force of the Royal Air Force (created in April 1918 by the merger of the RFC and RNAS) received its first complete O/400 unit, when No 97 Squadron arrived in France, this being followed later in the month by No 215 Squadron from England and No 100 Squadron that converted in France from the Royal Aircraft Factory F.E.2b bomber.

In France, the O/400 eventually equipped Nos 58, 207 and 214 Squadrons of the IX Brigade's 82nd, 54th and 82nd Wings respectively, as well as Nos 97, 100, 115, 215 and 216 Squadrons of the 83rd Wing of the Independent Force's VIII Brigade. In Palestine, one O/400 was attached to No 1 Squadron of the Australian Flying Corps, and numbers of O/400 warplanes were also used in the UK by No 1 and No 2 Schools of Air Navigation and Bomb-dropping, which were based in the West Country, at Stonehenge and Andover respectively.

In the last three months of World War I, the aircraft based in France began to exert a considerable effect on the German armies' lines of communication and on war industries in the west of Germany, on occasion dropping 1650 lb (748 kg) 'blockbuster' bombs that caused considerable devastation.

The success of the bombers was not achieved without loss, however, and between June and November 1918, the Independent Force lost 69 of the aircraft, 18 of them on operations and the other 51 in accidents. After the end of World War I, the RAF decided to standardise on the Airco (de Havilland) D.H.10 Amiens and Vickers F.B.27 Vimy bombers, and the number of O/400 bombers declined rapidly, the last two units being Nos 70 and 216 Squadrons, that flew the type from Egyptian bases up to 1920.

COMMANDANT DORAND

In the first 18 months of World War I, the responsibility for the design and production of French warplanes was the responsibility of the Service des Fabrications de l'Aviation (SFA, or Aircraft Production Service) that had been created in February 1914. However in February 1916, this responsibility was reallocated to a new body, the Section Technique de l'Aeronautique (STA, or Aeronautical Technical Section), directed by Commandant (later Lieutenant Colonel) Dorand.

One of Dorand's first moves was the creation of three requirements for new warplanes he felt were urgently required by the operational escadrilles (squadrons) of the French air force. The three requirements were firstly a tractor warplane to replace the Farman F.40 in the reconnaissance role, secondly a fighter with a machine gun firing forward through the propeller disc, and thirdly a twin-engined reconnaissance aeroplane with three-seat accommodation.

The last was apparently a legacy of Dorand's previous involvement with the Caudron R.4 three-seater with a twin-engined powerplant. When Gaston Caudron was killed in the crash of such an aeroplane during December 1915, Dorand was one of the officers allocated to the investigation of the crash, and proposed that his small and indeterminate detached body at Lyon should take over the Caudron design office. René Caudron, the surviving Caudron brother, strenuously opposed Dorand's suggestion, and Dorand then suggested the establishment of a new technical branch, and this was created at the STA.

To meet the first and third of its director's requirements, the STAÇ designed two aircraft as the AR two-seat tractor biplane, and also a three-seat biplane with a powerplant of two Hispano-Suiza 8 Vee piston engines, each rated at 150 hp (112 kW) and driving a two-blade tractor propeller. Dorand intimated that the aircraft were of his design, which has often led to their appellation as Dorand aircraft, but both machines were in fact the work of Capitaine Georges Le Père.

The three-seater proved satisfactory when tested in prototype form, and an order for 175 production aircraft (in no fewer than an eventual seven variants) was issued to Etablissements Letord, which had been established in 1908 for the manufacture of lighter-than-air craft (balloons and airships) before becoming involved in heavier-than-air craft (aircraft) in 1916. The first variant to enter service was the Let.1A.3 reconnaissance aeroplane, with a powerplant of two Hispano-Suiza 8A engines each rated at 150 hp (112 kW), and this model was followed by the Let.2A.3 with a powerplant of two Hispano-Suiza 8Ba engine, each rated at 200 hp (149 kW) or two Lorraine-Dietrich 8A Vee piston engines, each rated at 170 hp (127 kW). This latter powerplant was also installed in the Let.4A.3 that was the third reconnaissance variant.

The Let.3 was a derivative of the Let.2 with the same powerplant, no auxiliary nosewheel unit and a four-bay wing cellule increased in span to 55 ft 9.25 in (17.00 m). It was planned in two forms as the Let.3BN.3 night bomber with a maximum take-off weight of 5291 lb (2400 kg) and as the Let.3Ca.3 escort fighter variant, with a trainable armament of one 37 mm (1.46 in) Hotchkiss cannon and one 0.303 in (7.7 mm) Lewis gun.

Neither the Let.3BN.3 nor Let.3Ca.3 entered production, but paved the way for two further models. The concept of the Let.3BN.3 was developed into the Let.7BN.3 prototype that appeared in 1918, with a span of 62 ft 4 in (19.00 m), maximum take-off weight of 6305 lb (2860 kg) and a powerplant of two Lorraine-Dietrich engines, each rated at 275 hp (205 kW), while the concept of the Let.3Ca.3 paved the way for the Let.6Ca.3 that first appeared late in 1917, and which began trials in January 1918 but also failed to win a contract, as the superior Caudron R.11 was already in large-scale production.

The Let.4BN.3 was the only night bomber variant of the series to enter production, and then only in modest numbers, as only 51 aircraft were completed for service in the Bombardement de Nuit trois-place (three-seat night bomber) category. The type lacked the auxiliary nosewheel unit and was also notable for its three-bay wing cellule, which was of the unequal-span type, with a lower wing of less span than the upper wing. The outer parts of the aircraft's upper wing were therefore braced on each side by a kingpost-and-cable bracing arrangement.

ABOVE: The largest bomb used operationally by the British in World War I was the SN, a 1650-lb (748-kg) weapon of riveted construction that carried 800 lb (363 kg) of Amatol.

MACCHI BOMBERS

In the course of 1917, the Italian manufacturer Macchi, which by this time had considerable experience in the design and construction of flying boats, based on the Lohner concept, felt able to embark on more ambitious types, incorporating a higher percentage of its own concepts. Resulting from a programme of intensive studies into the static and aerodynamic qualities of the rigid airframe, one of these new types was the M.8 reconnaissance and bomber flying boat, introduced by Macchi at the end of 1917 on the basis of the aerodynamic design of the Lohner-derived M.3, but using a new form of wing bracing to provide a sturdy and rigid wing cellule that offered a considerable reduction in drag, as it required no flying or landing wires, and was also somewhat easier to rig, as the wires were limited to those needed for incidence bracing.

The result was therefore not only a stronger and more easily managed airframe, but also a boost in performance. The flight trials of the M.8 prototype revealed not only an improvement in performance over those of the M.3 and M.4, but also better handling characteristics, and the type was therefore ordered into production for the Italian navy air service, which received a total of 57 such 'boats in 1917 and 1918.

Accommodating a crew of two or three according to specific role, the M.8 carried the fixed armament of one 0.295 in (6.5 mm) Fiat-made Revelli trainable forward-firing machine gun on a Scarff-type ring mounting in the bow position, although a small number of the 'boats operated in the dedicated anti-submarine role had a 40 mm Coventry Ordnance Works cannon whose projectiles were capable of piercing the tin plate of current submarines. When operated in the pure bomber role, the M.8 could deliver 1213 lb (550 kg) of bombs, which was reduced to 661 lb (300 kg) when the 'boat was operated in the anti-submarine task.

The anti-submarine task became increasingly important from the later part of 1917, when German submarines started to use the bases of the Imperial Austro-Hungarian navy at the northern end and eastern side of the Adriatic Sea for operations in the Mediterranean.

During the later stages of World War I, the trend in the design of flying boats intended for the anti-submarine role was toward larger 'boats, so that the full complement of required equipment and armament could be carried for a useful time. Thus, the M.9 that was schemed as successor to the M.8 retained the basic design of its successful predecessor in a scaled-up form, although the less powerful of the two engines used in the M.8 was retained, as lifting and endurance qualities rather than outright flight performance were required in the anti-submarine and reconnaissance roles.

The embarked equipment of the M.9 included a revolving gun ring over the bow position, two bomb-throwers for four grenade mines, a reconnaissance camera, and radio apparatus, and, on some 'boats, provision was also made for the carriage of two spherical anti-submarine mines for a useful load of 1709 lb (775 kg) that could otherwise include four 220 lb (100 kg) aerial mines or two 298 lb (135 kg) anti-submarine bombs.

The other details of the M.9 included a powerplant of one Fiat A.12bis in-line piston engine rated at 300 hp (224 kW), span of 50 ft 8.25 in (15.45 m) with an area of 522.07 sq ft (48.50 m^2), length of 31 ft 2 in (9.50 m), height of 10 ft 4 in (3.15 m), empty weight of 2756 lb (1250 kg), maximum take-off weight of 3968 lb (1800 kg), maximum level speed of 116 mph (187 km/h) at sea level, maximum range of 559 miles (900 km), typical range of 435 miles (700 km), climb to 9845 ft (3000 m) in 19 minutes, and service ceiling of 18,045 ft (5500 m).

Following its official trials, the M.9 was accepted for series production by Macchi, with additional production planned for other manufacturers, but the effort had only just got under way by the end of World War I and deliveries amounted to only 30 Macchi-built 'boats (16 of them delivered in 1918), which remained in service up to 1924.

The layout of the M.9 proved so stable and effective that it was used with virtually no change other than enlargement in the M.12, which was completed in prototype form during the autumn of 1918, but was too late to enter production and service in World War I. Intended for the long-range reconnaissance role, the M.12 had the powerplant of one Ansaldo-San Giorgio 4 E/28 engine rated at 450 hp (335.5 kW). The most striking feature of the M.12 was the wider hull which, at a point to the rear of the wing cellule's trailing edges, bifurcated into two booms, each carrying a vertical tail surface, whose twin fixed elements were connected by a long-span tailplane.

The M.12 was armed with two 0.295 in (6.5 mm) Fiat-made Revelli trainable machine guns, the incorporation of a gangway in the hull allowing the gunner to move from his main position in the bow to a secondary position behind the wing cellule, from which he had good fields of fire, including the otherwise blind spot under the tail, now open to fire through the gap between the booms.

The other details of the M.12 included a span of 55 ft 9.325 in (17.00 m) with an area of 656.62 sq ft (61.00 m^2), length of 35 ft 9.125 in (10.90 m), height of 12 ft 0.125 in (3.66 m), empty weight of 3924 lb (1780 kg), maximum take-off weight of 5644 lb (2560 kg), maximum level speed of 118 mph (190 km/h) at sea level, maximum range of 590 miles (950 km), typical range of 466 miles (750 km), climb to 9845 ft (3000 m) in 28 minutes 30 seconds, and an effective service ceiling of 18,045 ft (5500 m).

THE ZEPPELIN-STAAKEN R VI

Although all the early bombers of the Zeppelin series, built at either Gotha-Ost or Staaken, had been produced only as single aircraft, which nevertheless gained considerably combat experience, it was with the R VI that the company reached an initial plateau of design and operational capability.

The R VI was therefore the first of the Zeppelin bombers to be placed in series production, and was also the largest aeroplane to be placed in series production during World War I. Deliveries of the type totalled 18 aircraft, excluding the seaplane variants, but of these only six were completed by the parent company, with the other 12 delivered by Automobil & Aviatik AG (six aircraft), Luftschiffbau Schütte-Lanz (three aircraft) and Ostdeutsche Albatroswerke GmbH (three aircraft).

The R VI was a consolidation of Zeppelin's previous experience in the design and production of Riesenflugzeug (giant aeroplane) bombers, and its primary differences from the earlier machines were its enclosed flightcrew positions, fixed tailskid landing gear (although an auxiliary nosewheel unit was still installed to reduce the chances of a nose-over accident while landing), and a powerplant of four engines located as tandem push/pull pairs between the wings, with no engine in the nose.

The most important of these changes was without doubt that of the powerplant, which was dictated by two factors, namely the desirability of removing the nose engine, and the need to get away from the coupled engine/gearbox arrangement. The nose engine demanded tall landing gear and with it there was an increased chance of a nose-over accident followed by a catastrophic fuel fire, as spilled fuel ran over the hot nose engine, while the design, development and manufacture of the gearboxes for coupled engines were costly and time consuming, resulting in a production bottleneck that would have made it impossible to produce bombers with such gearboxes on an effective production-line basis. Furthermore, combining gearboxes had revealed themselves to be unreliable, even when they were well made and maintained by highly skilled crew of the type that was always in short supply.

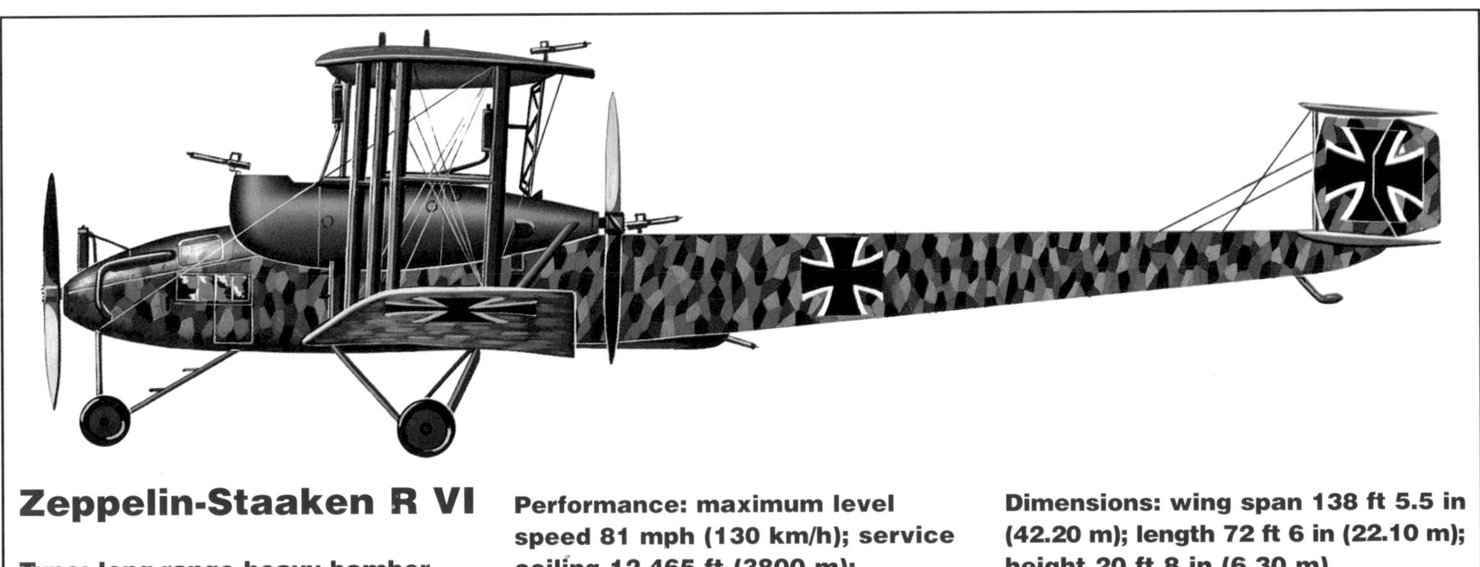

Zeppelin-Staaken R VI

Type: long-range heavy bomber
Country of origin: Germany
Powerplant: four 260-hp (194-kW) Mercedes D.IVa piston engines
Performance: maximum level speed 81 mph (130 km/h); service ceiling 12,465 ft (3800 m); endurance 8 hours
Weights: empty 16,934 lb (7680 kg); max take-off 25,269 lb (11,460 kg)
Dimensions: wing span 138 ft 5.5 in (42.20 m); length 72 ft 6 in (22.10 m); height 20 ft 8 in (6.30 m)
Armament: up to four 0.312-in (7.92-mm) LMG 14 machine guns, up to 9921 lb (4500 kg) of bombs

Tests of the tandem push/pull arrangement were undertaken by Zeppelin Werke Staaken's sister company, Zeppelin Werke Lindau (Dornier), during 1916 and revealed a level of efficiency almost as high as propellers operating singly. With this fact confirmed, Zeppelin (Staaken) could proceed with the design and construction of the first R VI without delay. Thus the first two R VI bombers were accepted by the IdFlieg (Inspektion der Fliegertruppen, inspectorate of flying troops) in June and July 1917, although the date of their first flights (probably late in 1916) has been lost. The success of these first two aircraft is attested by the fact that orders for additional aircraft were placed not only with Zeppelin (Staaken), but also with Aviatik, Sch¸tte-Lanz and Ostdeutsche Albatros.

As a consolidation of Zeppelin's (Staaken) earlier aerodynamic and structural concepts, the R VI was of mainly wooden construction, covered largely with fabric. The core of the structure was the fuselage, which was of basically rectangular section (wooden longerons and welded steel tube frames) with rounded-off corners and covered with fabric except on the forward section, which was skinned with plywood. From front to rear, this fuselage carried the open nose position for the bombardier/gunner, the enclosed and very well-equipped flightdeck for the two pilots seated side-by-side, commander/navigator, radio operator and fuel attendant, eight or ten 53.9 Imp gal (245 litre) fuel tanks, the lower-fuselage weapons bay rated at 3968 lb (1800 kg) but also able to carry two 2205 lb (1000 kg) bombs semi-externally, the open dorsal gunner's position with an open ventral position below it, and the tail unit. The aircraft were powered initially by four Mercedes D.III in-line piston engines, each rated at 260 hp (194 kW) for take-off, but these were generally replaced in the earlier aircraft by the powerplant installed from the start in later aircraft, namely four Maybach Mb.IVa in-line piston engines, each rated at 245 hp (183 kW) at 6560 ft (2000 m), which was equivalent to 300 hp (224 kW) at sea level, at which these high-compression engines could not be run at full throttle. Each engine was cooled by a radiator attached to the struts above it, the radiators for the two pusher engines being located higher than those of the two tractor units.

The Maybach-powered R VI differed from the Mercedes-powered variant in details such as its internal fuel capacity of 659.9 Imp gal (3000 litres), empty weight of 17,465 lb (7921 kg), maximum take-off weight of 26,125 lb (11,848 kg), maximum level speed of 84 mph (135 km/h) at optimum altitude, endurance of 10 hours 0 minutes, climb to 6560 ft (2000 m) in 23 minutes 0 seconds, and service ceiling of 14,175 ft (4320 m).

The preferred defensive weapon was the Lewis gun, of which limited supplies were available in the form of captured weapons, but the aircraft were also fitted at times with LMG 14 Parabellum machine guns. The three main positions for the trainable weapons were the nose, dorsal and ventral positions, equipped with one, two and one guns respectively, but in at least two of the aircraft, their were also single-gun positions above the upper wing for the use of the flight mechanics, who in their secondary gunner role stood on platforms above the rear engines, with their heads and shoulders above the upper wing.

SUCCESS STORY

The R VI bombers formed the main equipment of the two Riesenflugzeug-abteilungen (giant aeroplane detachments), namely Rfa 500 and Rfa 501, on the Western Front, flying raids against targets in the UK and France. The aircraft proved notably successful by the standards of the day, although 11 of the 18 machines were lost during the war: two were shot down (one by anti-aircraft guns and the other by a fighter), seven were written off in crash landings, one crashed as a result of engine failure on take-off, and one was destroyed after being overstressed in the air. Of the

BELOW: One of the best of the French bombers of World War I was the Breguet Bre.16, which is seen here in its Bre.16BN.2 two-seat night bomber form.

Ansaldo SVA-10/IF
Type:two-seat day bomber and reconnaissance aeroplane
Country of origin: Italy
Powerplant: one 250-hp (186-kW) Isotta-Fraschini Semi-Asso in-line piston engine
Performance: maximum level speed 133.5 mph (215 km/h); service ceiling 16,405 ft (5000 m); endurance 5 hours
Weights: empty 1609 lb (730 kg); maximum take-off 2337 lb (1060 kg)
Dimensions: wing span 30 ft 1.4 in (9.18 m); length 29 ft 10.25 in (9.10 m); height 10 ft 2 in (3.10 m);
Armament: one 0.303 in (7.7 mm) Vickers machine gun, one 0.303 in (7.7 mm) Lewis machine gun in the rear cockpit, and bombs

aircraft that survived to the end of the war, several were retained for post-war use as civil machines.

THE ANSALDO SVA-10

Following the success of the Ansaldo SVA-5 reconnaissance fighter with limited bombing capability, Ansaldo pursued the development of this type, which had been designed by Umberto Savoia and Rodolfo Verduzio of the Direzione Tecnica dell'Aeronautica Militare (Military Aviation Technical Directorate), with great vigour and considerable success, with a total of 1248 SVA-series aircraft delivered in the course of World War I. A comparatively simple development process resulted in the unarmed SVA-9 two-seat reconnaissance aeroplane with the observer seated in front of the pilot. It soon became clear, however, that the SVA-9's performance was not high enough to offer a virtually complete immunity to interception, and Ansaldo therefore developed the SVA-10 as the armed version of the SVA-9, with the positions of the pilot and observer reversed so that the latter now occupied the rear cockpit in his capacity as an observer/gunner, equipped with a rearward-firing machine gun. The pilot was also provided with armament, although to save weight and therefore maintain performance to the maximum possible degree, it was only one of the two fixed forward-firing machine guns that had featured on the SVA-5; provision was also made for the carriage of a light bomb load, as on the SVA-5.

The SVA-10 was an unequal-span biplane that inherited the SVA-5's primary structure, which had been designed most skilfully to ensure high performance, together with ease of manufacture and simplicity of maintenance. The SVA-10, which was introduced to service in 1918 and remained in service to the second half of the 1920s, was delivered with two different types of engine, namely the Isotta-Fraschini Semi-Asso in-line unit rated at 250 hp (186 kW) to create the SVA-10/IF, and the SPA 6 in-line unit rated at 220 hp (164 kW) to create the SVA-10/SPA, which was slightly slower at 130.5 mph (210 km/h) but possessed a better rate of climb including a climb to 9845 ft (3000 m) in 11 minutes 0 seconds rather than 12 minutes 0 seconds.

Designed for the short-range role in the Bombardement de Nuit deux-place (two-seat night bomber) category, the Bre.16BN.2 was basically an enlarged version of the Bre.14, with the same type of light alloy- and fabric-covered metal structure (Dural members and steel fittings). In layout, the major differences between the Bre.14 and Bre.16 were the latter's equal-span biplane wing cellule of the three rather than two-bay type, with aerodynamically-balanced ailerons on the lower as well as the upper wing. The larger wing area allowed a useful increase in the weight of the bomb load that could be lifted.

The Bre.16 first flew in prototype form during June 1918 with a powerplant of one Renault 12Jb Vee piston engine rated at 450 hp (335.5 kW) and driving a two-blade wooden propeller, and plans were laid for the type to enter large-scale service in time for the major Allied offensives planned for the Western Front in 1919. World War I (1914–18) ended in November 1918 without the need for these offensives, and by this time only a few examples of the Bre.14BN.2 had entered service in its original form, with a powerplant of one Renault 12Fe Vee piston engine rated at 300 hp (224 kW), and a revised vertical tail surface of considerably more angular shape than that of the prototype. Some of the aircraft were evaluated with the Packard Liberty 12 Vee piston engine rated at 400 hp (298 kW) and also with the Panhard 12 Vee piston engine rated at 350 hp (261 kW), but neither type was selected for any production variant of the Bre.16.

Production of the Bre.16BN.2 continued after the end of World War I with the powerplant of one Renault 12Fe engine, and it is thought that more than 200 of the type were delivered up to 1923.

CHAPTER 2

Bombers of the Inter-War Period

Although the end of the war saw rapid disarmament, progress continued to be made in bomber development. Rearmament began again in earnest in the 1930s, and new, sleek monoplanes became the order of the day.

The period following the end of World War I in November 1918 was a time of effective dissolution for the armed forces of the nations that had lost the war. At the same time, the victorious Allies felt that the 'Great War' had been the 'war to end all wars' and that there was therefore no need for anything but the most vestigial of armed forces. In the realm of aviation, the Allied nations were happy to rely, in the short term at least, on the aircraft with which they had ended the war, leavened with a small number of advanced machines under final development or initial production as the war ended.

Although his D.H.3 bomber of 1916 had not been notably successful and had therefore failed to attract a production order, Geoffrey de Havilland was confident that the basic design of this aeroplane possessed merit, and revived it for the D.H.10 that appeared in prototype form during 1918. The D.H.10 was of wooden construction, covered with plywood and fabric, and in configuration was a four-bay biplane with fixed tailskid landing gear. The powerplant of the Amiens Mk I (as it was rechristened) prototype, which made its maiden flight on 4 March 1918, was a pair of BHP in-line piston engines, each rated at 230 hp (171.5 kW) and driving a two-blade wooden propeller of the pusher type behind the wing trailing edges. The Amiens Mk II second prototype was completed with a powerplant of two Rolls-Royce Eagle VIII Vee piston engines, each rated at 360 hp (268.5 kW) and driving a two-blade wooden propeller of the tractor type forward of the wing leading edges. This improved the aircraft's performance considerably, but the engine selected for the production model was a new American engine, the Packard Liberty 12 Vee unit, rated at some 400 hp (298 kW). This powerplant was evaluated in the Amiens Mk III third and fourth prototypes.

Orders had already been placed for an initial 800 aircraft and further options increased the planned total to 1275. Deliveries of the Amiens Mk III were seriously delayed by problems in the final development, production and shipment of Liberty 12 engines from the USA, so the first aircraft were delivered only in October 1918, initially equipping No 104 Squadron of the Independent Force, which was the strategic air formation of the Royal Air Force in France. This squadron did not reach operational status until after the end of World War I in November 1918.

Known to the manufacturer as the D.H.10A, the Amiens Mk IIIA was a simple development of the Amiens Mk III with the engine nacelles lowered to the upper surface of the lower-wing centre section, for a simplified strut arrangement and reduced drag. The D.H.10B designation was reserved for civil variants of the D.H.10, and the designation D.H.10C was used for a small number of aircraft completed with a powerplant of two Eagle VIII engines, each rated at 375 hp (280 kW), probably as a result of the end of Liberty 12 deliveries in July 1918. None of these Eagle-powered aircraft entered service. By December 1918, D.H.10 production ended after the delivery of 258 aircraft,

LEFT: The Hawker Hart, seen here over terrain typical of northern India, was a two-seat light bomber that formed the mainstay of the British day bomber force in the mid-1930s.

■ABOVE: **A type that equipped the Royal Air Force's bomber squadrons for a short time into the early 1920s, the de Havilland D.H.10 Amiens was designed late in World War I.**

and in 1920, the financially troubled Airco was bought by Birmingham Small Arms. De Havilland had left Airco in 1918 as a result of nervous exhaustion, and in September 1920 created the de Havilland Aircraft Co Ltd, which now became responsible for logistic support of the D.H.10 and other ex-Airco warplanes.

The existing aircraft remained in service up to 1923 with a number of squadrons, including No 60 (ex-No 97) Squadron on the Northwest Frontier of India, and No 216 Squadron in Egypt. No 60 Squadron saw active service against rebel tribesmen in November 1920 and early 1922, and No 216 Squadron pioneered the air transport and air mail services between Cairo in Egypt and Baghdad in Mesopotamia (Iraq).

NIGHT BOMBING

The Air Board decided in July 1917, as a result of the German bomber campaign against London, to pursue the development and procurement of long-range night bomber aircraft capable of attacking targets deep in Germany from bases in France. In the short term, the solution to the British night bomber requirement was found in the O/400 development of the Handley Page O/100 bomber, but more capable types were wanted as longer-term solutions and here prototypes were ordered of the Handley Page V/1500 four-engined bomber and the Vickers F.B.27 twin-engined bomber. It was in July 1917 that Vickers received its order for three prototypes of a bomber able to attack Berlin from bases in France. The result was the F.B.27 design for a large equal-span biplane with a twin-engined powerplant and a crew of three, and the first of its three prototypes made its maiden flight on 30 November 1917, with a powerplant of two Hispano-Suiza 8 Vee piston engines, each rated at 200 hp (149 kW).

The first F.B.27 prototype was submitted for official trials in January 1918, and caused something of a sensation by carrying a bomb load heavier than that of the O/400. The Hispano-Suiza 8 engines were later replaced by a pair of Salmson (Canton-Unné) water-cooled radial engines, each rated at 260 hp (194 kW). The second F.B.27 prototype was completed in April 1918, with changes that included a powerplant of two Sunbeam Maori Vee engines, each rated at 260 hp (194 kW) and driving a four-blade wooden propeller, a third 0.303 in (7.7 mm) Lewis trainable rearward-firing machine gun added in the ventral position, and the wing cellule revised with plain inversely tapered ailerons with no overhanging balance areas, for a span of 68 ft 4 in (20.83 m) with an area of 1376 sq ft (127.83 m2). This machine was lost as a result of engine failure. The same fate befell the third prototype, which first flew a few weeks after the second prototype using two Fiat A.12 in-line piston engines, each rated at 260 hp (194 kW).

By this time, the F.B.27A production variant had received the official name Vimy, and was ordered into large-scale production. Vickers received an initial order for 150 aircraft, most of them to be completed as anti-submarine patrol machines to replace the inadequate Blackburn Kangaroo, during March 1918, and then a second contract for 200 machines. Thereafter, a higher rate of production was envisaged for the delivery of large numbers of bombers to support the great Allied offensives planned for 1919, and soon the order book totalled 1130 Vimy aircraft.

There remains some dispute about the official nomenclature adopted for these early aircraft. The more likely account suggests that the first prototype with Hispano-Suiza engines was the Vimy Mk I, the second prototype with Sunbeam engines was the Vimy Mk II, and the third prototype with Fiat engines was the Vimy Mk III, which was therefore the designation applied to the Fiat-engined production model. The less likely account suggests that the Vimy Mks I and II were the Sunbeam- and Fiat-powered prototypes, with the designation Vimy Mk III reserved for a BHP-engined prototype conversion that was not completed.

The Vimy Mk III differed from the Vimy Mk IV in its offensive armament of up to 4408 lb (2000 kg) of bombs in the form of eight 250 lb (113 kg) and four 112 lb (51 kg) bombs carried internally, plus two 520 lb (236 kg) bombs carried under the fuselage, and four 230 lb (104 kg) bombs carried under the lower-wing centre section. The two variants were dimensionally identical. Only three Vimy bombers had reached the Western Front by the time of the Armistice that ended World War I in November 1918, and none of these was used operationally. The Vimy was one of the few British warplanes to survive World War I as a major type, for it was retained as the major post-war heavy bomber of the Royal Air Force. Production eventually totalled at least 224 aircraft in the form of 143 from Vickers, 25 from Westland, 16 or more from the Royal Aircraft Establishment, and at least 40 from Morgan. Some of these machines were of the Vimy Mk III type with the Fiat A.12bis powerplant, but the considerable majority was of the Vimy Mk IV type that had been pioneered by the fourth prototype which first flew in September 1918 with a powerplant of two Rolls-Royce Eagle VIII Vee piston engines, each rated at 360 hp (268 kW) and driving a four-blade wooden propeller, considerably enlarged fuel capacity, and rudders with larger balance areas. The production standard added a small fixed fin ahead of each rudder.

The Vimy entered full service in July 1919, when it replaced the O/400 bombers of No 58 Squadron based in Egypt. Its type was replaced in first-line bomber service between 1925 and 1929 by the Vickers Virginia. The Vimy is of enormous historical importance as the aeroplane on which the first non-stop aerial crossing of the Atlantic Ocean was completed, when in June 1919 Captain John Alcock and Lieutenant Arthur Whitten-Brown flew a Vickers-owned Vimy Mk IV with additional fuel tankage over the 1890 miles (3042 km) between St Johns in Newfoundland and Clifden in Ireland. Another highly notable success was the first flight between the UK and Australia, a feat achieved by the brothers Captain Ross Smith and Lieutenant Keith Smith (with Sergeants Bennett and Shiers as their mechanics) in November and December 1919, when they flew a Vimy Mk IV over this 11,130 mile (17,910 km) distance in a flying time of just under 136 hours.

VIMY REPLACEMENT

In 1920, the Air Ministry issued a requirement for a long-range bomber to replace the Vimy. Vickers initially responded to the specification attached to this DoR Type 4 requirement with its Type 57 development of the Vimy, with the span increased to 86 ft 6 in (26.21 m), a biplane tail unit and a powerplant of two Napier Lion W-type piston engines, each rated at 450 hp (335.5 kW). The name Vulcan was at first allocated to the type, but as work proceeded on the design the name was altered to Virginia, in accordance with the Royal Air Force's recently adopted policy of naming bombers, transports and flying boats after places. The Air Ministry ordered an initial pair of prototypes that were at first designated as the Virginia I and Virginia II, but later accorded the retrospective designations Virginia Mk I and Virginia Mk II. The Virginia Mk I made its first flight on 24 November 1922, and immediately revealed inadequate directional control. The vertical tail surfaces and rudder-control system were modified, and then the rudders were increased in area, and this latter finally produced effective although very heavy directional control. In this form, the Virginia Mk I completed its initial trials and was then taken in hand, at express Air Ministry order, for revision with upper-wing 'fighting tops': located just outboard of the discs swept by the two propellers, these were long nacelles, installed with most of their depth below the wing and each carrying a fore-and-aft pair of gunner's positions, each equipped

Airco (de Havilland) D.H.10 Amiens Mk III

Type: three-seat bomber
Country of origin: UK
Powerplant: two 405-hp (302-kW) Packard Liberty 12 Vee engines
Performance: maximum level speed 124 mph (199.5 km/h); service ceiling 17,500 ft (5335 m); endurance 6 hours
Weights: empty 5585 lb (2533 kg); maximum take-off 9000 lb (4082 kg)
Dimensions: wing span 65 ft 6 in (19.96 m); length 39 ft 7.5 in (12.08 m); height 14 ft 6 in (4.42 m)
Armament: up to four 0.303 in (7.7 mm) Lewis machine guns, up to 1380 lb (626 kg) of bombs

with a Scarff ring mounting for one 0.303 in (7.7 mm) Lewis trainable machine gun, which complemented the standard pair of 0.303 in (7.7 mm) Lewis trainable machine guns installed singly in the nose and dorsal positions. The bomb load comprised nine 112 lb (51 kg) bombs carried in a lower-fuselage weapons bay.

Late in 1924, the Virginia Mk I was revised with a powerplant of two Rolls-Royce Condor III Vee piston engines, each rated at 650 hp (485 kW), and at the same time the aileron-control circuit was modified and a third rudder was added on the centre-line. When the aeroplane made its first flight in this revised form during October 1924, it revealed great instability in the longitudinal plane and considerable heaviness in the lateral plane. The latter was cured by a modification of the gear ratio in the aileron control system, but the former proved insensitive to the addition of ballast weight in the nose and was cured only be the relocation of the engines some 2 ft 1 in (0.635 m) farther forward. In this form the aeroplane was much improved, and further enhancement of the type's handling characteristics was effected by the addition of a fixed fin ahead of the central rudder. After the completion of flight trials in this form, the Virginia Mk I was further modified as the Virginia Mk VIII prototype, the changes including a 6 ft 0 in (1.83 m) lengthening of the rear fuselage, the addition of a new forward fuselage, the modification of the upper- and lower-wing outer panels with 2.5º of dihedral, and the alteration of the 'fighting tops' to much smaller units with their forward positions removed. After another round of trials, the aeroplane was again modified, in this instance to typical Virginia Mk VII standard, with outer wing panels swept at 6º. In this form the aeroplane was used by Nos 7 and 10 Squadrons for operational trials of the 'fighting top' concept. At the end of 1928, the Virginia Mk I received its final modification, in this instance to Virginia Mk X standard, for the use of No 7 Squadron. By this time, the aeroplane retained virtually nothing of its original features, and had an essentially metal airframe in place of its original wood.

The second aeroplane was completed to Type 76 standard with the RAF designation Virginia Mk II, and was somewhat different from the Virginia Mk I in details such as its Lion II engines in better streamlined nacelles, and cooled by semi-circular Lamblin radiators installed between the main landing gear unit Vee strut pairs, a longer nose incorporating an improved bombardier position, provision for the incidence of the tailplane to be altered in flight by the incorporation of a hinged joint in the rear fuselage, and the provision of greater legroom in the cockpit by altering the weapons bay for a maximum of eight rather than nine 112 lb (51 kg) bombs. The Virginia Mk II first flew in April 1924, and on the completion of its trials was allocated to No 7 Squadron for operational trials.

FIRST PRODUCTION VIRGINIA

The Type 79 model was the first production version of the Virginia family, but was produced to only six aircraft, the first two of them as prototypes to Specification 1/21, which was based on the Virginia Mk II with dual controls, provision for the underwing carriage of two bombs of up to 550 lb (249 kg) weight for a maximum bomb load of 1996 lb (905 kg), and provision for a 0.303 in (7.7 mm) Lewis trainable machine gun in a position under the fuselage. The Type 99 (Mk IV) variant was identical to the Type 79 (Mk III) in all except its extra electric gear, an increase in the number and positioning of bombs that could be carried and, as a retrofit, an additional centrally mounted rudder. Production totalled a mere three Virginia Mk IV aircraft. The Virginia Mk V was a development of the Virginia Mk IV, with the centrally mounted rudder and, for the first time in a British bomber of the period between the world wars, an overall finish of dark green in place of the standard silver of that time. Ordered to Specification 12/24, this was the first major production model of the Virginia bomber family, and production totalled 22 aircraft.

The Virginia Mk VI, known as the Type 108 in the company nomenclature, resulted from criticism of the Virginia Mk V's outer-wing panel folding system for easier hangarage. A revised folding system was therefore introduced together with a revision of the outer panels so that they had 2.5º of dihedral on both the upper and lower panels rather than 4º on only the lower panels, as had hitherto been the case. Orders for the Virginia Mk VI totalled 25 new-build aircraft, and six Virginia Mk V bombers were revised to the same standard.

There was considerable service criticism of the Virginia which, it was justly claimed, lacked real use in the bomber role, as the pilot had to concentrate all his attention on the flying of the aeroplane, rather than on its best employment in operational terms. The problem here was the poor handling in the air of the Virginia, which was still longitudinally unstable under all conditions, directionally unstable as soon as the pilot had lost the horizon, and

Vickers Vimy Mk IV

Type: three-seat heavy bomber
Country of origin: UK
Powerplant: two 360-hp (268.5-kW) Rolls-Royce Eagle VIII Vee piston engines
Performance: maximum level speed 103 mph (166 km/h); service ceiling 7000 ft (2135 m); typical range 900 miles (1448 km)
Weights: empty 7101 lb (3221 kg); maximum take-off 12,500 lb (5670 kg)
Dimensions: wing span 68 ft 0 in (20.73 m); length 43 ft 6.5 in (13.27 m); height 15 ft 7.5 in (4.76 m)
Armament: three 0.303 in (7.7 mm) Lewis machine guns, plus up to 4804 lb (2179 kg) of stores

laterally unstable in turbulence. It was soon established that this problem resulted in part from the addition of extra equipment, including the tail gun position, which had moved the centre of gravity too far to the rear, and in part from deficiencies that had been evident even in the Virginia Mk I. The solution to this problem, it was felt, was a combination of a slight sweepback angle on the outer wing panels to move the centre of lift back into the right position relative to the centre of gravity, for improved longitudinal stability and controllability, and the adoption of Frise ailerons for better lateral control. The chosen sweepback angle was 2.5º, but then the Air Ministry intervened with a demand that the radio equipment should be moved to a position behind the rear spar bulkhead, which moved the centre of gravity so far to the rear that a sweepback angle of 7.5º would have been required. This would have raised considerable structural problems, so a compromise angle of 6º was chosen for the converted Virginia Mk III prototype,

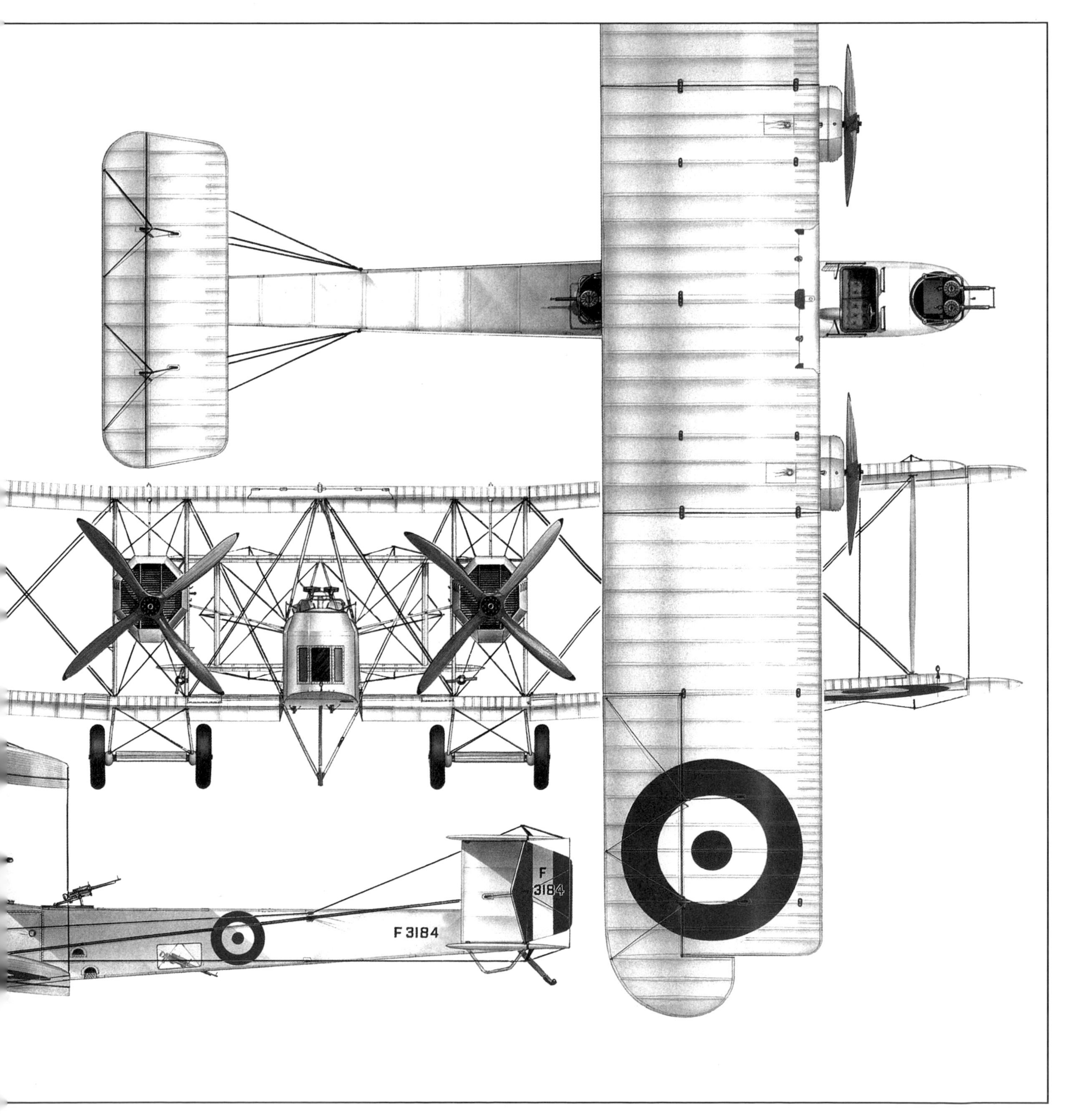

ABOVE: A typical example of the level of flight instrumentation in a bomber in the period immediately after World War I; shown here is the cockpit of the Vickers F.B.27 Vimy.

which became the Type 112 and as such the Virginia Mk VII prototype. In its fully revised form, this machine made its first flight in August 1925, and revealed handling characteristics transformed wholly for the better. The decision was thus taken to built 11 aircraft to the definitive Type 122 standard with Lion II engines replaced by Lion V engines, each rated at 570 hp (425 kW), as well as the other changes incorporated in the Type 112 prototype, and to convert another 38 existing aircraft to this standard.

Trials of a rear gun position in a converted Virginia Mk VII proved so successful that all thoughts of 'fighting tops' were immediately abandoned. Production of this revised Type 128, the Virginia Mk IX, totalled eight aircraft, and another 27 existing aircraft were adapted to this standard. As was the case with the Virginia Mk VII, aircraft of the Virginia Mk IX series were used widely for experimental work in addition to their standard squadron duties.

After the concept of metal wings had been validated by structural tests of a set of metal wings for the Vimy bomber, within the context of the Vickers Vigilant flying boat design of 1920, the Air Ministry asked Vickers to design fabric-covered metal wings for trials on the Virginia bomber. Vickers was already working on a metal rear fuselage for the Virginia Mk VII for a weight saving of 49 lb (22 kg), and the sensible decision was made to add metal wings to this prototype conversion for an overall weight saving of 1100 lb (499 kg). The revised aeroplane first flew in May 1927, and, after a number of teething problems, proved so successful that it was decided to proceed with the full metalisation of the airframe, including a revised tail unit with a pair of aerodynamically balanced rudders without fins. The Virginia Mk VII conversion proved so successful that its standard was accepted for all future Virginia orders. Production to this Type 139 standard totalled 50 Virginia Mk X aircraft, and 53 existing aircraft were rebuilt to the same standard.

FIAT AVIATION

Founded in 1899 as a Turin-based manufacturer of automobiles, the Fabrica Italiana Automobili Torino (FIAT, generally rendered as Fiat) moved into aviation in 1908, when thc company started to make aero engines, and in 1914 it entered the aircraft manufacturing field, when it established the Società Italiana Aviazione (SIA) for the licensed construction of the Farman Type VB biplane. SIA then progressed to the design and manufacture of its own aircraft, and the company was important in the Italian air effort of World War I, with a series of important aircraft including the Savoia-Pomilio series. Further strength was added to Fiat's aviation interests in 1926 when it acquired the Società Anonima Aeronautica Ansaldo, the aeronautical subsidiary of the Ansaldo shipbuilding company, that had become celebrated in World War I for its SVA series of bomber and reconnaissance warplanes. From 1926, SIA and Ansaldo design and manufacturing efforts were combined under the aegis of the Società Anonima Aeronautica d'Italia, but the aircraft were always known as Fiat machines, with a designation whose lettered portion indicated the individual aeroplane's role and/or design origin.

The most talented designer available to Fiat was Celestino Rosatelli, who had started work for SIA during 1918 with the initial task of developing an effective warplane out of the SIA.9 reconnaissance biplane, on which great hopes had been pinned, but which had proved to be structurally unsound. The new type appeared in 1919 as the BR (Bombardamento Rosatelli, or Rosatelli Bomber), and a few examples of the type were ordered for the Italian air force during the early 1920s. By comparison with the SIA.9, the BR had cleaner lines and a considerably stronger airframe, but inherited from its predecessor the fabric-covered wooden construction, the powerplant of one Fiat A.14 Vee piston engine rated at 700 hp (522 kW) and driving a two-blade wooden propeller of the fixed-pitch type, the two-bay biplane wing cellule, the fixed tailskid landing gear with a main unit of the through-axle type, and the two-seat accommodation that located the pilot in an open cockpit below a cut-out in the trailing edge of the upper wing's centre section, with the observer gunner immediately behind him. A notable external departure was the vertical tail surface, which introduced the distinctively shaped fin/rudder assembly characteristic of Rosatelli aircraft for the next decade.

In 1923, Rosatelli started work on an improved version of the BR, and this entered service with the Italian air force in the following year as the BR.1. The improved type was basically similar to its predecessor except in four important features: the overall size was increased, a lower-drag frontal radiator was adopted for the A.14 engine, the through-axle type of main landing gear unit was replaced by a main unit of the divided type and, most distinctively of all, the standard combination of interplane struts and bracing/flying wires was replaced by Warren-type interplane struts, whose W-shaped arrangement was used in all subsequent Rosatelli biplanes. The BR.1

had better performance and load-carrying capability than the BR, and was also used for trials of a new rotary-type bomb rack. Production was some 150 aircraft.

NEW AMERICAN DESIGNS

On the other side of the Atlantic Ocean, the Martin MB-1 twin-engined medium bomber, designed in World War I and produced to the extent of only 22 aircraft, paved the way for the MB-2 design that was conceived as a short-range night bomber derivative of the MB-1, with speed and manoeuvrability sacrificed to the carriage of a considerably heavier bomb load. The MB-2 was basically similar to the MB-1 in its construction and overall configuration. During 1920, Martin received an initial order for 120 such aircraft, of which 100 were then cancelled, for service initially with the manufacturer's MB-2 designation, although from the sixth aeroplane, the revised designation NBS-1 in the NBS (Night Bomber, Short-distance) category, that lasted only to 1924. Ultimately, 110 MB-2/NBS-1s were built. The feat for which the NBS-1 is most strongly remembered is the sinking of the surrendered German battleship *Ostfriesland* during the notorious July 1921 bombing trials, in which Brigadier General William 'Billy' Mitchell sought to persuade the US authorities of the utility of heavy bombing and of its capabilities for the coast-defence role.

AERO A.11

First flown in 1923 as an early example of the capabilities of the fledgling aircraft industry in Czechoslovakia, a country that had been created (from northwestern parts of Austria-Hungary) only in the aftermath of World War I, the Aero A.11 was a classic 'pilot's aeroplane' in which a number of largely unspecifiable factors combined to produce a machine that was both a delight to fly and the basis of a large number of developments in the A.11, A.21, A.25, A.29 and A.125 variants. The A.12 was an unequal-span biplane of the single-bay type with fixed tailskid landing gear, unremarkable in concept and structure. Production for the Czech army air service totalled 93 such aircraft, which remained in useful service up to the later 1920s. The key factors that made the A.12, and also its successors, so successful were its speed, agility, ruggedness and overall reliability.

Making its appearance late in World War I in the form of Farman FF.60, with the letter suffix in the designation indicating Farman Frères (Farman brothers), the F.60 was numerically the most important large aeroplane in the

■BELOW: The Vickers Virginia was a classic heavy bomber of the 1920s, and the type went through a large programme of development in new-build and converted aircraft.

world in the decade following the war. The type was originally designed purely for military service, but with the end of World War I, the two FF.60 prototypes currently under construction were revised to civil standard. The first of these machines flew in January 1919, with accommodation for 12 passengers in enclosed nose and midships compartment, carrying four and eight persons respectively. The FF.60 entered production for the civil market as the F.60 Goliath, with a powerplant of two Salmson (Canton-Unné) 9Z or, later, Salmson (Canton-Unné) 9CM water-cooled radial piston engines, each rated at 260 hp (194 kW).

France had meanwhile decided that this capable type should form the core of its post-war bomber force, and a third prototype was built in bomber form. The type's conceptual and structural origins can clearly be discerned in Farman's new thinking as first exemplified by the F.50, and the FF.60 was therefore a substantial three-bay biplane, with fixed tailwheel landing gear, and was of thoroughly orthodox fabric-covered wooden construction. The military version of the Goliath entered production in 1922 and service in 1924, and production of the F.60BN.2 in the Bombardement de Nuit deux-place (two-seat night bomber) category, despite its three-seat accommodation, totalled enough aircraft to equip six squadrons as well as a small number of French naval air arm units, in whose service the 24 aircraft were designated F.60Torp in the torpedo bomber role, with twin-float alighting gear, a redesigned nose position with minimal glazing, and a powerplant of two Gnome-Rhône (Bristol) 9A Jupiter radial piston engines, each rated at 420 hp (313 kW). The F.60BN.2 had a powerplant of two Salmson (Canton-Unné) 9Az piston engines and a maximum bomb load, carried under the fuselage and lower wing, of 2293 lb (1040 kg).

The F.62 was the export version of the F.60M with four-seat accommodation and a powerplant of two Lorraine-Dietrich piston engines each rated at 450 hp (335.5 kW) and a 'balcony' type bombardier position in the nose. The USSR bought enough aircraft of this model to equip two squadrons but, recognising that the type was already obsolescent, decided in 1926 to use the type as a trainer to familiarise Soviet pilots with the flying techniques required for the handling of large twin-engined aircraft in nocturnal operations.

Operated by the French air force as the F.63BN.4, the F.63 was a derivative of the F.62, with the revised powerplant of two Gnome-Rhône (Bristol) 9Aa Jupiter radial piston engines, each rated at 450 hp (335.5 kW). The French procured 42 of this variant, which saw comparatively little service use as a result of several airframe problems. Delivered to the French naval air service from 1925 to the extent of some 100 F.65Torp aircraft, the F.65 was in essence an upgraded version of the F.60Torp and F.60M, with a blunt nose section and interchangeable wheel/float landing gear.

Known to its manufacturer as the Super Goliath, the F.140 was the last attempt to wring additional performance out of the basic F.60 design by the adoption of an enlarged airframe with a powerplant of four Farman 12We W-type piston engines, each rated at 500 hp (335.5 kW), in tandem push/pull pairs located on the lower wing. Built to the extent of six aircraft for trials of the Très Gros Porteur (very heavy lifter) concept, the F.140 first flew in April 1924. One of the F.140 bombers was lost as a result of structural failure in 1930, and the French air force then grounded and scrapped all its surviving F.60, F.63 and F.140 bombers. The French naval air arm operated its F.60Torp and F.65Torp aircraft for a short time longer.

CAPRONI'S NEW AIRCRAFT

The standard bombers of the Italian air force during the early and mid-1920s were types such as the Caproni Ca 36M, that had been developed in the closing stages of World War I. This type was clearly ripe for replacement, and one of the first tasks faced by Rodolfo Verduzio, newly arrived in 1924 as Caproni's chief designer, was the development of a suitable bomber. Verduzio realised that he did not have the time to produce a 'clean sheet of paper' design, and

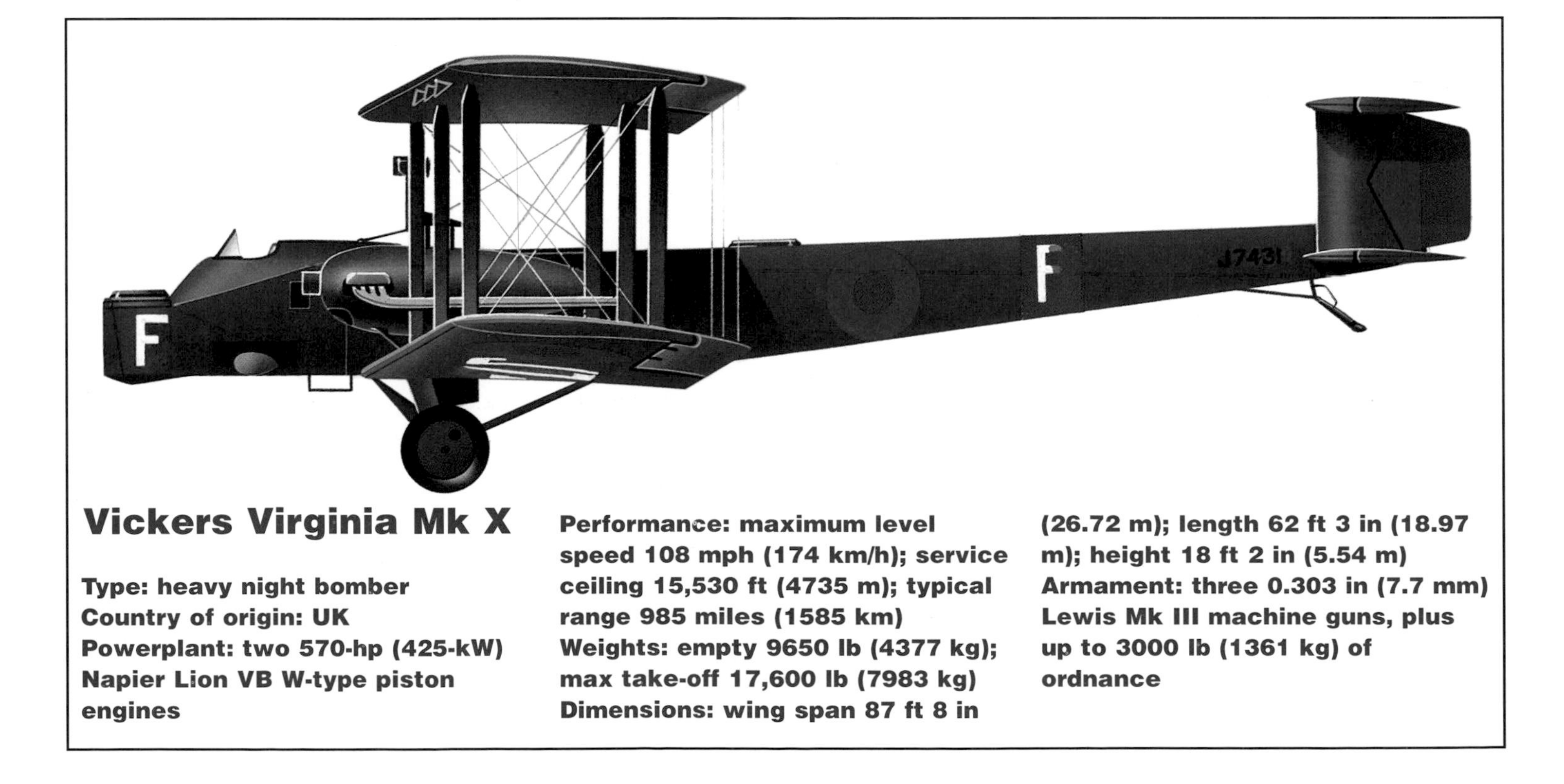

Vickers Virginia Mk X

Type: heavy night bomber
Country of origin: UK
Powerplant: two 570-hp (425-kW) Napier Lion VB W-type piston engines
Performance: maximum level speed 108 mph (174 km/h); service ceiling 15,530 ft (4735 m); typical range 985 miles (1585 km)
Weights: empty 9650 lb (4377 kg); max take-off 17,600 lb (7983 kg)
Dimensions: wing span 87 ft 8 in (26.72 m); length 62 ft 3 in (18.97 m); height 18 ft 2 in (5.54 m)
Armament: three 0.303 in (7.7 mm) Lewis Mk III machine guns, plus up to 3000 lb (1361 kg) of ordnance

therefore opted for the development of the Ca 66 four-engined experimental bomber into a more capable type that could serve in the civil transport (as well as the military bomber) role.

The resulting Ca 73 was distinctly unusual in appearance, with a rectangular-section fuselage whose curved lower line gave it a boat-like appearance, an inverted-sesquiplane backward-staggered wing cellule and a biplane tail unit. The initial Ca 73 model entered service in 1925, with a powerplant of two Lorraine-Dietrich 12 W-type piston engines, each rated at 410 hp (306 kW), and there followed in 1926 the Ca 73bis that was a simple derivative of the Ca 73, with the powerplant modified to a pair of Lorraine-Dietrich 12 engines each rated at 450 hp (335.5 kW) for modestly improved performance, and the Ca 73ter that was a development of the Ca 73, and Ca 73bis with greater fuel capacity and a powerplant of two Isotta-Fraschini Asso Vee piston engines, each rated at 510 hp (380 kW). The Ca 73ter was later redesignated as the Ca 82 after the lateral bomb racks had been replaced by underwing racks, and a number of the aircraft were subsequently converted for the Sanitario (air ambulance) role, with the further revised designation Ca 80S or for the Coloniale (colonial transport) role, with the designation Ca 82Co with accommodation for two crew and 10 passengers in a revised fuselage with an internal cabin. The Ca 74 was the overall designation accorded later by the Italian air force to all variants of the Ca 73 and its descendants, to reduce the confusion caused by the multitude of designations.

The Ca 80 was a development of the Ca 73 series, with the revised powerplant of two Bristol Jupiter radial piston engines, each rated at 400 hp (298 kW) for more reliable and effective operation in 'hot and high' conditions, such as those typical of the Italian possessions in North and East Africa; the main subvariant of this model was the Ca 80S for use in the air ambulance role. The Ca 88 was a development of the Ca 73ter (Ca 82) with a semi-enclosed cockpit, a manually operated dorsal turret for one 0.303 in (7.7 mm) machine gun, and a retractable ventral turret of the manually operated 'dustbin'-type, armed with a single 0.303 in (7.7 mm) machine gun. Originally designated Ca 73quaterG, the Ca 89 was a development of the Ca 88, in which the nose was revised with a fully enclosed and extensively glazed bombardier position without the trainable machine gun of all earlier variants. The Ca 73 and its successors may have appeared strange, but for their time were excellent aircraft, with adequate performance and good agility in combination with viceless handling characteristics. The aircraft saw extensive service with the squadriglie da bombardamento notturno (night bomber squadrons), saw considerable operational use in Italy's African possessions during the late 1920s and early 1930s, and were on occasion used as paratroop transports.

ABOVE: The Fiat BR.1 was designed by Celestino Rosatelli, whose name appeared in the designation (Bombardamento Rosatelli, or BR). Approximately 150 were built.

THE KEYSTONE BOMBERS

In the early 1920s, the standard bomber of the US Army Air Service was the Martin MB-2 and its derivatives that stemmed directly from the MB-1, designed in World War I. By 1923 the MB series was obsolescent, and in that year the USAAS contracted with Huff-Daland for a single prototype of its Pegasus design as the XLB-1 first machine of the new LB (Light Bomber) category. The XLB-1 was a three-seat single-bay biplane of conventional fabric-covered wooden construction, but introduced novel features in the form of its single rather than twin-engined powerplant, tapered rather than constant-chord outer wing panels, and a ventral rather than nose bomb-aiming position. The XLB-1 was powered by one Packard 1A-2540 Vee piston engine rated at 750 hp (559 kW) and driving a two-blade wooden propeller, and its armament included a gun element of two 0.3 in (7.62 mm) fixed forward-firing weapons in the lower wing, two 0.3 in (7.62 mm) trainable rearward-firing weapons in the open dorsal position and one 0.3 in (7.62 mm) trainable rearward-firing weapon in the ventral position, the dorsal and ventral guns being operated by one man, as well as a 2000 lb (907 kg) bomb load carried internally. The XLB-1 could carry a 1500 lb (680 kg) bomb load over a range of almost 1000 miles (1609 km) at a maximum level speed of 114 mph (183.5 km/h). There followed 10 LB-1 bombers, ordered in November 1925 and intended mainly for the service test role, and these warplanes were completed to a standard that differed from that of the XLB-1 only in the addition of a fourth crew member, and the introduction of the uprated 2A-2540 engine rated at 787 hp (587 kW), driving a two-blade wooden propeller and cooled by a radiator installed in the nose below the engine.

Delivery of these aircraft was made from July 1927, and the data for the machines included a span of 66 ft 6 in (20.27 m) with an area of 1137.00 sq ft (105.63 m2), length of 46 ft 2 in (14.07 m), height of 14 ft 11 in (4.55 m), empty weight of 6237 lb (2829 kg), maximum take-off weight of 12,415 lb (5631 kg), maximum level speed of 120 mph (193 km/h) at sea level, cruising speed of 105 mph (169 km/h) at optimum altitude, typical range of 430 miles (692 km), maximum rate of climb at sea level of 530 ft (162 m) per minute, and service ceiling of 11,150 ft (3400 m).

By the time the LB-1 aircraft were being delivered to the US Army Air Corps, as the USAAS had become in 1926, the service had decided that future procurement of light bombers would be based in a twin-engined powerplant for improved flight safety and to allow the incorporation of a nose gunner's position. The XBL-2 was a single twin-engined prototype derived from the Atlantic (Fokker) C-2 transport, so the next Huff-Daland bomber was the Pirate which was ordered initially to the XLB-3 prototype standard, that was essentially the LB-1 reworked to a twin-engined configuration by the replacement of the nose mounted engine by a nose gunner installation, and the location above the lower wing of the new powerplant of two Packard V-1410-1 inverted-Vee piston engines, each rated at 410 hp (306 kW) and installed in a nacelle, whose upper surface carried the bottom of one of the two additional sets of interplane struts that turned all later variants into two-bay biplanes. The engine was an experimental air-cooled version of the celebrated Liberty 12 unit of World War 1, but was not successful, so these engines were replaced by two Pratt & Whitney R-1340-1 radial piston engines, each rated at 410 hp (306 kW), to turn the XLB-3 into the XLB-3A that also had its crew increase to five, and the bomb-aiming position relocated to the nose under the nose gunner's open position. The XLB-3A was one of the first aircraft delivered by the company after it had been reorganised from Huff-Daland into Keystone, but before this, Huff-Daland had received an order for one prototype and 10 production aircraft to an improved XLB-3A standard with a powerplant of two Packard V-1650-3 Liberty Vee piston engines, each rated at 420 hp (313 kW). The designation LB-4 had already been allocated, in XLB-4 form, to a Martin bomber prototype of all-metal construction, with a powerplant of two Pratt & Whitney R-1690-1 radial piston engines, each rated at 525 hp (391 kW), so despite the cancellation of this machine before delivery, the new Keystone type became the LB-5 that was preceded by one XLB-5 prototype.

With the LB-6, known to the manufacturer as the Panther, there was a considerable change in the series, as the original tapered outer wing panels were replaced by longer-span panels of constant thickness and chord with ailerons of increased chord, and the powerplant of two Pratt & Whitney R-1750-1 radial piston engines, each rated at 536 hp (400 kW), was installed in nacelles strut-braced in mid-gap between the upper and lower wings, rather than on the upper surface of the lower wing. The XLB-6 prototype was a conversion of the last LB-5, and the 17 LB-6 production aircraft that followed differed only in minor details and a revision of the two rudders to a more angular shape.

The LB-5 and LB-6 bombers were complemented by 18 LB-7 bombers (and three LB-6 conversions) completed by Keystone to a standard that differed from that of the LB-6 only in its powerplant of two Pratt & Whitney R-1690-3 radial engines. Changes in the powerplant and shape of the vertical tail surfaces resulted in a number of differently designated bombers within the Keystone LB series at this time, the different powerplant installations being designed for the evaluation of various engines.

NEW DESIGNATIONS

In 1930, the USAAC abandoned its current pair of LB (Light Bomber) and HB (Heavy Bomber) categories in favour of the single B-for-Bomber category, and this affected the designations of the 73 Keystone bombers currently on order as 63 examples of the LB-10A, seven examples of the LB-13 and three examples of the LB-14. The LB-10A was the production version of the LB-10, and the 63 aircraft were delivered with the revised designation B-3A. The main changes were the single vertical tail surface, a reduction in the number of defensive guns to three, and an increase in the bomb load to 2500 lb (1134 kg). Of the seven LB-13 bombers on order, the first five were completed to Y1B-4 service test standard with a single vertical tail surface and a powerplant of two R-1860-7 radial engines, each rated at 575 hp (429 kW) and driving a three-blade metal propeller. The USAAC then ordered 25 basically identical B-4A production aircraft, which were dimensionally identical to the B-3A bombers but differed in details.

The three LB-14 bombers were completed as Y1B-5 aircraft, but were not, apparently, ever taken onto USAAC

RIGHT: Sturdy and reliable, the Ansaldo A.300 was an Italian bomber of the inter-war period. The variant seen here is an A.300/4 machine, flying over the north of Italy.

charge. There was nothing wrong with the type, however, for there followed 27 basically identical B-5A production aircraft, with a powerplant of two R-1750-3 radial engines, each rated at 525 hp (391 kW) and driving a three-blade metal propeller. The last two aircraft ordered to LB-13 standard were in fact completed to Y1B-6 service test standard with a powerplant of two R-1820-1 radial engines, each rated at 575 hp (429 kW), driving a three-blade metal propeller and drawing its fuel from main fuel tankage in the upper-wing centre section, with auxiliary fuel in lower-fuselage tankage. Three B-3A bombers were also converted to this standard. There followed 39 basically identical B-6A production aircraft, to a standard that included a crew of five (gunner/bombardier in an open nose position, pilot and co-pilot/navigator side-by-side in an open cockpit, radio operator in a fuselage compartment, and gunner in an open dorsal position), armament of one or two 0.3 in (7.62 mm) Browning trainable forward-firing machine guns in the nose position, two 0.3 in (7.62 mm) Browning trainable rearward-firing machine guns in the dorsal position, and one 0.3 in (7.62 mm) Browning trainable rearward-firing machine gun in the ventral position also manned by the dorsal gunner, and a disposable armament of up to 2150 lb (975 kg) of bombs carried in a lower-fuselage weapons bay.

Deliveries of the B-3A, B-4A, B-5A and B-6A ended in 1932, and the aircraft served with the 2nd and 5th Bombardment Groups in succession to these units' LB-series bomber, and also

ABOVE: The Farman F.60 Goliath was a mainstay of French aviation in the 1920s, when the type was built and operated in both bomber and airliner variants.

with the squadrons of the 7th and 19th Bombardment Groups that were formed in 1928. The Keystone bombers remained in first-line service up to the mid-1930s, when they were replaced by monoplane bombers, and then saw short second-line service as trainers.

In 1925, Aero responded to the requests of the Czechoslovak army air service for an improved version of its A.11 bomber and reconnaissance aeroplane and its A.12 reconnaissance and bombing aeroplane by starting work on the A.11LD version of the A.11, with a powerplant of one Lorraine-Dietrich 12 W-type piston engine rated at 450 hp (336 kW). Trials soon confirmed that this was too much engine for the airframe, and Aero thereupon undertook the design of an enlarged airframe from 1926. This emerged as the A.30, which was an unequal-span biplane of the single-bay type, with fixed tailskid landing gear, and was in no way remarkable in its concept or structure, although the machine was notable for its more nearly sesquiplane layout, as the upper wing was of considerably greater span and chord than the lower wing. In prototype form the A.30 offered adequate performance, but also possessed a number of unfortunate attributes, especially in its handling, and considerable development had to be undertaken before the Czechoslovak air force ordered the type into production during 1927, with an initial order for five aircraft with the powerplant altered to one Skoda L Vee piston engine rated at 500 hp (373 kW). Further contracts added 17 more aircraft to the production run, whose total of only 22 aircraft is telling evidence that the A.30 was not as successful as its predecessors.

Introduced in 1930, the A.230 was an improved version of the A.30, with a powerplant of one Avia (Lorraine-Dietrich) 12 engine rated at 490 hp (365 kW), a differently shaped lower wing, divided main landing gear units, and revised bomb racks under the fuselage and lower wing. The A.330 was the final production version, built up to 1933 to end deliveries of the A.30 and its successors at 79 aircraft in total, including prototypes, and was basically a development of the A.230, with the powerplant changed to one Praga (formerly Breitfeld Danek) ESV Vee piston engine rated at 650 hp (485 kW). The A.330 and its predecessors remained in service with the Czechoslovak air force into the second half of the 1930s, when the surviving aircraft were replaced by machines of the Aero A.100 series.

LIORÉ-ET-OLIVIER

First flown in June 1924, the Lioré-et-Olivier LeO 12 was a two-seat night bomber prototype of sturdy fabric-covered Dural construction, with an unstaggered three-bay biplane wing cellule and fixed tailskid landing gear, that included wide-track main units enclosed in large pantalon (pantaloon) fairings, extending downward from the undersurface of the lower wing. The aeroplane was powered by two Lorraine 12Db Vee piston engines, each rated at 400 hp (298 kW) and driving a two-blade wooden propeller of the tractor type, located in lower-wing nacelles immediately above the main landing gear pantalons. Five such aircraft were built for limited service use, and as a result there appeared in the middle of 1925 the LeO 122.01 prototype, which was, in effect, the prototype for the LeO 20, which first flew in 1926 as a development of the LeO 122.01, with a revised nose accommodating the 'balcony' position at the front of a lengthened nose for a third member of the crew, namely the bombardier/gunner, and the Lorraine-Dietrich engines replaced by two examples of the French licence-built version of the Bristol Jupiter radial piston engines, located in more refined nacelles, but still driving the same type of propeller. The LeO 20.01 prototype was evaluated in 1926, and won the French air ministry's night bomber competition, largely as a result of its world record for the carriage of a 4,409 lb (2000 kg) payload over a range of 1131 miles (1820 km) in a time of 9 hours 30 minutes.

An initial order was placed for 50 LeO 20BN.3 service aircraft which were delivered in 1927 for service in the Bombardement de Nuit trois-place (three-seat night bomber) category and were later joined by an additional 261 aircraft, which were delivered by December 1932 to give the French air force a total of 311 such aircraft. Although nominally three-seat machines, the LeO 20 warplanes were generally flown in four or even five-seat configuration, with a pilot and co-pilot side by side in the open cockpit, a bombardier/gunner in the nose balcony, a dorsal gunner in an open position on the rear fuselage, and a ventral gunner in a retractable ventral installation.

By the beginning of 1937, the French air force still had 224 LeO 20 series aircraft on strength, but with a maximum level speed of less than 124 mph (200 km/h) the type was thoroughly obsolete and replaced in first-line service during that year by the Bloch MB.200 monoplane bomber. On the eve of World War II (1939-45) in September 1939, the French air force still had 92 LeO 20 series aircraft in flying condition and a further 23 in storage, but all of these obsolete aircraft had been phased out of service before France's acceptance of defeat by Germany in June 1940.

THE ANSALDO A.120

Of metal construction, covered almost entirely with fabric, the Ansaldo A.120 was a simple parasol-wing monoplane typical of European design practices in the mid-1920s. The type was based on a rectangular-section fuselage carrying the nose-mounted engine and its associated radiator, the cockpits for the pilot and observer/gunner, and the tail unit, which was a braced structure including an aerodynamically balanced rudder and two aerodynamically balanced elevator halves, all three surfaces having wire trailing edges that resulted in a scalloped effect. The wing was supported over the fuselage by a standard cabane arrangement, had a large cut-out in the centre-section trailing edge to improve the pilot's upward fields of vision, carried outboard ailerons, and was braced to the lower longerons on each side by two struts. The airframe was completed by the landing gear, which was of the fixed tailskid type, with a main unit of the through-axle type.

The A.120 Ady was developed from the A.115m and A.115bis experimental parasol-wing monoplanes, and first flew during 1925 in the form of two prototypes that combined the parasol wing, with a fuselage based largely on those of the Dewoitine D.1 and D.9 fighters built under licence in Italy by Ansaldo, which became a subsidiary of Fiat in 1926. The two prototypes were the A.120 reconnaissance fighter, with a powerplant of one Lorraine 12Db W-type piston engine rated at 400 hp (298 kW) and the A.120bis reconnaissance aeroplane with a powerplant of one Fiat A.20A Vee piston engine also rated at 400 hp (298 kW). In 1926 there appeared a revised A.120 that had been redesigned by Celestino Rosatelli with an improved fuselage, tail unit and landing gear. The new version was initially flown with the Lorraine 12Db engine, but was later evaluated with the Fiat A.20 and A.22 engines. It was the last that was selected, in its A.22T form with a saddle-type radiator installation, for the A.120 Ady production model, of which the Italian air force received 57 examples. Other orders were received from Austria (two aircraft) and Lithuania (12 aircraft). Lithuania was the last operator of the type, its surviving machines operating latterly in the army co-operation role and being taken over and subsequently scrapped by the Soviet air force after the USSR's annexation of the country in 1940.

The A.120R was an improved version of the A.120 Ady, with the A.22R Vee piston engine using a tunnel-type radiator under the nose, and also featured a revised observer/gunner's cockpit, with a larger windscreen and rounded glazed side panels. Austria took six such aircraft, which were apparently produced as conversions of ex-Italian air force A.120 Ady machines.

A NEW CZECH DESIGN

The standard two-seat reconnaissance aeroplane operated by the Czechoslovak army air service in the mid-1920s was the Aero A.11 and when, late in the decade, the air service decided that it needed a version offering higher performance, Aero revised a single example of the A.11 with a considerably more powerful engine, the Bristol Jupiter radial piston engine built under licence in Czechoslovakia by Walter. The new engine transformed performance for the better, and the air service ordered the type with the designation A.11J. As Aero prepared the type for production, however, it incorporated so many changes that the new designation A.32 was allocated for a machine that matured as an equal-span biplane, with upper-wing ailerons which were mass rather than horn-balanced, and elevators that were now of the plain rather than horn-balanced type. The A.32 entered service in 1928, and a five-year production programme saw the delivery of 116 A.32 series warplanes for the home and export markets. The A.32 was the baseline version for the Czechoslovak army air service, which received 32 such aircraft.

The A.32IF was the initial attack variant for the Finnish air force, which received a single such aeroplane in 1929, with a powerplant of one Isotta-Fraschini Asso Caccia Vee piston engine rated at 450 hp (335.5 kW). The A.32GR was the definitive model for the Finnish air force, which received 15 aircraft with a revised version of the A.32's powerplant, namely one Gnome-Rhône (Bristol) Jupiter radial engine rated at 450 hp (336 kW). These 15 aircraft had been delivered by the end of 1930, and after a short period of service in the attack role, they were relegated to use as trainers up to the end of the 'Continuation War' with the USSR (1941-44). Although mainly used in the training role, the aircraft saw limited operational use as reconnaissance and communications aircraft.

The Ap.32 was the definitive version of the A.32 for the Czechoslovak army air service, with a number of detail refinements, including a divided main landing gear arrangement with streamlined fairings over the shock absorbers. The powerplant remained unaltered, but the reduced drag of this variant increased performance to figures that included a maximum level speed of

BELOW: The Keystone (originally Huff-Daland) LB series of light bombers served the US Army Air Corps faithfully and well during the later 1920s and into the early 1930s.

146 mph (235 km/h) at 8200 ft (2500 m), cruising speed of 124 mph (200 km/h) at optimum altitude, typical range of 559 miles (900 km), and service ceiling of 21,980 ft (6700 m). A subvariant of this improved model was the Apb.32, and production of these two improved models reached 68 aircraft.

ABOVE: The Tupolev TB-1 used the same type of corrugated metal skin as aircraft built by Junkers, who had a clandestine factory in the Soviet Union for some years after World War I.

FRENCH DEVELOPMENTS

First flown in 1928, the Farman F.160 was a development of the operational, aerodynamic and structural thinking that had first appeared in mature form with the F.60 series. The F.160 was therefore a substantial three-bay biplane with fixed tailwheel landing gear and thoroughly orthodox fabric-covered wooden construction. The type entered service in 1929 as the F.160BN.4 with a bomb load of 3307 lb (1500 kg), but was built in only modest numbers including single aircraft for evaluation by Italy and the Imperial Japanese army air force. The F.161 was a development with three-seat accommodation and the bomb load reduced to 2205 lb (1000 kg), and was intended for the longer-range role in the BN.3 category. The type did not enter production, and the same fate befell the F.162 seaplane version that was intended for the level and torpedo bombing role in the Torp.4 (Torpilleur quattre-place, or four-seat torpedo bomber) role, as a development of the F.161 with a powerplant of two Salmson radial piston engines, each rated at 500 hp (373 kW) and provision for the wheeled landing gear to be replaced by side-by-side single-step floats complemented, as on the floatplane versions of the F.160 series, by a pair of fixed stabilising floats.

Built only in small numbers and notionally operated as F.165BN.2 aircraft, the F.165 was a floatplane type that was used mainly in the training role. As delivered, the aircraft had a powerplant of two Salmson radial piston engines, each rated at 260 hp (194 kW), but these engines were later replaced by two Gnome-Rhône (Bristol) 9 Jupiter radial piston engines, each rated at 380 hp (283 kW). Built in larger numbers and intended right from the beginning for the full operational rather than training role with a somewhat strengthened airframe, the F.166Torp.4 featured the powerplant of two Gnome-Rhône 9 Jupiter radial engines, side-by-side accommodation for the pilot and co-pilot/navigator, twin rather than single trainable machine guns on the ring mountings on the nose and dorsal positions, provision for an offensive armament of bombs or a single 1764 lb (800 kg) torpedo, and provision for the wheeled landing gear to be replaced by two floats. The F.167 was a development of the F.166, with outer wing panels that folded to the rear to reduce width and thereby ease hangarage problems, and served as the F.167Torp.4.

The F.168 was the definitive model of the series, with an uprated powerplant and a revised forward fuselage with a rounded and slightly elevated upper decking between the rear of the nose position and the forward edge of the dorsal position. This raised section carried the pilot and co-pilot/navigator in separate open cockpits with full dual controls and considerably improved fields of vision. Other changes in the F.168 were the installation of the uncowled Jupiter engines in more tapered nacelles which extended to a point well to the rear of the wing trailing edges, and the use of more modern floats attached to the underside of the engine nacelles and fuselage by a simplified arrangement of struts. Production of the F.168Torp.4 totalled about 100 aircraft, some 60 of these for the French naval air service, and the other 40 for the French air force. The aircraft of the naval air service operated with the Escadrilles (Squadrons) 1B1, 3B2, 4B1 and 4B3 up to 1936, when they were replaced by Lioré-et-Olivier LeO 258 warplanes and then relegated to training duties at the St Raphaël and Hourtin bases. The air force aircraft were retired in 1937.

SOVIET GROWTH

While it was countries such as France, Italy, the UK and the USA that led the way in the concept of strategic heavy bombing, another that came to the same conclusion in the later 1920s was the USSR, which saw its growing air power and the steadily enlarging industrial base on which it was dependent as means for the protection of the fledgling communist state and, if required, the projection of its power into other parts of the Western world. As leader of the AGOS (Department of Aviation, Hydro-aviation and Experimental Construction) within the TsAGI (Central Aerodynamics and Hydrodynamics Institute), Andrei Nikolayevich Tupolev was one of the founding fathers of all-metal aircraft construction in the USSR. The ANT-3 was one of two projects allocated to Tupolev in July 1924, at the time in which the Soviet air forces decided that all subsequent major warplane types would be fabricated of Kolchug (a Soviet copy of the German-developed Dural aluminium alloy). The ANT-3 (R-3) was the lighter and less ambitious of the two aircraft, the other being the heavier and altogether more ambitious ANT-4 that was schemed from the beginning as a heavy bomber. This machine eventually matured as one of the most important aircraft of its type anywhere in the world during the later 1920s, and was a major milestone in the development of the USSR's aeronautical industry and military aviation. Tupolev was aided in the task of drafting the design of the ANT-4 by Vladimir Mikhailovich Petlyakov, and the two men drew extensively on their experience with Junkers design and fabrication techniques. (Junkers in fact took the USSR to court for infringement of its patents, but lost the action.) Tupolev and Petlyakov designed the ANT-4 as the world's first large low-wing monoplane of all-metal construction, with a twin-engined powerplant, and the aeroplane was completed in August 1925, although it was November of the same year before the machine made its first flight. It took two months to extricate the seven major assemblies from the second-floor room in which they had been built and assemble them into the complete aeroplane.

ABOVE: With bombers such as the Lioré-et-Olivier LeO 20, the French began to develop the type of angular ugliness that typified most of their bombers until the later 1930s.

The prototype made its first flight with ski landing gear and a powerplant of two Napier Lion W-type piston engines, each rated at 450 hp (336 kW) and driving a two-blade propeller of the fixed-pitch type. This first flight revealed that the skis were both heavy and weak, and no further flight was essayed until February 1926, when revised skis had been designed, built and fitted. Wheeled landing gear was installed after the winter snow had melted, and a series of 25 successful evaluation flights led to the decision for a major production programme for use in several roles (most importantly the heavy bombing task), with a cheaper powerplant for which the Lorraine-Dietrich was preferred, as this had already been selected and ordered in substantial numbers from France for use in the R-3 aircraft. In April 1927, it was decided to use the BMW VI engine imported from Germany, although the M-17 Soviet development of this engine was also substituted.

Production was entrusted to the factory at Fili, where Junkers was now winding down its secret manufacturing operation and which had a core of workers skilled in the manufacture of metal aircraft. The ANT-4 second prototype was completed in February 1928 to bomber standard, with a number of revisions, including powerplant of two BMW VI engines, three gun positions each carrying one 0.303 in (7.7 mm) Lewis trainable machine gun, and provision for 1609 lb (730 kg) of bombs. The ANT-4bis third prototype was the first to be built at Fili with the standardised BMW VI engine installation, full military equipment, six 0.3 in (7.62 mm) DA trainable machine guns in three twin installations, and provision for 2205 lb (1000 kg) of bombs.

The ANT-4bis paved the way for the TB-1 bomber, of which 152 were delivered between 1929 and August 1932. These aircraft saw extensive service, but were obsolescent by the mid-1930s and from 1935 were relegated to second-line duties, including the development of the Soviet airborne forces. A total of 66 aircraft was completed to the TB-1P revised form with twin-float alighting gear. The decision to proceed with this model was made in 1926, but it was 1928 before real progress was made with the receipt of a pair of prototype floats designed and made in the UK by Short Brothers. A revised version of this float design was placed in production in the USSR, delivery of more than 100 pairs of floats being made from 1932. The TB-1P was used mainly in the torpedo attack role, with a single torpedo under the fuselage.

Félix Amiot established the SECM (Société d'Emboutissage et de Constructions Mécaniques) during 1916,

■ **ABOVE: The K 43 was a development of the W 34 civil aircraft, and its design was typical of several Junkers types of the period. All the Junkers aircraft had corrugated metal skinning.**

and initially concentrated the efforts of his company on the repair and overhaul of other companies' products, most notably the Breguet Bre.14. It was only after this that the company branched into the design and construction of its own aircraft, starting with the Amiot 22 and 24 touring biplanes, and then in 1923 by the Amiot 26 trainer. These comparatively small aircraft were followed in 1925 by three examples of an altogether larger unequal-span biplane, the Amiot 120. The first two of these were intended for attempts on long-range flying records, but the first crashed on take-off in June 1925 and the other was unsuccessful in an effort to capture the world absolute distance record for France. Two related record-breaking aircraft were the Amiot 121, which was lost in a rough landing during June 1927, and the Amiot 122S that completed two long flights, in the forms of a circuit of the Mediterranean and a circuit of the Sahara, in the hands of Capitaine Pelletier d'Oisy. These aircraft were powered by Renault Vee or Lorraine-Dietrich W-type engines, the latter generally proving more reliable.

As these record attempts were being made, Amiot had completed the third example of the original type as the Amiot 122 prototype of a three-seat warplane, intended for the bomber and bomber escort roles. In this capability, the prototype was designed to combine the flying characteristics of the lighter type of single-engined biplane with the load-carrying capability of the twin-engined warplanes currently serving with the French air force. This prototype first flew in 1928, and was extensively displayed to the air arms of friendly nations, as well as to the French air force. The prototype was deficient in lifting capability by the standards of the late 1920s, however, and when the type was selected for service with the French air force, it was in the modified form as the Amiot 122BP.3 (Bombardement de Protection trois-place, or three-seat bomber and escort aeroplane) with wings of increased span and area.

The Amiot 122 was of light alloy construction, covered with fabric except over the engine and forward fuselage, which were skinned in light alloy. The French air force started with an order for 50 examples of the Amiot 122BP.3, and these entered service during 1930 with the 11th Regiment based at Metz in eastern France. Brazil ordered five aircraft in 1931, and in 1934 the French air force received a final batch of 30 aircraft. Poland also considered an order for the type in its Amiot 123 two-seat form, but lost interest after the loss of the prototype in the Azores during an attempt to make the first Polish flight across the Atlantic Ocean. During 1932, three Amiot 122 aircraft were revised as test beds for different engines as the Amiot 124, 125 and 126. The Amiot 124 had the Hispano-Suiza 18Sb W-type piston engine rated at 1000 hp (746 kW), the Amiot 125 the Renault 18Jbr piston engine rated at 900 hp (671 kW), and the Amiot 126 the Lorraine-Dietrich 18Gad Orion W-type piston engine rated at 900 hp (671 kW). Although all of these engines offered improvements in performance, the Amiot 122 was conceptually obsolete although it was still a robust type with powerful offensive and defensive armament, and no production plans were seriously considered.

JUNKERS K 43

Typical of the new generation of German warplanes was the Junkers K 43, which was the three-seat reconnaissance bomber derivative of the W 34 transport and built in 1927 by A.B. Flygindustri, the Junkers subsidiary in Sweden, for the export market, with a number of powerplant options and the possibility of fitting wheeled, float or ski alighting gear. The type had provision for a bomb load of 661 lb (300 kg) and a defensive armament of three machine guns, two of them trainable weapons in open positions, and production was undertaken in Germany and Sweden for export sales to countries such as Argentina, Bolivia, Finland and Portugal, the latter two generally operating its aircraft on twin floats or, for Finnish winter operations, twin-ski alighting gear.

The K 43 was a cantilever low-wing monoplane of all-metal construction, with a skinning of corrugated light alloy. The prototype made its first flight in 1926 with a powerplant of one Gnome-Rhône (Bristol) Jupiter VI radial piston engine rated at 480 hp (358 kW), and was a two-seat machine with a defensive armament of two 7.62 mm (0.3 in) machine guns in the form of one fixed forward-firing weapon operated by the pilot and one trainable rearward-firing weapon operated by the dorsal gunner. Production aircraft, now built in Germany as well as in Sweden, were revised with an additional dorsal position, offset to port as the other dorsal position was offset to starboard, for a third member of the crew, who doubled as the radio operator, bombardier and additional dorsal gunner. These aircraft were also structurally revised to allow operation at weights considerably higher than the prototype's 3527 lb (1600 kg) and with powerplants of up to 750 hp (559 kW). The type was produced in two subvariants as the K 43L landplane and K 43W seaplane, the latter with the normal wheels landing gear replaced by a side-by-side pair of single-step floats that increased length to 36 ft 9 in (11.20 m) and height to 12 ft 9 in (3.90 m). The K 43 could also be fitted with ski alighting gear for continued operability under winter conditions.

LIORÉ-ET-OLIVIER 200 SERIES

With its LeO 20 in full production for the French air force, Lioré-et-Olivier turned its attentions to the development of a more capable bomber in which greater payload and/or performance would be provided by an uprated powerplant. The first step in this direction was the LeO 202, which was in essence the LeO 20 with the revised powerplant of two Salmson 9Abc radial piston engines. Flight trials of the LeO 202 with this uprated powerplant persuaded the Lioré-et-Olivier design team that it was on the right track. Desiring to provide still greater power without too much alteration of the basic airframe, the design team decided that the optimum solution could be provided by a four-engined powerplant with two pairs of push/pull engines in which the forward and rear units would drive tractor and pusher propellers ahead and to the rear of the lower-wing leading and trailing edges respectively. The first result of this process was the LeO 203.01 prototype, which first flew in May 1930 with a powerplant of four Gnome-Rhône 7Kb Titan radial piston engines, each rated at 350 hp (261 kW) for take-off, and the outer wing panels revised with a sweepback of 4.5º. A floatplane version of the LeO 203 first flew in 1931 as the LeO H-204 with twin-float alighting gear, and another development of the same year was the LeO 205 with a powerplant of four Renault 9Ca radial piston engines. Neither the LeO H-204 nor the LeO 205 was ordered into production, but in 1932 the French air force ordered 40 examples of the LeO 203, although the order was almost immediately transferred to the improved LeO 206 that first flew in June of the same year with a revised 'balcony' nose and a long ventral gondola accommodating the weapons bay over its forward and middle sections, with a defensive gun position at its rear.

Some 37 aircraft were completed, and proved popular for their tractable flight characteristics and ability to maintain altitude on three or even two engines.

JAPANESE ATTACK AIRCRAFT

As it was developing its technical capabilities during the 1920s, the Imperial Japanese army air force was also considering the uses to which its new air power might be used. One of the targets already envisaged for Japanese territorial expansion was the Philippines, the American protectorate with its capital at Manila on a large bay, whose seaward side was controlled by the very heavily fortified island of Corregidor off the southern tip of the Bataan peninsula. The Imperial Japanese army air force therefore conceived a requirement for a heavy bomber that could be used to neutralise the American defences on Corregidor for the nearest possible Japanese base at Pingtung on the island of Formosa. The design of a bomber to carry the required bomb load over the range to tackle Corregidor from Formosa was currently beyond the capabilities of the Japanese aero industry, and Mitsubishi accordingly reached a secret September 1928 arrangement with Junkers for the design data, working drawings, manufacturing techniques and production rights to its K 51 bomber design, which was a clandestine development of the G 38 transport that Germany was then banned from producing by the terms of the Treaty of Versailles which had ended Germany's involvement in World War I. As part of this secret contract, Junkers produced plans for the installation of the armament and other internal equipment required by the Imperial Japanese army air force.

Originating in Junkers' Nurflügel (wing only) concept for a virtual flying wing, the G 38 was a truly remarkable design in which the crew, payload, engines and fuel were all accommodated in the very large wing and stumpy forward fuselage, the vestigial rear fuselage being used mainly to support the tail unit that provided stability and control in pitch and yaw. Work on the design began in 1928, and the G 38a prototype made its first flight in November 1929 with a powerplant of two Junkers L-88 piston engines, each rated at 800 hp (596.5 kW), inboard and two Junkers L-8 piston engines, each rated at 400 hp (298 kW), outboard: each of these engines drove a four-blade propeller of the fixed-pitch type. The structure was of the typical Junkers all-metal type, with a stressed corrugated skinning. In its basic

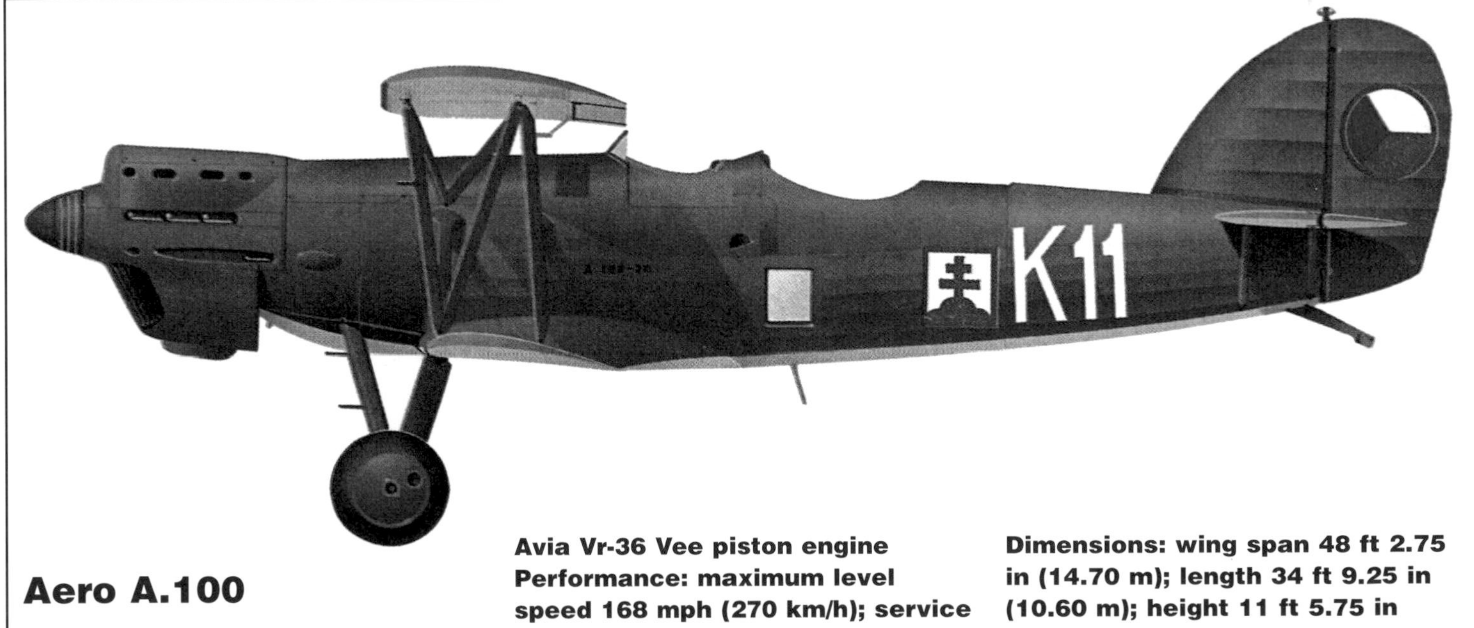

Aero A.100

Type: light bomber and long-range reconnaissance aeroplane
Country of origin: Czechoslovakia
Powerplant: one 725-hp (541-kW) Avia Vr-36 Vee piston engine
Performance: maximum level speed 168 mph (270 km/h); service ceiling 21325 ft (6500 m); typical range 570 miles (917 km)
Weights: empty 4497 lb (2040 kg); max take-off 7099 lb (3220 kg)
Dimensions: wing span 48 ft 2.75 in (14.70 m); length 34 ft 9.25 in (10.60 m); height 11 ft 5.75 in (3.50 m)
Armament: four 0.312 in (7.92 mm) vz.30 machine guns, plus up to 1323 lb (600 kg) of stores

Farman F.222.2BN.5

Type: five-seat heavy night bomber
Country of origin: France
Powerplant: four 950-hp (708-kW) Gnome-Rhône 14N-11/15 radial piston engines
Performance: maximum level speed 199 mph (320 km/h); service ceiling 26,245 ft (8000 m); typical range 1243 miles (2000 km)
Weights: empty 23,148 lb (10,500 kg); max take-off 41,226 lb (18,700 kg)
Dimensions: wing span 118 ft 1.33 in (36.00 m); length 70 ft 4.5 in (21.45 m); height 17 ft 0.33 in (5.19 m)
Armament: three 0.295 in (7.5 mm) MAC 1934 machine guns, plus up to 9259 lb (4200 kg) of stores

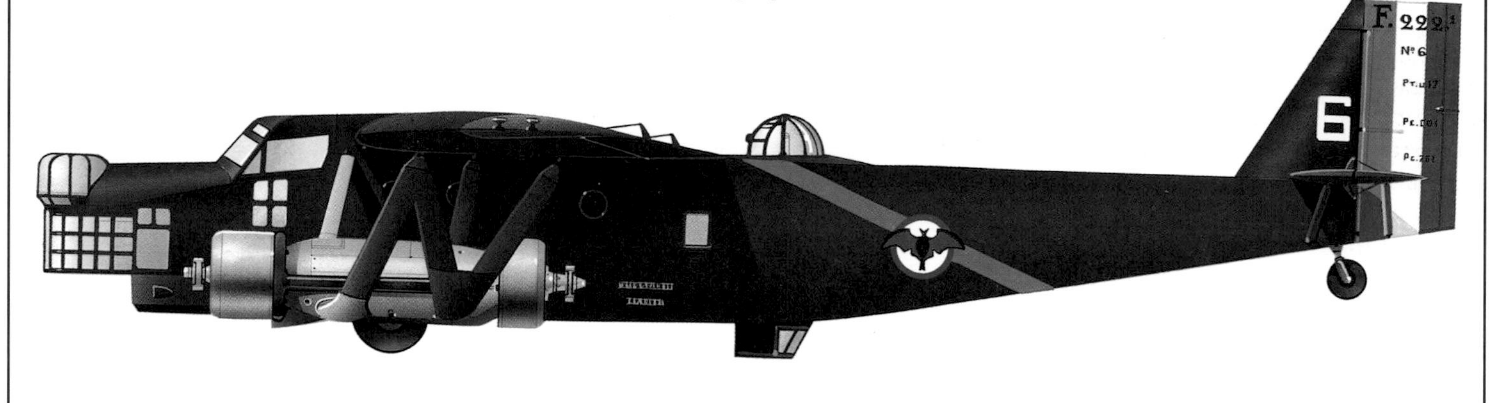

structure and configuration, the K 51 differed in no major respect from the G 38, and the first two aircraft produced in Japan were constructed from assemblies and components supplied by Junkers. The only major difference between the transport and the bomber was therefore the latter's armament, which comprised an offensive element of between 4409 and 11,023 lb (2000 and 5000 kg) of bombs carried externally and a defensive element of cannon and machine guns in six positions.

The first Army Type 92 Heavy Bomber, which later received the short designation Ki-20, was completed in 1931 and first flew with a powerplant of four Junkers L-88 Vee piston engines each rated at 800 hp (596.5 kW) and driving a four-blade wooden propeller of the fixed-pitch type. This powerplant was installed in the first four aircraft, but the fifth and sixth aircraft were completed with a powerplant of four Junkers Jumo 204 Diesel engines each rated at 750 hp (559 kW) for an improvement in range as a result of this engine type's lower specific fuel consumption, and the earlier aircraft were then flown on occasion with a mixed powerplant of two L-88 engines inboard and two Jumo 204 engines outboard. Some of the aircraft were also flown experimentally with the Kawasaki Ha-9 for trials in methods of extending range still farther. By the time these trials had been completed, the Imperial Japanese army air force had decided that production should be limited to just six aircraft as the type was already obsolete. The six aircraft were then used mainly for research purposes, still under a cloak of great secrecy, and the first Ki-20 made its public debut only in January 1940, only a short time before the type disappeared from service.

SOVIET ADVANCES

At the time of its introduction in the early 1930s, the Tupolev TB-3 was the most advanced four-engined heavy bomber in service anywhere, and was the largest landplane to have been completed anywhere in the world: it also established the basic configuration that was followed (albeit with many detail improvements) by virtually every heavy bomber and large aeroplane then produced, up to the end of the era of piston-engined warplanes, and represented a very considerable achievement in purely technical terms as a cantilever all-metal monoplane, with corrugated Dural skinning and tailskid landing gear of the fixed type with tandem main units. What made the type all the more remarkable was not just its vast size, but the fact that the ANT-6, unlike other contemporary giants such as the Beardmore (Rohrbach) Inflexible and Dornier Do X, was carefully designed to use this size to meet a carefully-framed operational requirement through sophisticated aerodynamic and structural thinking. Western thinking about the ANT-6 was later coloured by the fact that the type was kept in service far longer than it should have been, since the most enthusiastic supporters of the strategic bombing concept were 'liquidated' by Stalin. The heavy bomber programme faded toward obscurity in the later 1930s, with the resulting lack of a successor type compelling the retention of the ANT-6 into a twilight of complete technical obsolescence. The ANT-6 survived to the time of the considerably more advanced Avro Lancaster and Boeing B-17 Flying Fortress, but should be compared with more exact contemporaries, such as the Handley Page Heyford and Curtiss B-2, rather than the much later bombers.

The origins of the ANT-25 can be traced to 1925 and discussions about a successor to the ANT-4 bomber, which had entered service as the TB-1. These discussions decided that the next logical step in the soviet development of the heavy bomber should be a large monoplane powered by engines delivering some 2000 hp (1491 kW) and capable of operation on wheel, ski or float alighting gear. The basic configuration of the new ANT-6 bomber was established by Andrei Nikolayevich Tupolev and then passed for detail design to the brigade headed by Vladimir Mikhailovich Petlyakov. Finalisation of the design was considerably delayed by the Soviet air force's stream of requirement changes and by lack of production capacity. The latter meant that the service debut of the TB-1 was delayed, and the air force wanted experience of the type before finalising the details of its successor.

The delay allowed Tupolev to design the ANT-14 transport that had a measure of commonality with the ANT-6, but required the use of five Gnome-Rhône 9Akx radial piston engines, each rated at 480 hp (358 kW), to secure modest performance at a lower weight than that projected for the ANT-6. Greater power would be therefore required for the bomber, and as a five-engined powerplant was not feasible, it was decided to adopt a powerplant of four Curtiss V-1570 Conqueror Vee piston engines, each rated at 600 hp (447 kW). Wind tunnel tests of definitive models began in December 1929 and, following the successful examination of a mock-up in March 1930, the first of three ANT-6 prototypes was completed in October 1930 for a maiden flight in December of the same year as what was, in some respects, a scaled-up version of the ANT-4 with exactly the same configuration.

The first flight nearly ended in disaster as the pilot needed both hands to overcome the heavy control loads, and the throttles slipped closed before being seized and pulled open by a mechanic at the last moment. The weight of the control loads was reduced by alteration of the control surfaces, and even before the prototype had flown in this revised form the ANT-6 had been ordered into production during February 1931, with a powerplant of four M-17 Vee piston engines each driving a two-blade wooden propeller of the fixed-pitch type. Production began in late 1931.

The revised first prototype was tested from January 1931, and revealed fully satisfactory flight characteristics. The revision had also included the provision of armament, in the form of girder-type racks under the fuselage and inner wing panels for a maximum disposable load of 4409 lb (2000 kg) of bombs carried in Der-9, Der-13, Der-15 and Der-16 containers, and 6300 rounds of ammunition in 100 drums for eight 0.3 in (7.62 mm) DA trainable machine guns. These latter were disposed as two weapons on the Tur-6 ring mounting in the nose positions, two weapons on the Tur-5 ring mountings in the diagonally-opposed corners of a large gunners' cockpit to the rear of the wing, and one weapon in each of the two B-6 retractable turrets under the wing near the outboard engines. The first prototype continued its trials during 1931, and underwent a great deal of development as efforts were made to improve operational capability yet keep weight growth under control, as changes such as a switch from imported to Soviet steel threatened to erode performance. A further contribution to the flight test and development programs was made by the second and third prototypes, which were each powered by four BMW VI Vee piston engines each rated at 730 hp (544 kW) for take-off. (The BMW VI was the German engine from which the Soviet M-17 was derived.)

The success of these machines paved the way for the TB-3/M-17 initial

BELOW: The Martin Model 139 (B-10 and B-12) was the world's first 'modern' bomber of all-metal cantilever construction with retractable landing gear, and enclosed accommodation.

production model, of which some 400 were delivered up to the end of 1933, with a powerplant of four M-17F Vee piston engines, each rated at 715 hp (533 kW) for take-off, and a combination of offensive and defensive armament modelled exactly on that of the revised first prototype.

In 1931, it became clear that the more powerful Mikulin M-34 (redesignated AM-34 in 1940) Vee piston engine derived ultimately from the BMW VI would become available in a production version towards the middle of the decade, and it was decided to create a version of the TB-3 with a powerplant of four such engines at their baseline rating of 830 hp (619 kW). A prototype with four M-34 engines first flew in February 1933, and trials were undertaken with two similar aircraft from October of the same year. The success of the trials prompted a switch to the improved model, which entered production late in 1933 with an improved radiator installation (with water and oil cooling elements located in a duct set farther back under the engine) and a bombardier's position in a gondola under the nose. Fewer than 100 examples of this TB-3/M-34 model were delivered.

The TB-3/M-34R version was powered by the improved M-34R engine which was rated identically with the M-34 but offered better altitude performance. This model also introduced a number of airframe refinements, a main landing gear arrangement with brakes on the rear wheels and oleo-pneumatic rather than rubber shock absorption, a castoring tailwheel in place of the original fixed skid, and a tail gunner's position. This last was originally a plain position under a cut-out in the bottom of the rudder with two 0.3 in (7.62 mm) DA trainable rearward-firing machine guns, but in its production form was a neatly-faired installation that provided access to the rear fuselage and was linked to the other crew stations by an intercom. In 1935, the TB-3/M-34R was improved with drag-reducing fairings on the wing roots, tail unit, engine nacelles and main landing gear units, and the two windmill-driven electrical generators became retractable.

Introduced late in 1935, the TB-3/M-34RN had a powerplant of four M-34RN Vee engines, each rated at 970 hp (723 kW) for improved performance at high altitude. Other changes included four-blade wooden propellers of the fixed-pitch type on the inboard engines; revised nose, dorsal, tail and new ventral gunners' positions, each equipped with a Tur-8 mounting with a single 0.3 in (7.62 mm) ShKAS machine gun; and a 4409 lb (2000 kg) disposable weapons load carried in Der-19, Der-20 or KD-2 containers.

Built to the extent of about 90 aircraft with a powerplant of four M-34FRN engines, each rated at 900 hp (671 kW) and driving a three-blade metal propeller, the TB-3/M-34FRN had a smooth rather than corrugated skinning, an enclosed turret in the nose, extra fuel tankage in the outer wing panels, radiators of reduced size in improved ducts, better wing root fairings for reduced drag, and revised main landing gear units with large single wheels. Included in the total of 90 TB-3/M-34FRN series bombers, the TB-3/M-34FRNV had a powerplant of four M-34FRNV engines, each rated at 1200 hp (895 kW) and also introduced an enclosed dorsal turret. The TB-3 was used operationally against the Japanese in the border clashes of 1938 and 1939, but the series was clearly obsolete by this time since production had ended late in 1937 after the delivery of 818 aircraft, including the three prototypes. The type remained in service as a bomber into the early stages of World War II, but was then retired to second-line tasks.

THE AERO A.100 AND A.101

The Aero design team evolved the A.430 prototype with a more powerful engine and a number of aerodynamic refinements. Trials with this prototype revealed improved performance and overall capabilities, but also suggested that further enhancement was possible through the adoption of additional changes. This led to the A.100 design that was offered in response to a requirement issued in 1933 by the Czechoslovak ministry of defence for a two-seat warplane optimised for the light bomber and reconnaissance roles. The A.100 design was declared winner of the resulting competition, and over the following two years, some 44 examples of the A.100 were delivered to the Czechoslovak army air service. The A.100

Martin B-10B

Type: four-seat medium bomber
Country of origin: USA
Powerplant: two 775-hp (578-kW) Wright R-1820-33 radial piston engines
Performance: maximum level speed 213 mph (343 km/h); service ceiling 24,200 ft (7375 m); maxi range 1240 miles (1995 km)
Weights: empty 9681 lb (4390 kg); max take-off 16,450 lb (7462 kg)
Dimensions: wing span 70 ft 10.5 in (21.60 m); length 44 ft 8.75 in (13.63 m); height 11 ft 5 in (3.48 m) with the tail down
Armament: three 0.3 in (7.62 mm) Browning machine guns, plus up to 2260 lb (1025 kg) of ordnance

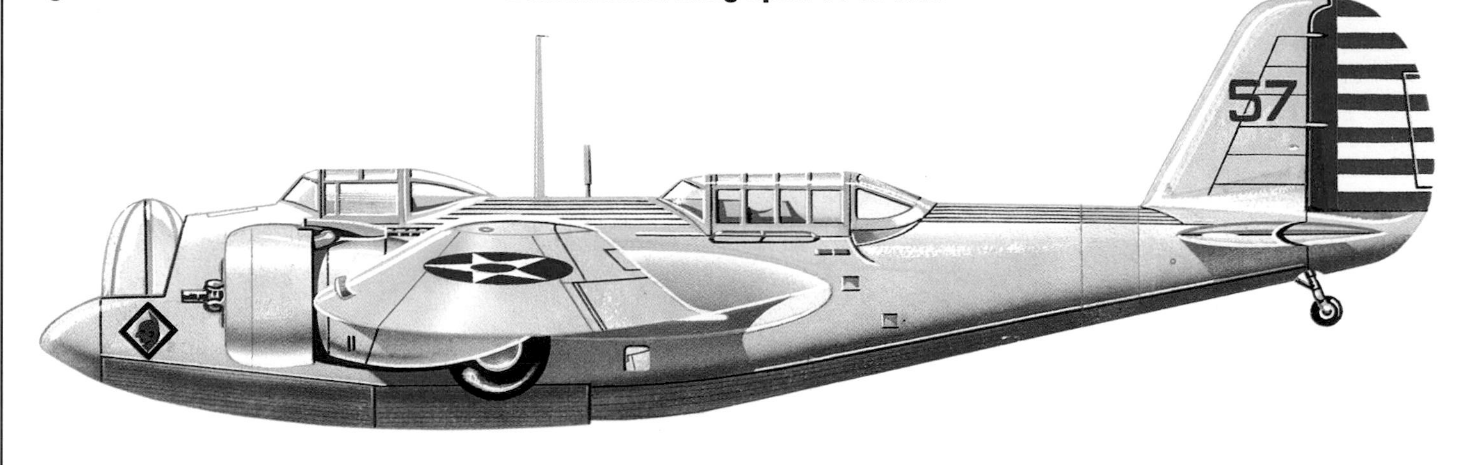

was an unequal-span biplane of unadventurous but nonetheless workmanlike design, with a fuselage and tail unit of welded steel tube construction and wooden wings, all covered with fabric with the exception of the forward fuselage, where the engine had a light alloy cowling. Most of the aircraft were still operational when, in March 1939, Germany occupied Czechoslovakia.

In 1934, Aero produced the A.101 as a development of the A.100, with wings of greater span and area, a larger rudder, a more capacious rear cockpit, and an uprated powerplant in the form of the Isotta-Fraschini Asso-1000 W-type piston engine built under licence by CKD-Praga at a maximum rating of 1000 hp (746 kW) and a normal rating of 800 hp (596 kW). The A.101 thus had considerably greater power than the A.100, but this was offset by the fact that the Asso-1000 was 617 lb (280 kg) heavier than the Vr-36. Production amounted to 29 aircraft, whose performance was inferior to that of the A.100 as a result of the engine's greater weight. The Czechoslovak army air service was therefore happy when in 1936 the Republican government, faced with a Nationalist insurgency at the beginning of the Spanish Civil War, offered to buy the Czechoslovak aircraft. Not all of the aircraft reached their intended operator: in April 1937 a Nationalist cruiser intercepted the Panamanian vessel carrying 22 of the aircraft, which thus entered service with the Nationalist air force. The other machines did reach the Republican air force for extensive service, and at the end of hostilities six of these were captured by the victorious Nationalists.

THE VERY HEAVY BOMBER

When it first appeared in 1932, in response to a French air ministry requirement for a Bombardier Très Gros Porteur (very heavy bomber) for what were then regarded as medium and long ranges, the Farman F.211 bomber established a basic configuration that was retained for a whole series of Farman aircraft, civil as well as military. This configuration was based on an angular fuselage that carried a large high-set wing supported by a mass of bracing, extending outward and upward from low-set stub wings that themselves carried the main landing gear units and the powerplant of four piston engines arranged in two tandem push/pull pairs, to drive two pusher and two tractor propellers. The whole arrangement was aesthetically unappealing and produced considerable drag, but it was extremely strong, remained comparatively simple to produce and maintain, and allowed the carriage of a large bomb load.

■ABOVE: The Japanese Army Type 93 Single-engined Light Bomber, or Ki-3 for short, entered service in 1935, but problems with its engine gave the aircraft a short service life.

The F.211 was intended as the prototype of a five-seat night bomber but, with a powerplant of four Gnome-Rhône Titan radial piston engines, each rated at 300 hp (224 kW), was underpowered and therefore followed by the F.212 with a number of detail refinements and a powerplant of four Gnome-Rhône 7Kds radial piston engines, each rated at 350 hp (261 kW). Farman had already appreciated that in addition to being underpowered, the F.211 and F.212 were both too small for the night bomber role and had therefore embarked on the creation of a larger type that retained the same basic configuration, as well as specific features such as the enclosed pilots' cockpit, the 'balcony' bombardier/ nose gun position, and the fixed tailwheel landing gear with wide-track main units.

This larger type emerged for a first flight in May 1932 as the F.220.01 prototype with a powerplant of four Hispano-Suiza 12Lbr Vee piston engines each rated at 600 hp (447 kW), and was later converted as a long-range mailplane for non-stop flights across the South Atlantic between Dakar in French West Africa and Natal in Brazil. The F.220.01 had revealed the potential of the larger airframe, and in May 1933 was followed into the air by the F.221.01 prototype that differed from the F.220.01 mainly in its redesigned vertical tail surface, fully enclosed nose and ventral gunners' positions, a semi-retractable 'dustbin' in place of the previous hatch position for the ventral gunner, and the considerably uprated powerplant of four Gnome-Rhône 14Kbrs Mistral-Major radial piston engines, each rated at 800 hp (596.5 kW) for take-off and installed in two long nacelles, that had cowlings for the tractor units but none for the pusher units.

A production batch of 12 F.221BN.5 bombers followed for service with Escadre de Bombardement II/15, and these aircraft differed from the F.221.01 mainly in the introduction of a manually operated dorsal gun turret, the adoption of a revised nose section that carried a manually-operated gun turret as well as revised glazing for the bombardier position under it, and the full long-chord cowling of the pusher, as well as the tractor engines. From August 1935, the F.221.01 was adapted as the F.222.01 improved prototype with revised main landing gear units that now retracted forward into the underside of the two engine nacelles for a slight but nonetheless valuable reduction in drag. The F.222.01 first flew in the winter of 1935-36, and 12 examples of the F.222BN.5 (later redesignated F.222.1BN.5) production version followed the F.221BN.5 on Farman's production line from April 1936.

As these aircraft were still in the early stages of their production programme, Farman was in the process of finalising the details of an improved version, the F.222.2BN.5 with dihedral of the outer wing panels for improved lateral stability, the removal of the step in the line of the fuselage underside behind the aircraft's bombardier position, and the lowering and lengthening of the forward

Fairey Fox Mk I

Type: two-seat light day bomber
Country of origin: UK
Powerplant: one 480-hp (358-kW) Curtiss D-12 Vee piston engine
Performance: maximum level speed 156 mph (251 km/h); service ceiling 17,000 ft (5180 m); max range 500 miles (805 km)
Weights: empty 2609 lb (1183 kg); max take-off 4170 lb (1892 kg)
Dimensions: wing span 37 ft 8 in (11.48 m); length 28 ft 3 in (8.61 m); height 10 ft 8 in (3.25 m)
Armament: two 0.303 in (7.7 mm) Vickers machine guns, plus up to 500 lb (227 kg) of stores

fuselage's upper line to give the pilots improved fields of vision. This was the standard of the following eight bombers.

The 15e Escadre de Bombardement started to convert onto the F.222.1 during April 1937, and by this time the nationalisation of the fragmented French aero industry had resulted in the combination of Farman with Hanriot to create the Société Nationale de Constructions Aéronautiques du Centre, which had received production orders for an additional 16 examples of the F.222.2, with the powerplant changed to four Gnome-Rhône 14N-11/15 radial piston engines in place of the Gnome-Rhône 14Kirs Mistral-Major engines of the earlier bombers. The last F.222.2 off the production line made its first flight in March 1938.

THE MITSUBISHI KI-1-I

In February 1931, a Japanese patriotic organisation imported a single example of the Junkers K 37 light bomber built by the German firm's Swedish subsidiary, and this aeroplane was then donated to the Imperial Japanese army air force. The service operated this machine with considerable success in Japan's conquest of Manchuria (1931–32), and was so impressed with its capabilities that in April 1932 it issued a requirement for a bomber, similar to the K 37, as replacement for the obsolete Kawasaki Type 87 Heavy Bomber. Having suffered the effects of imprecise specification in some of its earlier warplanes, the Imperial Japanese army air force accompanied its requirement with a tightly-framed specification that demanded the delivery by March 1933 of two prototypes of a bomber of modern monoplane configuration, with a powerplant of two engines in the 800 hp (596.5 kW) class.

Based on its experience with the Ki-20 (Army Type 92 Heavy Bomber), which was the Japanese licence-built version of the four-engined Junkers K 51, itself the bomber derivative of the G 38 transport, Mitsubishi decided that the requirement could be satisfied by an enlarged version of the K 37. Key features of the design were the close grouping of the crew for ease of tactical communication (including a Gosport tube link between the bombardier and pilot), the dispersal of the fuel into as many tanks as possible so that one hit would not empty the whole system, and ease of disassembly so that the aeroplane was readily transportable by railroad flatcar. Mitsubishi completed a mock-up of its design in August 1932, and the first prototype was completed on schedule in March of the following year as a cantilever low-wing monoplane of all-metal construction, with the Junkers type of corrugated metal skinning. In the absence of the planned Mitsubishi Type 93 Vee piston engines, each rated at 700 hp (522 kW), the prototype was powered by two Rolls-Royce Buzzard Vee piston engines, each rated at 800 hp (596.5 kW), driving a two-blade wooden propeller of the fixed-pitch type, and installed in nacelles over the outboard ends of the centre section. Even with this uprated powerplant, the new type was some 12.5 mph (20 km/h) below the demanded speed, but the Imperial Japanese army air force decided nonetheless to adopt the type without significant change as the Army Type 93-1 Heavy Bomber that also carried the short designation Ki-1-I. Deliveries began in the autumn of 1933, and the aircraft rapidly replaced the obsolete Ki-20.

There were continued problems with the Ki-1-I's powerplant of two Mitsubishi Type 93 (Ha-2-II) Vee engines, each rated at 940 hp (701 kW), and controlled level flight on only one engine was virtually impossible, so the 71st aeroplane was taken in hand for modifications designed to rectify the problems. The engine nacelles were lowered, resulting in the need for altered main landing gear units with longer legs and drag-reducing streamlined fairings, a heavily framed canopy was introduced over the two pilots' cockpits and later extended to the rear to cover the dorsal gunner, smooth skinning replaced some of the corrugated skinning on the outer wing panels, and landing lights were added at the front of fairings that helped to reduce the drag of the externally-carried bombs. These changes improved the Ki-1-I to a limited but useful degree, and the last 47 aircraft were completed to this Ki-1-II standard that had the full service designation Army Type 93-2 Heavy Bomber. Like the Ki-1-I, the Ki-1-II was disliked by its crews but remained in production up to April 1936, when the Mitsubishi Ki-21 was planned as its successor. Pending delivery of the Ki-21, the Imperial Japanese army air force bought 100 examples of the Fiat BR.20 Cicogna bomber for service, with the Japanese designation Type I Heavy Bomber. The Ki-1 was used operationally with limited success during the Japanese conquest of Manchuria (1931–32) and also against negligible Chinese fighter opposition during the early stages of the 2nd Sino-Japanese War (1937–45), but had been relegated to the bomber training role by the outbreak of the Pacific War of World War II.

THE KI-2-I

Even though its heavy bombers were little more than medium bombers by the reckonings of other air forces, the Imperial Japanese army air force still felt that it had need of medium and light bombers for the tactical support of its ground forces and the destruction of targets relatively close behind the front line. Thus, when in February 1931 a Japanese patriotic organisation imported a single example of the Junkers K 37 light bomber built by the German firm's Swedish subsidiary and donated the aeroplane to the army air force, the service was happy to operate this machine, which achieved considerable success in Japan's conquest of Manchuria. Impressed with its capabilities, especially in the ground-attack role, in September 1932 the army air force requested Mitsubishi to develop a Japanese version of the K 37 to supersede the Mitsubishi Type 87 and Kawasaki Type 88 Light Bombers, and to partner the somewhat larger Type 93 Heavy Bomber that the company was already designing, as a replacement for the by now obsolete Kawasaki Type 87 Heavy Bomber.

The design team decided to retain the basic concept and structure of the K 37, but opted for a virtually complete redesign of the aeroplane, retaining only the K 37's wing in a revised form with modified ailerons. The powerplant, for which the design team wanted to use the Mitsubishi A4 radial piston engine for an estimated maximum speed of 168 mph (270 km/h), was to be carried in wing-mounted nacelles inside Townend narrow-chord ring cowlings, and other features included a fully enclosed nose turret, a carefully designed dorsal position offering its gunner much improved downward fields of fire, and shock absorption by oleo-pneumatic struts rather than bungee chord. The Imperial Japanese army air force examined the draft design in November 1932 and approved it in general terms, with the exception of the powerplant that was to comprise the specified pair of Kotobuki engines, the nose turret that was to be replaced by a semi-enclosed position, the dorsal position that was to be modified for wider lateral angles of fire, the pilot's cockpit that was to be adapted so that a cover could be attached, and the powerplant installation that was to be modified with a shuttered front for each nacelle for improved cold-weather operability. Mitsubishi received approval for the mock-up of its modified design, and the first prototype was completed two months ahead of schedule, in May 1933, as a cantilever low-wing monoplane of all-metal construction with corrugated metal skinning.

BELOW: Although designed and used as a bomber, the Boulton & Paul Sidestrand was a beautifully harmonised aircraft, with a high level of agility in the air.

The first prototype revealed adequate performance and good handling characteristics, but was lost with fatal results owing to a structural weakness in the very narrow rear fuselage. The second prototype was therefore revised with a wider and stronger rear fuselage, and it was this standard that was accepted for production and service with the full designation Army Type 93-1 Twin-engine Light Bomber and short designation Ki-2-I. Production totalled 113 such aircraft by Mitsubishi up to 1936, with another 13 completed by Kawasaki between November 1934 and August 1935, for an overall total of 126 aircraft. In 1936, the production switched to the improved Army Type 93-2 Twin-engine Light Bomber or Ki-2-I standard with changes that included a powerplant of two Nakajima Type 94 (Ha-8) radial piston engines each rated at 750 hp (559 kW) and installed inside long-chord cowlings, a revised main landing gear arrangement with single-wheel units that retracted forward and upward into the underside of the engine nacelles, an enclosed pilot's cockpit with a rearward-sliding section of access and egress, smooth skinning on the outer wing panels in place of the original corrugated skinning, and on aircraft intended for operations in cold climes a virtually hemispherical framed cover for the nose gunner's position that was thus effectively transformed into an enclosed turret. Production of the Ki-2-II totalled 61 aircraft delivered by Mitsubishi between April 1937 and 1938. The Ki-2 was used operationally in the first stages of the 2nd Sino-Japanese War, most generally in the northern theatre, and the type was generally popular for the fact that it offered performance far superior to that typical of the Ki-1 and Ki-3 bombers. In the early 1940s, most of the surviving aircraft were transferred to second-line duties such as training for continued utility into the middle period of the Pacific War of World War II.

THE MARTIN B-10

Flown by the air forces of six countries and the first American-designed bomber to be flown in combat (albeit by an overseas air force), the Martin B-10 series of bombers was obsolete by the beginning of World War II, but was in its time was a pioneering type, the first American bomber of all-metal construction to enter large-scale production, the first American warplane to be fitted with turreted armament, and the US Army Air Corps' first cantilever low-wing monoplane. Martin was no novice in the design and construction of bombers when it set about the process of designing an altogether superior bomber. The design team was not working to any official requirement, and therefore had a free hand in the development of a design optimised for the maximum possible performance by the standards of the day. Martin's new bomber combined an all-metal airframe, cantilever flying surfaces and retractable main landing gear units, with a twin-engined powerplant and the defensive machine gun in the nose located in a manually operated turret to provide the gunner with protection against the slipstream that was becoming a major factor at the high speeds now attainable.

The new type was the Model 123 and Martin built a single prototype as a private venture with a powerplant of two Wright SR-1820-E radial piston engines each rated at 600 hp (447 kW). This machine was delivered to the USAAC during March 1932 for evaluation as the XB-907. It had a tandem arrangement of three open cockpits on the upper side of the fuselage for the pilot, radio operator and dorsal gunner, and the aeroplane's somewhat strange appearance derived largely from its deep belly, which provided internal accommodation for the bomb load, and the blunt nose incorporating the bombardier position. The official trials, which started in July 1932, revealed that the XB-907 could carry a disposable weapons load of 2200 lb (998 kg) over a range of 650 miles (1046 km) at a maximum speed of 197 mph (317 km/h) at 6000 ft (1830 m).

The performance of the XB-907 was somewhat higher than that of the two Boeing prototypes, but Martin felt that further gains could be made without too great a modification of the basic airframe.

■ABOVE: The Overstrand was a modernised development of the Sidestrand, with features such as a nose-mounted defensive gun turret and enclosed accommodation.

In the later summer of 1932, therefore, the XB-907 was returned to Martin for alteration to XB-907A standard with a power-operated nose turret. Its wings were increased in span from 62 ft 2 in (18.95 m) to 70 ft 7 in (21.71 m) for the lower drag associated with a higher aspect ratio, and the powerplant altered to two R-1820-19 radial engines each rated at 675 hp (503 kW) for take-off and enclosed in NACA cowlings of the long-chord type. Tested from October 1932, the XB-907A had lost something in range and climb rate, but was capable of reaching 207 mph (333 km/h) at 6,000 ft (1830 m), which allowed the bomber to outpace the USAAC's current fighter mainstays, the Boeing P-12 and Curtiss P-6.

This success was rewarded by a USAAC order for 48 examples of the Model 139 production version, and at the same time the service bought the XB-907A for further trials with the designation XB-10. The Model 139 differed from the Model 123 (XB-907 and XB-907A) in a number of details such as its fully enclosed accommodation (the pilot in a forward-mounted cockpit and the radio operator/ventral gunner and dorsal gunner in a somewhat longer rear cockpit), a defensive armament of three 0.3 in (7.62 mm) Browning trainable machine guns (installed in the single-gun nose turret and single-gun dorsal and ventral positions), a standard fuel capacity of 187.35 Imp gal; 851.7 litres) that could be doubled by use of a weapons bay auxiliary tank, a span of 70 ft 6 in (21.49 m), length of 45 ft 3 in (13.79 m) and height of 11 ft 0 in (3.35 m). The original batch of 48 aircraft ordered in 1933 was delivered in no fewer than five different configurations. The first 14 were completed to the YB-10 standard for service trials with a powerplant of two R-1820-25 radial engines each rated at 675 hp (503 kW). Then followed seven examples of the YB-12 service test model with the powerplant altered to two Pratt & Whitney R-1690-11 radial piston engines each rated at 775 hp (578 kW) for a maximum level speed of 212 mph (341 km/h) at optimum altitude. The same powerplant was retained for the 25 examples of the B-12A variant which was basically similar to the YB-12 with the exception of its provision for 303.9 Imp gal (1381.7 litres) of auxiliary fuel in a weapons bay tank. The fourth configuration was represented by the YB-10A, which was powered by two R-1820-31 turbocharged radial engines each rated at 675 hp (503 kW) for take-off and maintaining this speed at altitude for a maximum level speed of 236 mph (380 km/h) at 25000 ft (7620 m). The last aeroplane of the original 48 was completed to the fifth configuration as the sole XB-14 with a powerplant of two Pratt & Whitney R-1830-9 radial piston engines each rated at 950 hp (708 kW) for take-off. Another ten aircraft were ordered to the YB-13 standard with a powerplant of two Pratt & Whitney R-1860-17 radial piston engines, but these were cancelled before completion.

The USAAC and US Army Air Forces, which succeeded the USAAC in June 1941, operated three more aircraft with the designation B-10. Two of these were ordered directly by the USAAC with fiscal year 1936 funding, presumably as attrition replacement, and the third was received in July 1942 as an impressment of an ex-Netherlands East Indies' Model 139WH-3A after it had reached Australia in the closing days of the Japanese conquest of the Netherlands East Indies. The original 48 aircraft allowed a thorough evaluation of the Model 139 with a number of different powerplants, and paved the way for the first true production variant, which was the B-10B of which 103 were completed with a powerplant of two R-1820-33 radial engines each rated at 775 hp (578 kW) for take-off. The B-10B aircraft entered service in 1935, and served mainly with the squadrons of the 2nd, 7th, 9th and 19th Bombardment Groups in the continental USA, while the B-12A machines served overseas with the 6th Composite Group in the Panama Canal Zone between 1936 and 1939, and also with the 5th Composite Group in Hawaii. The aircraft of this latter unit were pressed into emergency use by the 15th Pursuit Group (Fighter) during 1942, when units based in Hawaii were desperately short of all types of aircraft. During their few years of first-line service, the B-10B and B-12A bombers (supplemented by a number of YB-10 and YB-12 aircraft brought up to B-10B and B-12A standards) acquired a good reputation for reliability and, most importantly of all, provided the USAAC with crews experienced in the operation of monoplane bombers. It is worth noting that a number of B-10B bombers had also operated in the coast defence role around the USA after being revised with twin-float alighting gear, and as they reached obsolescence in the bomber role, several of the aircraft were adapted to the target-

Boulton Paul Overstrand Mk I

Type: five-seat medium bomber
Country of origin: UK
Powerplant: two 580-hp (433-kW) Bristol Pegasus IIM3 piston engines
Performance: maximum level speed 153 mph (246 km/h); service ceiling 22,500 ft (6860 m); typical range 545 miles (877 km)
Weights: empty 7936 lb (3600 kg); max take-off 12,000 lb (5443 kg)
Dimensions: wing span 72 ft 0 in (21.95 m); length 46 ft 0 in (14.02 m); height 15 ft 6 in (4.72 m)
Armament: three 0.303 in (7.7 mm) Lewis machine guns, plus up to 1600 lb (726 kg) of stores

Handley Page Hyderabad Mk I

Type: four-seat heavy bomber
Country of origin: UK
Powerplant: two 454-hp (338.5-kW) Napier Lion IIB or Lion V W-type piston engines
Performance: maximum level speed 109 mph (175 km/h); service ceiling 14,000 ft (4265 m); max range 500 miles (805 km)
Weights: empty 8910 lb (4042 kg); max take-off 13,590 lb (6164 kg)
Dimensions: wing span 75 ft 0 in (22.86 m); length 59 ft 2 in (15.90 m); height 16 ft 9 in (5.11 m)
Armament: two 0.303 in (7.7 mm) Lewis machine guns, plus up to 1450 lb (658 kg) of bombs

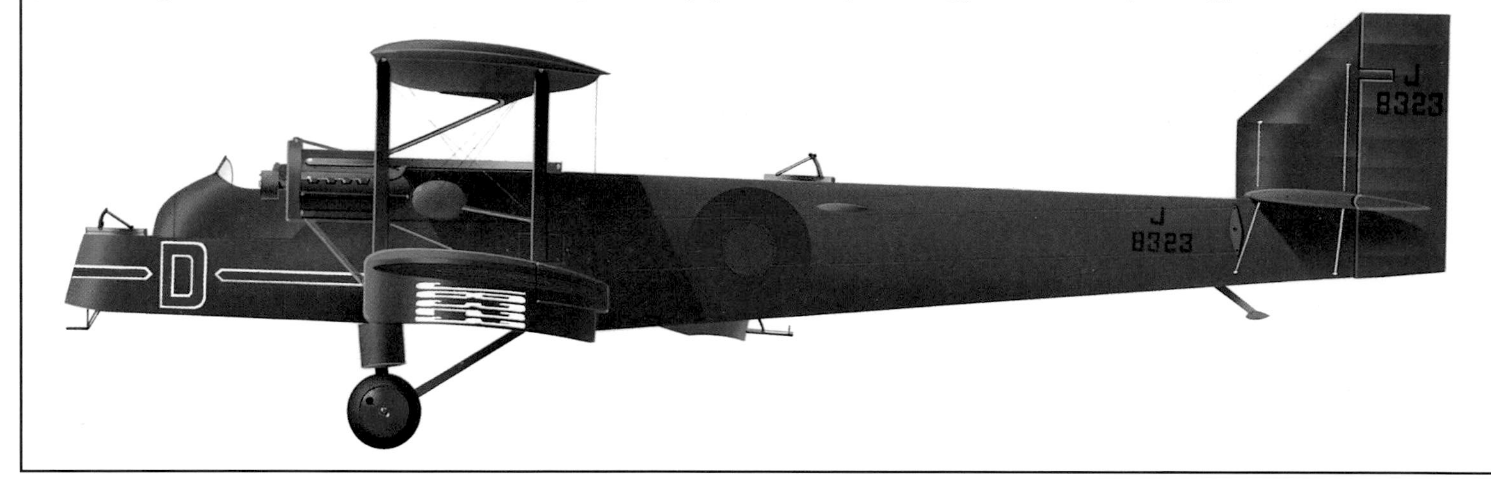

towing role with the revised designations B-10M and B-12AM.

In July 1936, the Martin bomber was released for export. The first sale was made to China, which bought six and three examples of the Model 139WC-1 and Model 139WC-2 respectively. An altogether larger number of aircraft was purchased by the Netherlands East Indies, which ordered 117 examples of the Model 139W bomber in 1936 and 1937. The aircraft were used to equip the 1e, 2e and 3e Vliegtuiggroep based at Andir, Malang and Madioen with two, one and three squadrons respectively. Each of these squadrons had nine aircraft, and the rest of the Model 139WH force was reserved for training and for use as attrition replacements. By the time of the outbreak of the Pacific War of World War II in December 1941, the Netherlands East Indies had slightly more than 100 of these aircraft still on strength with the same three groups now based at Andir, Singosari and Tjililitan respectively as well as two small detachments at Kali Djati. In the course of three months of sustained operations from mid-December 1941, all but one of the aircraft were lost, most of them on the ground to Japanese air attacks, and the others in the air where the lumbering and poorly-protected bombers were no match for agile Japanese fighters.

GERMAN REARMAMENT

The troublesome nature of the Dornier Do 11, the first relatively modern bomber to be adopted for service with the still-clandestine German air force since the end of World War I, especially in its retractable main landing gear units, were reflected in Dornier's decision before the end of 1932 to undertake the development of a simplified version with fixed landing gear and the Junkers type of 'double-wing' flaps extending right across the span of the wing trailing edges to serve collectively as camber-changing flaps and, differentially on their outboard ends, as slotted ailerons. This revised type first flew in February 1933 as the Do 13 prototype, which had faired main landing gear units carrying spatted wheels, but revealed serious instability as well as the same type of wing vibration that was being encountered on the Do 11 series. There followed two improved prototypes, the Do 13b and Do 13c, the latter adopting the reduced-span wing of thc Do 11D and the revised powerplant of two BMW VI Vee piston engines each rated at 750 hp (559 kW) for take-off and 500 hp (373 kW) for continuous running. The Do 13c proved the better of the two improved prototypes, and orders for the last 222 Do 11 bombers were transferred to the Do 13C production version of the Do 13c. Deliveries of the Do 13C were much delayed by engine cooling problems which were finally solved by the addition of flush radiators on the underside of the engine nacelles in place of the supplementary underwing radiators that had originally been evaluated but found to produce excessive drag. The Do 13C finally entered service in the fall of 1934, and almost immediately there followed a number of losses as a result of structural failure. Production was therefore halted after the delivery of 12 aircraft.

As a consequence of the problems with the Do 13, Dornier undertook a complete restressing of the structure, with particular emphasis on the fuselage, and also incorporated a number of revisions into the wing, which was reduced in span from 91 ft 10.33 in (28.00 m) to 83 ft 11.875 in (25.60 m). The immediate result of this process was the Do 13e prototype which made its maiden flight in September 1934 and, despite an increase of 981 lb (445 kg) in empty weight and a reduction in wing area, was finally deemed acceptable by the German air ministry. The ministry thus ordered that unfulfilled orders for the Do 11 and Do 13 should be transferred to the Do 23, the change in designation being thought sensible to avoid the stigma now attached to the Do 13. In structural terms the Do 23 was virtually identical to the Do 11 and Do 13, being a semi-cantilever monoplane of the shoulder-wing type with a rectangular-section fuselage of Dural construction with light alloy covering and fabric-covered Dural flying surfaces; the landing gear retained the basic layout pioneered in the Do 11, but like that of the Do 13 was of the fixed rather than retractable type.

The initial production model was the Do 23F with a powerplant of two BMW VIU Vee piston engines using water cooling. Only a very few Do 23F bombers were completed before production was switched to the Do 23G that differed only in the use of ethylene glycol rather than water for engine cooling. Construction of the Do 23F and Do 23G totalled about 210 aircraft in all, and the Do 23 series entered service in the summer of 1935. The type was delivered first to bomber training schools, and then entered operational service with Gruppen Fassberg, Finsterwalde, Giebelstadt, Gotha and Merseburg, and were soon redesignated as gruppen (wings) of Kampfgeschwadern (Bomber Groups) 153, 155, 253 and 254. In service the Do 23 proved disappointing and production of the limited but trouble-free Junkers Ju 52/3m ge interim bomber, which was to have been replaced by the Do 11, Do 13 and finally Do 23, continued. So disappointing was the Do 23, indeed, that the type was phased out of first-line service from the summer of 1936, although a number of the aircraft survived in second-line tasks until the beginning of World War II, when a few Do 23 aircraft were pressed into service as aerial mine-detectors until the advent of more suitable aircraft.

NEW JAPANESE DESIGNS

During the early 1930s, the Imperial Japanese army air force decided that its previous system of competitive designs for major warplanes was wasteful of scarce financial and design resources, and when in September 1932 it finalised a requirement for a new light bomber, the service issued this only to Kawasaki. The new type was to be used for the tactical support of ground forces, and was therefore required to have rugged reliability, great structural strength, and a judicious blend of adequate performance and considerable agility. The company entrusted the task of preparing the new type to its expatriate German chief designer, Dr. Richard Vogt, and Takeo Doi, and these two men used as the basis of the new design the A-6 high-speed communications aeroplane that had been developed from the KDA-6 experimental reconnaissance machine. The resulting aeroplane was therefore a trim biplane of all-metal construction covered with fabric except over the forward fuselage, which was covered with light alloy panels, tailwheel landing gear with a main unit of the divided type carrying spatted mainwheels, a simple tail unit with a strut-braced horizontal surface, and a slightly staggered single-bay biplane wing cellule with a flat upper wing and moderately dihedralled lower wing, I-type interplane struts, and strut-connected ailerons on the outboard trailing edges of both the upper and lower wings.

The first prototype was completed in April 1933 with a powerplant of one BMW IX Vee piston engine driving a two-blade wooden propeller of the fixed-pitch type, and in September of the same year Kawasaki put this engine in production for the service version of the new bomber. In its original form, the prototype had a horseshoe radiator with controllable shutters in front of the engine, but this was soon moved to a more conventional position under the nose. There followed two more prototypes, and in August 1933 the Imperial Japanese army air force then ordered the type into production as the Ki-3 for service with the full designation Army Type 93 Single-engined Light Bomber.

Production started in January 1934, and the Ki-3 entered service in 1935 as successor to the Kawasaki Type 88 light bomber with the 6th Mixed Air Regiment in Korea as well as the new 9th, 10th and 16 Air Regiments based in Manchuria and the central and northern parts of China. The Ki-3 was moderately effective in the tactical support, reconnaissance, and light freighting roles, but was plagued by engine problems centred mainly on the supercharger. Kawasaki could not eradicate these problems, and production of the Ki-3 was therefore terminated in March 1935 after the delivery of 240 aircraft excluding the prototypes but including 40 produced by Tachikawa. The service life of these aircraft was therefore short, although some of the aircraft remained in second-line service into the very early 1940s.

FAIREY AIRCRAFT

During 1924, and spurred by the success of the Curtiss R-3 twin-float racing seaplane in the 1923 Schneider Trophy race with a powerplant of one Curtiss D-12 Vee piston engine rated at 450 hp (335.5 kW), Fairey secured a licence to make the D-12 engine in the UK as the Fairey Felix, and also to manufacture the Curtiss-Reed metal propeller, Curtiss wing surface radiators, and Curtiss high-speed aerofoils. The forthcoming availability of this important engine, with its combination of a low frontal area and a high power/weight ratio, now persuaded the company to launch an intense development programme for warplanes with the new engine, although the D-12 never in fact entered British production as the Felix, and Fairey therefore relied on a batch of 50 imported engines.

The first result of this process was the Fox day bomber, which gave the British aeronautical establishment considerable food for thought when it revealed outright flight performance considerably better than that of the Royal Air Force's current generation of fighters as well as a speed some 50 mph (80.5 km/h) faster than the Fairey Fawn day bomber with the same bomb load. Design of this aeroplane started in April 1924, the design team setting itself the task of producing an airframe of the smallest possible dimensions, especially in frontal area, and particular emphasis was placed on a cleanliness of line, low structure weight, elimination of all possible drag-producing excrescences, and overall simplification of systems. The result was

BELOW: With its clean lines and fighter-like agility, the Hawker Hart two-seat day bomber was delightful to fly and marked the emergence of a far better British bomber capability.

an exceptional aeroplane that made its maiden flight in January 1925 as a trim single-bay biplane. Flight tests immediately revealed that these surface radiators were inadequate, and Fairey therefore added an interconnected honeycomb radiator just forward of the main landing gear unit as a retractable unit. Renewed trials showed that cooling was now adequate and that performance and handling were both excellent. Even so, there was considerable official resistance to a type powered by an American engine and fitted with internal fuel tankage of the type considered at that time to be a considerable safety hazard to pilots. In July 1925, however, Air Chief Marshal Sir Hugh Trenchard, the Chief of the Air Staff, decided to order enough aircraft to equip a single unit – No 12 Squadron, currently equipped with the Fawn bomber and based at Andover in Hampshire. The 18 aircraft of this order, later supplemented by nine more machines in subsidiary contracts for five and four aircraft, were completed to a modestly revised standard with a wing cellule increased in span by 4 ft 2 in (1.27 m) from 33 ft 6 in (10.21 m). No further aircraft were ordered as a result of continued official antipathy to the Fox and the desire to ensure that RAF day bomber squadrons were equipped with aircraft powered by British engines.

The first Fox Mk I flew in December 1925, and No 12 Squadron was soon the envy of all other day bomber units as well as the despair of fighter squadrons, which were unable to achieve realistic interceptions of this new high-speed bomber. No 12 Squadron operated the Fairey Fox up to 1931, when it received

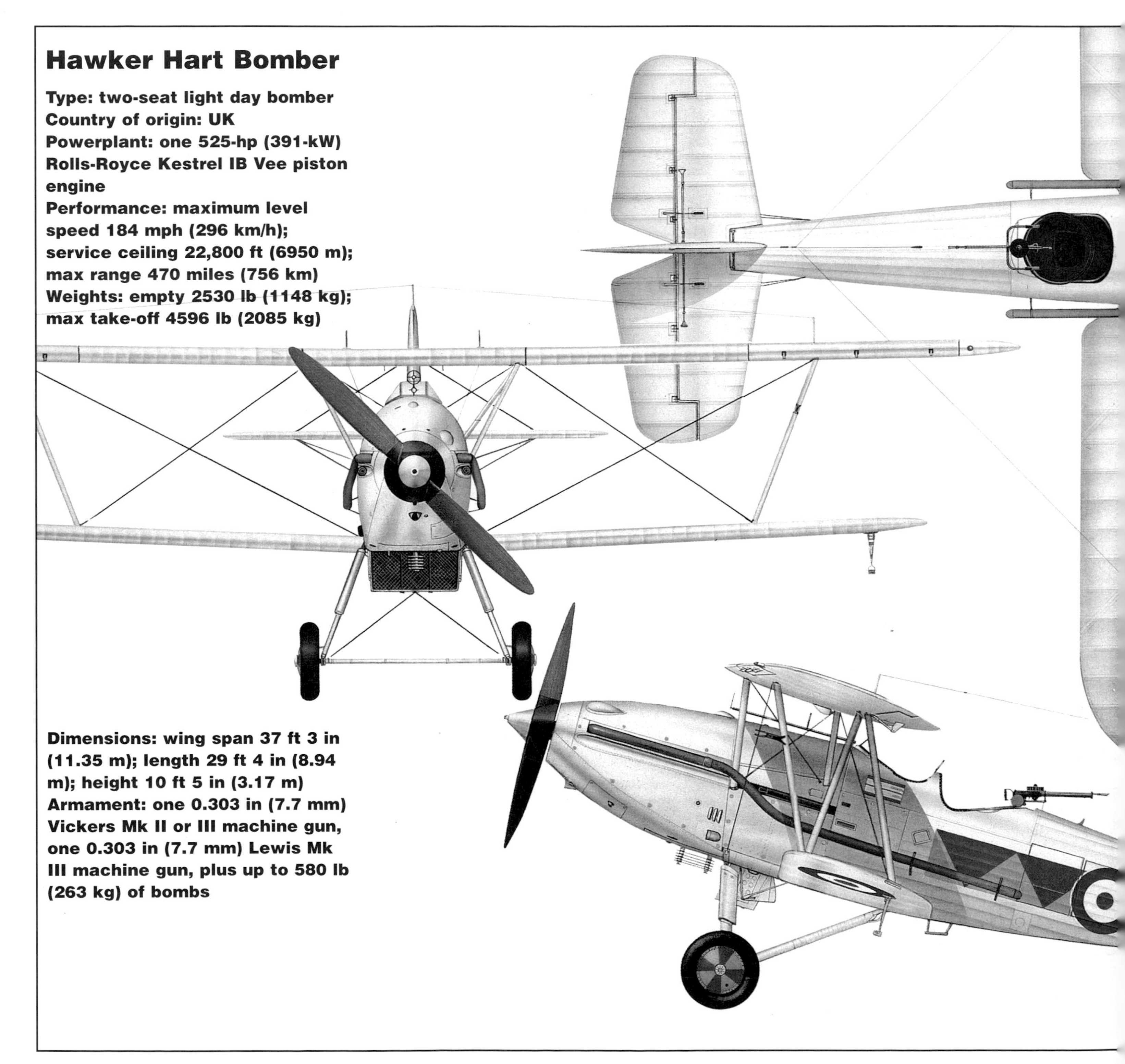

Hawker Hart Bomber

Type: two-seat light day bomber
Country of origin: UK
Powerplant: one 525-hp (391-kW) Rolls-Royce Kestrel IB Vee piston engine
Performance: maximum level speed 184 mph (296 km/h); service ceiling 22,800 ft (6950 m); max range 470 miles (756 km)
Weights: empty 2530 lb (1148 kg); max take-off 4596 lb (2085 kg)

Dimensions: wing span 37 ft 3 in (11.35 m); length 29 ft 4 in (8.94 m); height 10 ft 5 in (3.17 m)
Armament: one 0.303 in (7.7 mm) Vickers Mk II or III machine gun, one 0.303 in (7.7 mm) Lewis Mk III machine gun, plus up to 580 lb (263 kg) of bombs

Hawker Hart bombers as a replacement. Comprising the last four new-build aircraft and conversions of most of the existing aircraft, the Fox Mk IA was a later development of the Fox Mk I. It was equipped with the revised powerplant of one Rolls-Royce Mk XIIA (later Kestrel IIA) Vee piston engine, which gave a maximum take-off weight of 4640 lb (2105 kg) and a maximum level speed of 160 mph (257 km/h) at sea level. The first Fox Mk IA flew in December 1928, and the subvariant entered service in January 1929.

BOULTON AND PAUL BOMBERS

The first medium day bomber to enter service with the Royal Air Force, and also the first twin-engined bomber to enter service with the RAF after the retirement of the de Havilland D.H.10 Amiens, which had entered limited service after the end of World War I, the Boulton and Paul P.29 Sidestrand was a result of the manufacturer's experience with the P.7 Bourges and P.25 Bugle bombers that appeared in 1918 and 1924 respectively, but failed to secure production orders.

The P.29 was initially designed for a powerplant of two Napier Lion W-type piston engines that were replaced by a pair of Bristol Jupiter VI radial piston engines, each rated at 425 hp (317 kW), before the first of two Sidestrand Mk I prototypes made its maiden flight in about March 1926. Trials revealed that the Sidestrand Mk I was remarkably manoeuvrable for a twin-engined type, and the aeroplane could be looped, rolled and spun without difficulty. Thc Sidestrand was of fabric-covered metal construction. The Air Ministry's initial production order was for six Sidestrand Mk II bombers with a powerplant of two Jupiter VI ungeared (direct-drive) engines and a prone bombardier position in the nose. These six aircraft, later supplemented by three more, entered service in April 1928 with No 101 Squadron based at Bircham Newton in Norfolk, and soon revealed that they were excellent machines notable for their reliability and accurate bombing.

Produced to the extent of nine aircraft for the use of No 101 Squadron, which was the only operator of the Sidestrand and also had five of its Sidestrand Mk III aircraft upgraded to the same standard, the Sidestrand Mk III had the revised powerplant of two Jupiter VIIIF geared radial piston engines each rated at 460 hp (343 kW), a number of structural revisions, and a seated bombardier position. One of the aircraft was later adapted to Sidestrand Mk IV experimental standard with a power-plant of two Jupiter XF supercharged engines enclosed in Townsend narrow-chord ring cowlings. The Sidestrand was phased out of service in 1934 when it was replaced by the Boulton Paul Overstrand.

It was clear from the early 1930s, however, that the Sidestrand was obsolescent, and Boulton and Paul therefore undertook to modernise the type as the P.75 with an uprated powerplant in a strengthened airframe for higher performance and the carriage of a heavier bomb load, and with a number of improvements to enhance the type's operational capabilities. These improvements included an enclosed cockpit for the pilot, who was seated under a framed canopy with a rearward-sliding section for access, a power-operated nose turret (the first installed on an RAF warplane for a fivefold improvement in air-to-air firing accuracy), a windscreen for the dorsal gunner, better aerodynamic shielding for the ventral gunner, electric crew heating, Townend ring cowlings and exhaust collectors for the engines, and an automatic pilot to ease pilot workload. The prototype, designated Sidestrand Mk V, was a conversion of the eighth Sidestrand and made its maiden flight in August 1933, soon revealing capabilities that were considerably superior to those of the basic Sidestrand. In March 1934 the Sidestrand Mk V was officially renamed the Overstrand, which was to be placed in production at the Norwich factory that the renamed Boulton Paul Aircraft Ltd was about to close, as its new facility at Wolverhampton was approaching completion.

The RAF ordered 24 production aircraft to replace the Sidestrand in service with No 101 Squadron at Bircham Newton in Norfolk, and these aircraft were preceded into service by the prototype and three other Sidestrand Mk III conversions delivered in January and February 1935 with the interim powerplant of two Bristol Pegasus IM3 radial piston engines each rated at 555 hp (414 kW) and driving a four-blade wooden propeller of the fixed-pitch type. The fifth aeroplane was the first Overstrand Mk I off the production line and introduced the powerplant of two Pegasus IIM3 radial engines each rated at 580 hp (433 kW).

The last aeroplane was delivered in the closing stages of 1936, and the sole squadron that was fully equipped with the type was No 101 Squadron, although the re-formed No 144 Squadron had four of the aircraft. No 101 Squadron replaced its Overstrand Mk I biplane bomber with the considerably more advanced Bristol Blenheim Mk I monoplane during 1937, and the biplanes were relegated to secondary tasks that included air-to-air gunnery training. The last aircraft were fully retired in 1941. It is worth noting that Boulton Paul proposed a

Superstrand development with a cleaned-up airframe and retractable main landing gear units, but nothing came of this project, since the biplane was rightly seen as obsolete.

HANDLEY PAGE AIRCRAFT

When, in October 1920, the Air Ministry issued requirements for a long-range bomber, a coastal defence torpedo bomber and a troop carrier, Handley Page responded with three types based on its W.8 civil transport. This pioneering type had first been schemed in 1919 as the W/400, which was an aerodynamic derivative of the O/400 bomber with a revised fuselage whose lack of internal bracing allowed the incorporation of a large passenger cabin. The type was later revised with an equal-span wing cellule and entered production and service as the W.8 series with a number of different powerplant options. The W.8 derivatives that Handley Page offered for the 1920 requirements were based in a powerplant of two Napier Lion W-type piston engines each driving a tractor propeller, but secured no real official interest until 1922. By this time the Lion-engined W.8b transport had entered successful service, and the Air Ministry issued its Specification 31/212 for a twin-engined night bomber to supersede the Airco (de Havilland) D.H.10 Amiens and Vickers F.B.27 Vimy. The Vickers Type 57 design had already been introduced to service for this role as the Virginia, which equipped two squadrons, but the Air Ministry also wanted a slightly lighter type for procurement in smaller numbers, for comparison with the single-engined Avro Type 549 that had entered service with No. 99 Squadron as the Aldershot. To meet this revised requirement, Handley Page designed the W.8d as a derivative of the W.8b with a crew of four and provision for armament including an offensive element of two 550 lb (249 kg) bombs and a defensive element comprising three 0.303 in (7.7 mm) Lewis trainable machine guns in open nose, dorsal and ventral positions. The W.8d inherited the basic structure of the W.8b and was therefore of conventional design and construction with a covering of fabric over a structure of wood.

In January 1923, the Air Ministry ordered a single prototype of the W.8d, which in 1924 was allocated the retrospective company designation H.P.24, and this machine made its maiden flight in October of the same year. Service trials revealed that the W.8d had considerably better performance, with the same military load, than the Virginia Mk III, and as a result an initial batch of 15 Lion IIB-engined aircraft were ordered for service with No 99 Squadron at Bircham Newton in Norfolk, with the service designation Hyderabad Mk I. Production of the new bomber was slow, and this meant that it was 1927 before two further batches, of eight and 11 aircraft, each with the Lion V engine, were ordered respectively for Nos 99 and 10 Squadrons, the latter based at Upper Heyford in Oxfordshire.

A final batch of 11 Hyderabad bombers was ordered in 1928, but instructions were later issued that the final six of these aircraft should be completed to Hinaidi standard with a powerplant of two Bristol Jupiter radial piston engines; there was a shortage of this engine, however, and the aircraft were completed as Hyderabad Mk I bombers before being converted to Hinaidi standard in 1928-29. The Hyderabad was withdrawn from first-line service in 1930, but the surviving aircraft were then allocated for service up to 1933 with Nos 502 and 503 Squadrons of the Auxiliary Air Force, based respectively at Aldergrove in Northern Ireland and Waddington in Lincolnshire. The Hyderabad was finally declared obsolete in 1934, and has the distinction of having been the sole Royal Air Force type to have gone through the entirety of its career without suffering a single fatality.

BELOW: Many bombs used by the British until well into the 1930s were relics of World War I in concept if not manufacture, but lower-drag weapons were in the offing.

■ **ABOVE: The Hawker Hart secured useful export sales as well as large sales to the Royal Air Force for its day bomber squadrons, where it was replaced by its Hind derivative.**

THE HAWKER HART

A classic aeroplane that emerged in the late 1920s and resulted in more aircraft of the basic and derived series than any other British aeroplane of the period between the two world wars, the Hart Bomber was the result of the requirement embodied in the Air Ministry's Specification 12/26, issued in May 1926, for a fast day bomber to enter service in five or six years in the future, as replacement for the Airco (de Havilland) D.H.9A and Fairey Fawn, and to be capable of reaching a maximum level speed in excess of 160 mph (257 mph). The type was designed on the basis of two experimental fighter designs of the mid-1920s, the F.20/27 fighter powered by a Bristol Mercury radial piston engine and the Hornet interceptor powered by a Rolls-Royce F.XIS Vee piston engine, and emerged as a thoroughbred warplane of fabric-covered metal construction.

The prototype introduced a number of changes from the originally envisaged layout, most notably the revision of the main landing gear arrangement to the through-axle type with an oleo-pneumatic shock absorber in the forward legs of the two wire-braced Vee struts that carried the axle, lighter and stronger N-type interplane struts in place of the originally planned I-type interplane struts, a pump-operated rather than gravity-feed fuel system and, most importantly of all, the replacement of the original engine by the Rolls-Royce F.XIB Vee unit. This was a development of the Falcon with cast aluminium monobloc cylinder banks in place of the Falcon's individually cast cylinders for a weight saving of some 60 lb (27 kg), in combination with the greater strength that allowed the new engine's rapid development to higher powers. The F.XI engine was type-tested in the spring of 1927 at a rating of 490 hp (365 kW) at 2350 rpm, and in 1930 was named as the Kestrel.

The prototype made its maiden flight in June 1928, and as a result of its high-powered engine and clean lines immediately revealed an excellent combination of high performance (especially in level speed and climb rate), agility and viceless handling characteristics. The Hart was evaluated in competition with the Avro Antelope and the Fairey Fox II, and judged considerably better than the former as well as slightly better than the latter. There followed an initial production batch of 15 Hart Bomber aircraft that were used by No 33 Squadron for a full service evaluation of the type from January 1930, and then the Hart Bomber entered what was, for that time, large-scale production amounting to an eventual 450 aircraft, including the Hart (India) and Hart (Special) subvariants, for the Royal Air Force.

The initial 15 aircraft to Specification 9/29 were completed with a powerplant of one Kestrel IB or Kestrel IS engine, and later orders for the day bomber version, increasing the overall total to 311 machines up to 1935, were: 32 aircraft built by Hawker to the Hart Bomber (Improved) standard with the Kestrel IB engine and an improved prone bombing position for the bombardier/gunner in the rear seat; 50 aircraft built by Hawker to the Hart Bomber (Updated) standard with the Kestrel V, Kestrel VDR or Kestrel X engine; 65 aircraft built by Vickers with the Kestrel IB or Kestrel V engine and including one machine transferred to Canada with the Bristol Pegasus radial piston engine and provision for ski landing gear, two aircraft transferred to South Africa and two aircraft transferred to Southern Rhodesia; 24 aircraft built by Armstrong Whitworth with the Kestrel IB engine; and 125 examples of the Hart Single-Engine Day Bomber built between 1933 and 1935 by Armstrong Whitworth, of which two and three were transferred to South Africa and Southern Rhodesia respectively. The Hart was flown by seven home-based units (Nos 12, 15, 18, 21, 33, 57 and 142 Squadrons) and four overseas-based units (No 6 Squadron in Egypt and Palestine and Nos 11, 39 and 60 Squadrons in India) of the first-line RAF, and also by eight home-based units (Nos 600, 601, 602, 603, 605, 609, 610 and 611 Squadrons) of the Auxiliary Air Force. The last aircraft were withdrawn from British first-line service between 1936 and 1938, when they were replaced by the Hawker Hind, and from Indian service in 1939 when supplanted by the Bristol Blenheim. From 1936 a number of Harts surplus to British requirements were passed to South Africa, and the South African Air Force operated some of these aircraft in the utility and communications roles up to 1943 in the North African and then Italian theatres during World War II (1939–45). Some 507 Hart Trainer aircraft were also built, as were moderately large numbers for export with several types of engine.

BRITISH REARMAMENT

As a result of the first intimations of German rearmament following the advent to power of the Nazi party at the beginning of 1933, during 1934 the UK started a major programme of military expansion and rearmament. The Air Ministry, realising that it urgently needed a type on which new day bomber crews could learn their skills, issued its G.7/34 requirement for a light bomber to supersede the Hawker Hart Bomber. The ministry reasoned that this would be only an interim type that would allow the training of new crews to the state from which they could convert easily to more advanced monoplane types, such as the Bristol Blenheim and Fairey Battle, that would then be available in large numbers. Hawker's response to the

requirement was the Hind, which was little more than an updated version of the Hart with a fully supercharged Rolls-Royce Kestrel V Vee piston engine driving a two-blade wooden propeller of the fixed-pitch type, increased fuel tankage, a revised gunner's cockpit based on that of the Hart Two-Seat Fighter (later Demon) to provide the bombardier/gunner with an improved prone bombing position in his former capacity and the ring-mounted Lewis machine gun with an improved field of fire and reduced interference from the slipstream in his latter capacity, a tailwheel in place of a tailskid, and a number of other refinements including small 'ram's horn' exhaust manifolds.

The Hind prototype made its first flight on 12 September 1934 after construction in a very short time as Hawker was already planning such improvements before the issue of the G.7/34 requirement, and the first production Hind Mk I took to the air for the first time only a few days more than one year later. Deliveries amounted to 527 aircraft, and these served with an eventual 30 first-line and 13 Auxiliary Air Force squadrons all based in the UK. The last aeroplane was delivered in September 1938, and by 1939 the type had been phased out of first-line British service. Aircraft still in Royal Air Force markings were used for the training, communications and, later, glider towing roles until the middle years of World War II, and a number of surplus aircraft had been passed to other air forces. A number of the aircraft were also exported with several types of engine.

BOEING'S BOMBER

With its Model 200 Monomail mailplane that first flew in May 1930 with a powerplant of one Pratt & Whitney Hornet B radial piston engine rated at 575 hp (429 kW), Boeing started the process that led to the 'modern aeroplane' of the mid-1930s, for the Monomail introduced an advanced and prophetic combination of features, such as a ring-cowled radial piston engine, main landing gear units that semi-retracted to leave only the lower portions of the two wheels exposed, all-metal construction with smooth metal skinning, a semi-monocoque fuselage, and a low-set cantilever wing. The importance of this combination of aerodynamic and structural factors was reflected in the fact that while the Model 40B biplane mailplane, with basically the same engine and payload, had a maximum level speed of 137 mph (220.5 km/h), the Model 200 had a maximum level speed of 158 mph (254 km/h). Boeing rightly reasoned that what was applicable to the comparatively lightweight mailplane would probably be equally applicable to the bomber, which was another type of load-carrying aeroplane dominated by the biplane layout up to this time, at least in American service. Boeing therefore decided to use its own financial resources to develop a couple of basically similar prototype aircraft that differed mainly in their powerplants. These aircraft were the Models 214 and 215 with a power-plant of two Curtiss GIV-1570 Conqueror Vee piston engines each rated at 600 hp (447 kW) and two Pratt & Whitney R-1860-13 Hornet radial piston engines each rated at 575 hp (429 kW), in each case driving two-blade metal propellers.

In aerodynamic terms the design of the two private-venture bomber prototypes was basically a scaled-up version of the Model 200 with the single

■ABOVE: A true harbinger of bombers to come, the Boeing YB-9 pioneered the cantilever low-wing monoplane layout of essentially all-metal construction, offering strength and low drag.

nose-mounted engine replaced by two wing-mounted engines. As such, the Models 214 and 215 were of all-metal construction and cantilever low-wing configuration. As it was later than the Model 215, which had already completed successful initial trials that persuaded the US Army Air Corps to purchase both aircraft, the Model 214 was completed to full military standard and first flew in November 1931 with a powerplant of two Curtiss GIV-1510C Vee piston engines each rated at 600 hp (447 kW). These engines were later replaced by Curtiss GIV-1570-29 engines of the same rating, and after delivery to the USAAC with the designation Y1B-9 was later revised to exactly the same standard as the YB-9.

The Model 215 preceded the Model 214 into the air, but even so was not the first monoplane bomber to have been evaluated by the USAAC, this distinction having fallen to the Douglas B-7 series and the General Aviation (Fokker) XB-8. Although both of these types were monoplanes with retractable main landing gear arrangements, they were conceptually less advanced than the Models 214 and 215 in aerodynamic and structural terms. The Model 215 made its first flight in April 1931 with a powerplant of two Pratt & Whitney R-1860 Hornet radial piston engines each rated at 575 hp (429 kW), and in other respects its data were essentially similar to those of the Model 214. The USAAC was impressed with the type's performance, and undertook an initial evaluation of the type under the temporary prototype designation XB-901. Still further impressed by its own evaluation of the Model 215, the USAAC then bought this machine for full trials with the designation YB-9. The original R-1860-13 engines were later replaced by R-1860-11 engines with superchargers, and this increased the maximum level speed to 188 mph (302.5 km/h). Boeing believed that a large order would follow, but the problem of being first into a pioneering field was revealed when Martin quickly followed the Boeing lead with its Model 123, a somewhat more advanced type that was evaluated as the XB-907 prototype and then ordered as the B-10 and B-12 series.

Ordered to the extent of five aircraft by the USAAC at the time that it bought the Models 214 and 215, the Y1B-9A was the service test variant of the Model 215 and was known to the manufacturer as the Model 246. The aircraft were similar in their external details to the Model 215 with the exception of the rudder, which had the Model 214's type of trailing servo tab rather than the Model 215's inset servo tab, the metal rather than fabric skinning of the control surfaces, and three- rather than two-blade propellers. A number of structural and equipment changes were also introduced, and a later alteration was a fabric-covered rudder (with inset servo tab and more curvaceous trailing edge) as designed for the Model 247 transport. Boeing designed 'glasshouse' canopies to enclose the cockpits, but these were never installed and the Model 246 aircraft always flew with the same open accommodation as the Models 214 and 215. The first Model 246 made its maiden flight in July 1932 with a powerplant of two Pratt & Whitney Y1G1SR-1860B Hornet radial engines each rated at 600 hp (447 kW), and its other details included a fixed armament of two 0.3 in (7.62 mm) Browning trainable machine guns (one each in the nose and dorsal positions), a disposable armament of up to 2400 lb (1089 kg) in the form of four 600 lb (272 kg) bombs, span of 76 ft 10 in (23.42 m) with an aspect ratio of 6.19 and an area of 954.00 sq ft (88.63 m2), length of 51 ft 9 in (15.77 m), height of 12 ft 0 in (3.66 m), empty weight of 8941 lb (4056 kg), maximum take-off weight of 14320 lb (6496 kg), maximum level speed of 188 mph 302.5 km/h) at 6000 ft (1830 m), cruising speed of 165 mph (265.5 km/h) at optimum altitude, range of 540 miles (869 km), maximum rate of climb at sea level of 900 ft (274 m) per minute, and service ceiling of 20750 ft (6325 m). The last of the aircraft was delivered in March 1933, and the machines performed much important work in developing modern bomber concepts and tactics for the USAAC.

THE MB.200

The MB.200 was of all-metal construction, and in design was typical of the highly angular French warplanes of the late 1920s and early 1930s. The MB.200.01 prototype made its maiden flight in June 1933 with a powerplant of two Gnome-Rhône 14Krsd Mistral-Major radial piston engines each rated at 760 hp (567 kW) and driving a three-blade propeller. During its official trials undertaken later in the same year, the type revealed adequate if not good performance (maximum level speed was some 18 per cent below that suggested by the initial performance estimates), and in December 1933 the French air ministry ordered an initial 30 examples of the MB.200B.4 production model with the uprated powerplant of two Gnome-Rhône 14Kirs/Kjrs radial piston engines each rated at 870 hp (649 kW) at 10500 ft (3200 m) and 900 hp (671 kW) at 13780 ft (4200 m). Four of these were built by Bloch and the other 26 by Henry Potez, the first of them flying in July 1934 and deliveries amounting to 20 aircraft by the end of the year. Supplementary orders were later placed with Potez and Hanriot, which each received an order for 45 aircraft in contracts dated September 1934 and May 1935 respectively. The MB.200 entered service late in 1934, and by May 1935 some 38 aircraft were operational with the Groupes de Bombardement (Bomber Groups) I/12 and II/12 based at Reims and with Bomber Group II/22 based at Chartres. By the end of the following month the French air ministry had increased the total of MB.200 aircraft in service or on order to 208 with additional contracts for 40 aircraft placed with Potez, 19 with Breguet, 19 with Loire, and 10 with Sud-Ouest. Deliveries amounted to 136 aircraft during 1935, and the last 52 were handed over to the French air arm between January and July 1936.

The MB.200 was slow even by the standards of the early 1930s, and was obsolescent even as it entered service. Even so, some 169 of the aircraft were still on strength at the outbreak of World War II (1939-45) in September 1939: 77 of these were used in second-line tasks, but 69 were still operational with seven operational groups (GR I/31 and II/31 at Tours in France, GR I/32 and II/32 at Châteauroux in France, GR I/25 at Tunis-El Aouina in French North Africa, GR II/61 at Blida in French North Africa, and GR I/39 at Rayak in French Syria). The four groups based in metropolitan France undertook a number of daylight sorties in the first weeks of the war, but their losses soon persuaded the French that the aircraft were not suitable for modern warfare and the machines were rapidly relegated to second-line tasks.

In 1935, the Czechoslovak air force was facing a worsening threat of German aggression and started a major programme to bolster its air defences. As part of this programme it secured a licence to build the MB.200 in Czechoslovakia. The task was entrusted to Aero, which received an order for 124 bombers and subcontracted 70 to Avia. The aircraft were basically similar to

BELOW: With its mass of excrescences such as turrets, gondolas and fixed landing gear, the Bloch MB.200 virtually epitomised the concept of aerodynamic drag.

their French-built counterparts, with the exception of their powerplant, which comprised two Walter (Gnome-Rhône) 14-K radial engines each rated at 850 hp (634 kW) for a maximum level speed of 132 kt (152 mph; 245 km/h). Produced between 1936 and 1938, the aircraft were allocated to the 81st, 82nd, 83rd and 84th Bomber Squadrons of the 5th Bomber Regiment as well as the 85th and 86th Heavy Bomber Squadrons of the 6th Bomber Regiment. After Germany had occupied and annexed Czechoslovakia in March 1939, the Luftwaffe seized the surviving aircraft for use in its own multi-engine training schools, but later 25 aircraft were supplied to the Rumanian air force, and smaller numbers were delivered to the Bulgarian and Croatian air forces.

BLOCH REDESIGN

Even as it was designing the MB.200 bomber, the Bloch design team was aware that the type contained a number of obsolescent if not actually obsolete features, most notably its shoulder-set wing, fixed landing gear and three drag-producing defensive gun turrets. It was a natural progression, therefore, for the design team to turn next to a bomber that was essentially a modernised version of the MB.200 with improved features such as a low-set wing and tailwheel landing gear incorporating main units that retracted forward into the undersides of the engine nacelles. Possibly wanting to emphasise to the French air force the financial attractions of purchasing a type closely related to a type it had already ordered, the design team decided not to attempt any wholesale aerodynamic refinement of the basic concept along the lines that were being presaged by aircraft such as the Boeing Model 247 and Douglas DC series of civil transports that were opening the era of the 'modern aeroplane'. The resulting MB.210 must therefore be regarded as an interim type bridging the gap between France's very ugly high-wing bombers of the later 1920s and the extremely elegant low-wing bombers of the mid-1930s. Bloch produced the MB.210 as a private venture, intending the type for the dual roles of level and torpedo bombing, and the first of two prototypes made its maiden flight in November 1934 with fixed main landing gear units and a powerplant of two Gnome-Rhône 14Kdrs/Kgrs Mistral-Major radial piston engines each rated at 800 hp (596.5 kW) at 12,630 ft (3850 m). Built at much the same time but not flown until August 1935, the MB.211 Verdun second prototype had retractable main landing gear units and a powerplant of two Hispano-Suiza 12Y Vee piston engines each rated at 860 hp (641 kW) and installed in nacelles carrying frontal radiators for the engines' cooling water. Trials confirmed the superiority of the MB.210's powerplant and the MB.211's landing gear, revealed the need for greater horizontal tail area, and suggested that advantage would accrue from a movement of the dorsal turret to a position farther forward. The revised aeroplane took to the air again in January 1935, and was further revised with outer wing panels of greater sweep before being committed to official trials in February of the same year.

By the middle of 1935, the French air force had become firmly convinced that the MB.210 offered considerable operational advantages over its current types of medium bomber, and in September and October 1935 placed orders for 80 MB.210BN.4 bombers (30 each from Bloch and Potez-CAMS, and 20 from Hanriot) in the BN.4 category. The first of these aircraft was flown by the parent company in December 1935, and differed from the prototype in its retractable main landing gear units and a powerplant of two Gnome-Rhône 14Kirs/Kjrs radial piston engines each rated at 870 hp (649 kW) at 10500 ft (3200 m) and 900 hp (671 kW) at 13780 ft (4200 m). The second aeroplane introduced greater dihedral on the outer wing panels for improved lateral stability, and this became standard on all subsequent aircraft. During 1936 additional aircraft were ordered from a number of manufacturers (16 from Breguet, 20 from Hanriot, 20 from ANF

Bloch MB.200B.4

Type: medium bomber
Country of origin: France
Powerplant: two 870-hp (649-kW) Gnome-Rhône 14Kirs/Kjrs Mistral-Major radial piston engines
Performance: maximum level speed 176 mph (283 km/h); service ceiling 26,245 ft (8000 m); typical range 621 miles (1000 km)
Weights: empty 9840 lb (4300 kg); max take-off 16,490 lb (7480 kg)
Dimensions: wing span 73 ft 7.875 in (22.45 m); length 51 ft 10 in (15.80 m); height 12 ft 10 in (3.92 m)
Armament: three 0.295 in (7.5 mm) MAC 1934 machine guns, plus up to 2646 lb (1200 kg) of stores

Handley Page Heyford Mk IA

Type: four-seat heavy bomber
Country of origin: UK
Powerplant: two 575-hp (429-kW) Rolls-Royce Kestrel IIIS5 Vee piston engines
Performance: maximum level speed 142 mph (228.5 km/h); service ceiling 21,000 ft (6400 m); maximum range 400 miles (644 km)
Weights: empty 10,470 lb (4749 kg); max take-off 16,900 lb (7666 kg)
Dimensions: wing span 75 ft 0 in (22.86 m); length 58 ft 0 in (17.68 m); height 20 ft 6 in (6.25 m) with the tail down
Armament: three 0.303 in (7.7 mm) Lewis machine guns, plus up to 3500 lb (1588 kg) of stores

Les Mureaux, 10 from Potez-CAMS and 35 from Renault) to raise the total on order to 181 machines which, from the 51st aeroplane onwards, were delivered to the MB.210BN.5 standard with five rather than four crew members.

Further orders were placed during and after the virtually wholesale nationalisation of the French aircraft industry in November 1936, and production by the Sociétés Nationales de Constructions Aéronautiques du Centre, de l'Ouest and du Sud-Est raised the MB.210 total to 257 aircraft. Of these machines, 233 were delivered to the French air force and 24 to the Rumanian air force, which received its aircraft between June 1937 and the middle of 1938. Once in service, the MB.210 proved popular and successful. Its only problem could be traced to a lack of power, which meant that for take-off at maximum weight the engines had to be run at maximum power and were therefore prone to overheating and seizing, resulting in a crash. The aircraft were therefore revised with a powerplant of two Gnome-Rhône 14N-10/11 radial piston engines each rated at 910 hp (679 kW) for take-off and 950 hp (708 kW) at 12140 ft (3700 m).

At the beginning of World War II in September 1939, the French air force had already started to discard the type, some 35 of its surplus aircraft having been passed to the air force of the Spanish Republican government for service in the closing stages of the Spanish Civil War, but its 12e, 19e, 21e, 23e and 51e Escadres de Bombardement were still operational with the MB.210; each had two groupes de bombardement and a complement of between 13 and 16 bombers. Despite the facts that many of the aircraft had been delivered only recently and were numerically among the most important of the French bombers, the MB.210 was considered obsolescent and used only sparingly in service. Operator units were re-equipped with more advanced warplanes as soon as possible, whereupon their MB.210 aircraft were relegated to secondary tasks such as training. Even so, the MB.210 was used for a number of nocturnal raids on targets in the Rhineland, Belgium and France after the start of the German invasion in May 1940. In June the last two operational units, Bomber Groups GB I/21 and GB II/21, were evacuated to North Africa where they were disbanded in the summer of 1940. The aircraft were generally scrapped, but some were stored and a number of these were refurbished in 1942 for use as navigation trainers. The Germans seized 37 examples of the MB.210 when they occupied Vichy France in November 1942, and it has been claimed that six of these machines were passed to the Bulgarian air force, although there is no conclusive documentary evidence for this assertion.

THE HEYFORD

The Handley Page H.P.50 Heyford was the last biplane heavy bomber to reach squadron service with the Royal Air Force, and resulted from the Air Ministry's B.19/27 requirement that also led to the Fairey Hendon, which was the first cantilever low-wing monoplane of all-metal construction to serve with the RAF. Unlike the Hendon, which was much delayed and served with only one full squadron, the Heyford was an ultimate expression of the biplane layout and as such was developed rapidly and served with no fewer than 11 squadrons right up to the eve of World War II. The B.19/27 requirement was intended to provide a successor to the Handley Page Hinaidi and Vickers Virginia biplane bombers, and the H.P.38 design prepared under the supervision of George Volkert was very carefully considered for the minimum possible drag and the maximum possible operational utility. The latter was provided by the attachment of the fuselage to the underside of the upper wing to provide the crew members with the best possible fields of vision and of fire, and the use of the thickened centre section of the lower wing as the main weapons bay. The H.P.38 prototype was of fabric-covered metal construction, and made its first flight in June 1930 with a powerplant of two Rolls-Royce Kestrel II Vee piston engines each rated at 550 hp (410 kW) and driving a two-blade wooden propeller of the fixed-pitch type. Trials revealed adequate performance and good handling, although doubts about the strength of the main landing gear units seemed well founded as the prototype was damaged when its landing gear collapsed during a landing in June 1932. By this time, however, the H.P.38 had been accepted for production in revised form as the H.P.50 to the B.23/32 requirement, and this introduced main landing gear units that were structurally strengthened and fitted with deeper wheel spats which left only the very lowest part of each main wheel exposed, and a revised powerplant of two Kestrel IIIS or Kestrel IIIS5 engines with shorter exhausts and carried in smoother nacelles incorporating a radiator in an underslung tunnel installation.

The first Heyford Mk I off the production line flew in June 1933, and deliveries to operational units followed in November of the same year. Production of the Heyford Mk I for No 99 Squadron at Upper Heyford in Oxfordshire totalled 15 aircraft with a powerplant of two Kestrel IIIS Vee piston engines each driving a four-blade wooden propeller of the fixed-pitch type. This initial model had a maximum take-off weight of 16,750 lb (7598 kg) and a maximum level speed of 138 mph (222 km/h) at optimum altitude. Another 23 aircraft were completed to the Heyford Mk IA standard that differed only in its use of the Kestrel IIIS5 engine with an engine-driven electrical generator that allowed the removal of the slipstream-powered generator of the Heyford Mk I.

The 16 Heyford Mk II aircraft each had a powerplant of two Kestrel VI Vee engines derated from their nominal rating of 640 hp (477 kW) and installed in nacelles of smaller cross section and raised by 1 ft 6 in (0.46 m). These changes reduced weight, drag and fuel consumption with consequent improvements in performance, including a maximum level speed of 154 mph (248 km/h) at optimum altitude, despite an increase in maximum take-off weight to 17000 lb (7711 kg). There followed 70 examples of the Heyford Mk III, of which the last was delivered in July 1936, to a standard that differed from that of the Heyford Mk II only in having fully rated Kestrel VI Vee engines. The Heyford series served with Nos 7, 9, 10, 38, 78, 97, 99, 102, 148, 149 and 166 Squadrons in the home-based bomber role, and from 1937 was gradually replaced by the Armstrong Whitworth Whitley and Vickers Wellesley, the last aircraft in front-line service being replaced in 1939 by the Vickers Wellington. On the outbreak of World War II in September 1939, the RAF still had some 40 of the aircraft in second-line service, mostly as bombing and air gunnery trainers, and these machines remained in declining service up to the middle of 1941, before the last aircraft were scrapped.

RIGHT: Through a more advanced type than the bombers it replaced, the Handley Page Heyford was still a lumbering biplane with open defensive gun positions.

THE FAIREY HENDON

The Fairey Hendon, which was built in numbers large enough to equip only a single squadron, has the distinction of having been the first all-metal cantilever low-wing monoplane heavy bomber to enter British service. The type was designed to meet the Air Ministry's B.19/27 requirement for a heavy night bomber. The far-sighted nature of the Fairey design can be gauged from the fact that its primary competitor was the Handley Page H.P.50 biplane that was ordered as the Heyford and in fact built in larger numbers than the Fairey bomber for service with a total of eight squadrons. The B.19/27 requirement demanded a bomber able to deliver a 1500 lb (680 kg) bomb load over a range of 920 miles (1480.5 km) at a speed of 115 mph (185 km/h) at a height of 10000 ft (3050 m) after 30 minutes of flight at sea level at full throttle. Fairey proposed two variants of the same basic design in 1928, and in October 1929 the Air Ministry placed an order for one prototype with a powerplant of two Bristol Mercury V (later Pegasus) radial piston engines in place of the alternative with a powerplant of two Rolls-Royce F.XIS Vee piston engines. At this time British warplanes were built of metal, with steel in the primary structure and aluminium alloy limited to the secondary structure, and the Night Bomber, as the type was known up to October 1934 when the name Hendon was adopted, was no exception to this rule, with a structure mainly of steel under a covering of fabric, except the extreme nose and tail which were covered with light alloy panels.

The Night Bomber prototype made its first flight in November 1930 with a powerplant of two Bristol Jupiter XF radial piston engines each rated at 525 hp (391 kW), enclosed in a narrow-chord Townend ring cowling and driving a two-blade wooden propeller of the fixed-pitch type. There were a number of teething problems with the Night Bomber, including heaviness of the rudder and

ailerons, inadequate longitudinal stability, elevator oscillation, and a tendency for this lightly-loaded aeroplane to 'float' during landing as it lacked flaps. Many of these problems were addressed and rectified during the reconstruction of the prototype after a landing accident in March 1931. Other changes were the adoption of a powerplant of two Kestrel IIIS Vee piston engines, each rated at 480 hp (358 kW), to overcome the problems caused by turbulent airflow round the original radial engines, the operating cables for the tail controls were replaced by rods to reduce an oscillation problem, the enclosure over the pilot's cockpit was removed, and a second cockpit was added for the navigator/radio operator.

It was in this revised form that the Night Bomber returned to flight trials in November 1941, and from May 1932 the prototype was used for armament trials, following which the aeroplane was competitively evaluated by No 10

■ **ABOVE: The Fairey Hendon can be characterised as three-quarters of the way to modernity, but still had fixed landing gear, fabric covering and open accommodation.**

Squadron at Boscombe Down in Wiltshire, against the Heyford and Vickers Vannox prototypes. The service pilots preferred the Heyford, largely for its more conventional handling characteristics, and it was this type that was ordered into production. The Night Bomber was then revised with different ailerons of the Frise type and with servo tabs on the tail control surfaces, the lightening and better balance of the controls in all three planes resulting in a more favourable report when the Night Bomber was again evaluated in 1933. By this time the conceptual obsolescence of the Heyford had been fully appreciated, and an order was therefore placed for 14 Night Bomber production aircraft, largely to provide RAF pilots with experience in the handling of multi-engined monoplane bombers pending the delivery of the service's first 'modern' bombers, the Armstrong Whitworth Whitley and Vickers Wellington. Further orders were placed for another four aircraft in mid-1934 and for an additional 58 aircraft in July 1935, but these were soon cancelled.

As far as was possible, the Hendon Mk II production model, the designation Hendon Mk I having been accorded retrospectively to the Night Bomber prototype, conformed to the B.20/34 standard ordained for the cancelled aircraft. This standard included a powerplant of two Kestrel VI engines each rated at 695 hp (518 kW) and driving a three-blade Fairey-Reed metal propeller of the fixed-pitch type, a canopy enclosing the pilot's and navigator/radio operator's cockpits, a nose turret in place of the original open position, and slipstream deflectors for the dorsal and tail positions. The Hendon Mk II was delivered to No 38 Squadron, which was based at Mildenhall in Suffolk and the only complete squadron equipped with the type, from November 1936. The aircraft remained in service up to January 1939, when No 12 Squadron re-equipped with the Wellington.

AMIOT'S NEW AIRCRAFT

Amiot was one of four French companies that responded to a 1928 requirement issued by the technical department of the French air ministry for a four-seat multiplace de combat (multi-seat warplane) suitable for the day and night bomber, long-range reconnaissance, and bomber escort roles. None of the other three contenders, which were the Blériot 137, Breguet Bre.410 and SPCA 30, could be described as an elegant aeroplane, but the Amiot 140 design was positively ugly. The first of two Amiot 140 prototypes flew in April 1931 with a powerplant of two Lorraine 12Fas W-type piston engines each rated at 650 hp (485 kW).

After a protracted flight test programme and competitive evaluation, the type received an initial production order for 40 aircraft during November 1933. Amiot had meanwhile developed a number of alternative designs as the Amiot 141 with a powerplant of two Lorraine 18 Orion W-type piston engines, each rated at 700 hp (522 kW), the Amiot 142 with a powerplant of two Hispano-Suiza 12Ybrs Vee piston engines each rated at 860 hp (641 kW), and the Amiot 143 with a powerplant of two Gnome-Rhône 14K Mistral-Major radial engines each rated at 870 hp (649 kW).

Early in 1934, the French air ministry decided to revise its order for the Amiot 140 to cover the more powerful Amiot 143 with Gnome-Rhône engines each driving a three-blade Gnome-Rhône propeller with blades whose pitch could be adjusted on the ground. Another change in the Amiot 143 was the replacement of the original open cockpit by a fully-enclosed cockpit. The first of these aircraft flew in August 1934, with a powerplant of two Gnome-Rhône 14Kdrs/Kgrs Mistral-Major radial engines, each rated at 800 hp (595.5 kW) for take-off and 770 hp (574 kW) at 14435 ft (4400 m), and after initial trials the vertical tail surface was enlarged, the engine bearers were lengthened, and the original open nose and dorsal gun positions were replaced by manually operated enclosed turrets. The nose turret accommodated one 0.303 in (7.7 mm) Lewis machine gun with eight 97-round ammunition drums, and the dorsal turret carried two examples of the same weapon with 12 97-round ammunition drums, while the rest of the defensive armament comprised two more Lewis guns in the rear of the ventral gondola also with 12 97-round ammunition drums. Revised with Gnome-Rhône 14Kirs/Kjrs engines, this was the standard adopted for the Amiot 143 production model, which was itself revised, from the 31st aeroplane onwards, with a longer nose increasing overall length from 58 ft 10.5 in (17.95 m) to 59 ft 11 in (18.26 m), and from the 41st aeroplane, with a different arrangement of fuel tanks and armament. The latter now comprised single 0.295 in (7.5 mm) MAC 1934 machine guns in the two turrets, the ventral position and a new position in the floor of the ventral gondola's forward section.

The first Amiot 143 bombers entered service in July 1935 with the 22e Escadre de Bombardement, and production of this ungainly type eventually amounted to 138 aircraft. The first aircraft were delivered in Amiot 143M.4 configuration, but after the obsolescence of the multiplace de combat concept had been recognised, the aircraft received the revised designation Amiot 143BN.4 and some late aircraft were delivered in Amiot 143B.5 day bomber configuration with an additional gunner for improved defensive capability.

The Amiot 143 was wholly obsolete as a bomber when World War II (1939-45) broke out in September 1939, but the French air force still had 91 of the type in service: of these six were in storage and 29 were operated by training units, leaving 56 in the hands of five first-line bomber groups (GB I and II/34, GB II/35, and GB I and II/38). These units flew nocturnal leaflet-dropping raids over Germany in the first months of the war, and after GB II/35 had transitioned to the Breguet Bre.691 and Bre.693 its aircraft were passed to GB I and II/38. Thus there were still four units equipped with the Amiot 143 when Germany unleashed her May 1940 onslaught against France, and many of these were lost in futile efforts to destroy the bridges over which the Germans forces were crossing the River Meuse in their armoured drive to split the Allied armies in two. Night raids were far less costly, and a number of aircraft were still operational when France capitulated toward the end of June 1940. GB I and II/38 continued to fly the Amiot 143 as part of the Vichy French air force up to May 1941, when the aircraft were transferred to the three units of Groupe de Transport (Transport Group) I/15. The last aircraft were withdrawn from service only in February 1944.

EVOLUTION OF THE BOMBER

As remarkable as it was, the metamorphosis during the early 1930s of the fabric-covered biplane fighter with an open cockpit and fixed landing gear into the all-metal cantilever monoplane fighter with an enclosed cockpit and retractable landing gear was not as startling as the transformation of the bomber during the same period. For whereas the evolution of the 'modern' fighter was achieved in a number of steps, the transformation of the bomber was completed in just one step. The fabric-covered biplane bomber with its fixed landing gear, open gun positions and externally carried bombs was thus replaced almost directly by the cantilever low-wing bomber with retractable landing gear, enclosed crew positions and internally-carried bombs.

The first Italian bomber of the new type was the Fiat BR.20 Cicogna (stork), which first flew in February 1936. The new machine was by no means the first of the modern bombers to fly, but was so well designed that it made the translation from drawing board to operational service in a remarkably short and trouble-free time. Design work by Celestino Rosatelli started in the autumn of 1935; the design was completed and the prototype built in less than six months, and the type's service debut followed little more than six months after that. The key to this rapid development was the adoption of a modern configuration in combination with well proved structural features.

Amiot 143B.5

Type: reconnaissance/night bomber
Country of origin: France
Powerplant: two 870-hp (640-kW) Gnome-Rhône 14Kirs/Kjrs Mistral-Major radial piston engines
Performance: maximum level speed193 mph (310 km/h); service ceiling 25,920 ft (7900 m); max range 1243 miles (2000 km)
Weights: empty 13,448 lb (6100 kg) max take-off 21,385 lb (9700 kg)
Dimensions: wing span 80 ft 5.75 in (24.53 m); length 59 ft 11 in (18.26 m); height 18 ft 7.75 in (5.68 m)
Armament: four 0.295 in (7.5 mm) MAC 1934 machine gun, plus up to 3527 lb (1600 kg) of stores

Deliveries of the BR.20 began in the autumn of 1936, the first aircraft going to the 7o and 13o Stormi Bombardamento Terrestre (land-based bombing wings). Their crews soon came to appreciate the considerable structural strength of the BR.20 bombers as well as their excellent handling in the air, but were less happy with the vibration associated with the A.80 engine at certain revolutions: the vibration tired both the crew and airframe, which despite the introduction of modified engine bearers, suffered several failures in the wing's secondary structure. The problem was eased, but never fully cured, by a strengthened wing centre-section structure.

Further difficulties arose when three BR.20 bombers were sent to Libya for trials: these revealed that the A.80 lost power rapidly under hot conditions, and was also seriously prone to wear as a result of dust ingestion. Another six BR.20 bombers were sent to Spain for operational trials within the context of the Aviazione Legionaria that was the air component of the forces that Italy contributed to the Nationalist insurgent cause in the Spanish Civil War (1936-39). The aircraft was faster than the Polikarpov I-15 fighter fielded by the Republican government forces, and even when intercepted proved able to defend itself without problem. The only aeroplane lost in the first six months of war in Spain was written off after an airfield collision. As these trials were proceeding, production was accelerating in Italy. The first 20 aircraft had been delivered by February 1937, the second production batch of 29 aircraft was delivered between February and July, and delivery of a third batch began in May 1937 from a second production line.

JAPANESE INTEREST

The performance of the BR.20 had also caught the attention of the Imperial Japanese army air force, which needed a modern bomber for operations over China pending the availability of the indigenously designed Mitsubishi Ki-21. The Japanese evaluated the Caproni Ca 135 in addition to the BR.20, but opted for the latter and in the fall of 1937 placed an order for 72 aircraft that was supplemented early in the following year by a contract for an additional ten aircraft of the same type. The BR.20 was designated as the Army Type 1 Heavy Bomber Model 100 by the Japanese, and deliveries began in February 1938 as the aircraft were shipped to Talien in Manchukuo (occupied Manchuria) and assembled locally before issue to units operating against the Chinese, as replacements for their obsolete Mitsubishi Ki-1 bombers. The Army Type 1 bombers were committed to long-range missions at the very limit of their tactical radius and suffered comparatively heavy losses as they were operated without fighter escort and the Chinese had begun to receive supplies of the Polikarpov I-152 fighter. The surviving aircraft were gradually concentrated in a unit based in Manchukuo, and were finally phased out of service in 1940 after suffering heavy losses in the campaign waged between Japan and the USSR along the Manchukuoan/Mongolian border (May-September 1939).

The need to complete the valuable export order to Japan had seriously slowed the delivery of aircraft to the Italian air force, but its basic capabilities seemed to be confirmed by the use of another six aircraft in Spain, where the type served to the end of the Spanish Civil War for the loss of only one

LEFT: The Fiat BR.20 Cicogna was Italy's first modern bomber built in useful numbers. For its time it was a considerable achievement, marking a significant conceptual advance.

Fiat BR.20 Cicogna

Type: five-seat medium bomber
Country of origin: Italy
Powerplant: two 1030-hp (768-kW) Fiat A.80 RC.41 piston engines
Performance: maximum level speed 267 mph (430 km/h) at 13125 ft (4000 m); service ceiling 23620 ft (7200 m); typical range 770.5 miles (1240 km)
Weights: empty 14,859 lb (6740 kg); max take-off 22,795 lb (10,340 kg)
Dimensions: wing span 70 ft 8.8 in (21.56 m); length 53 ft 0.5 in (16.17 m); height 14 ft 1.25 in (4.30 m)
Armament: five 0.303 in (7.7 mm) Breda-SAFAT machine gun, plus up to 3527 lb (1600 kg) of stores

aeroplane. Deliveries of the BR.20 ended in November 1939 after the delivery of 320 aircraft, all delivered to the Italian air force with the exception of 82 aircraft to Japan and one other to Venezuela.

Delivered from February 1940, the BR.20M was an improved version as suggested by its M (Modificato, or modified) suffix. The desirability of the modification programme had been suggested by operational experience in Spain, and the changes included the strengthened centre section, improved armour protection for the crew, a faired tailwheel, several aerodynamic improvements, the lengthening of the nose by 2 ft 3.5 in (0.70 m) and, later in the production run, the replacement of the M.1 turret by an aerodynamically superior Caproni-Lanciani turret carrying the same 0.5 in (12.7 mm) Breda-SAFAT machine gun. These changes increased the BR.20M's empty weight to 15,102 lb (6850 kg) and its maximum take-off weight to 23,038 lb (10,450 kg), but the aerodynamic improvements meant that performance was essentially unaltered. By the time of Italy's entry into World War II in June 1940, the 7o and 13o Stormi had converted to the improved model, which was also in service with the 25o and 43o Stormi. A number of operations were flown against targets in southern France, and then the Italian air force allocated a major role to the type in the Corpo Aereo Italiano (Italian Air Corps) created to fight alongside the Luftwaffe in the Battle of Britain during the late summer of 1940. The BR.20M bombers flew their first mission against a British target without encountering opposition, but on the next mission lost five out of ten bombers to British fighters, whereupon further BR.20M daylight missions were cancelled in favour of night operations that proved wholly ineffective. The CAI was finally withdrawn in January 1941 after contributing nothing of value to the Axis air effort against the UK.

The BR.20M enjoyed slightly better fortunes against the British in Malta and North Africa, and against the Soviets in the southern part of the USSR, but the age of the basic design was now telling against the type and production of the BR.20M ended in April 1942 after the delivery of 264 aircraft. At the time of Italy's September 1943 armistice with the Allies, only 67 BR.20Ms were operational, almost all of them in occupied Albania, Greece and Yugoslavia where they were used for operations against the partisans fighting Axis occupation. A few of the aircraft survived to the end of the war and were then scrapped.

The obsolescence of the BR.20 and BR.20M resulted in a major effort to improve the aeroplane's operational efficiency. The BR.20C was a development with a revised nose carrying a 37 mm (1.46 in) cannon, but this did not enter production and considerable effort was therefore expended on the BR.20bis in an effort to revitalise the type with increased performance, heavier defensive armament and improved armour protection. First flown in September 1942, the BR.20bis had a powerplant of two Fiat A.82 radial piston engines each rated at 1250 hp (932 kW) and installed in close-fitting cowlings for reduced drag, had its fuselage lengthened to 57 ft 3 in (17.45 m), and was carried by a wing increased in span to 71 ft 8.25 in (21.85 m) with an aspect ratio 6.37 and an area of 807.29 sq ft (75.00 m2). It also featured a revised forward fuselage section that was extensively glazed and generated less drag. The defensive armament was bolstered by the replacement of the 0.303 in (7.7 mm) weapons in the nose turret and ventral position by 0.5 in (12.7 mm) machine guns, the replacement of the Caproni-Lanciani dorsal turret by a power-operated Breda V turret with the same 0.5 in (12.7 mm) machine guns, and the addition of two 0.303 in (7.7 mm) Breda-SAFAT trainable rearward-firing machine guns in blisters on the fuselage sides in line with the wing trailing edge. These changes improved performance and defensive capabilities to a marked extent, but the Italian air force had meanwhile decided to concentrate its orders on the CANT Z.1018 and placed an order for only 49 examples of the BR.20bis, of which only ten were completed after the Italian armistice with the Allies in September 1943. There is no evidence that these few aircraft ever entered service with the air force of the Italian Fascist state that was recreated in the German-occupied portion of Italy.

The other details of the BR.20bis included an empty weight of 16534 lb (7500 kg), maximum take-off weight of 25,353 lb (11,500 kg), maximum level speed of 286 mph (460 km/h) at 16405 ft (5000 m), cruising speed of 230 mph (370 km/h) at optimum altitude, range of 1243 miles (2000 km), and climb to 13125 ft (4000 m) in 10 minutes 10 seconds.

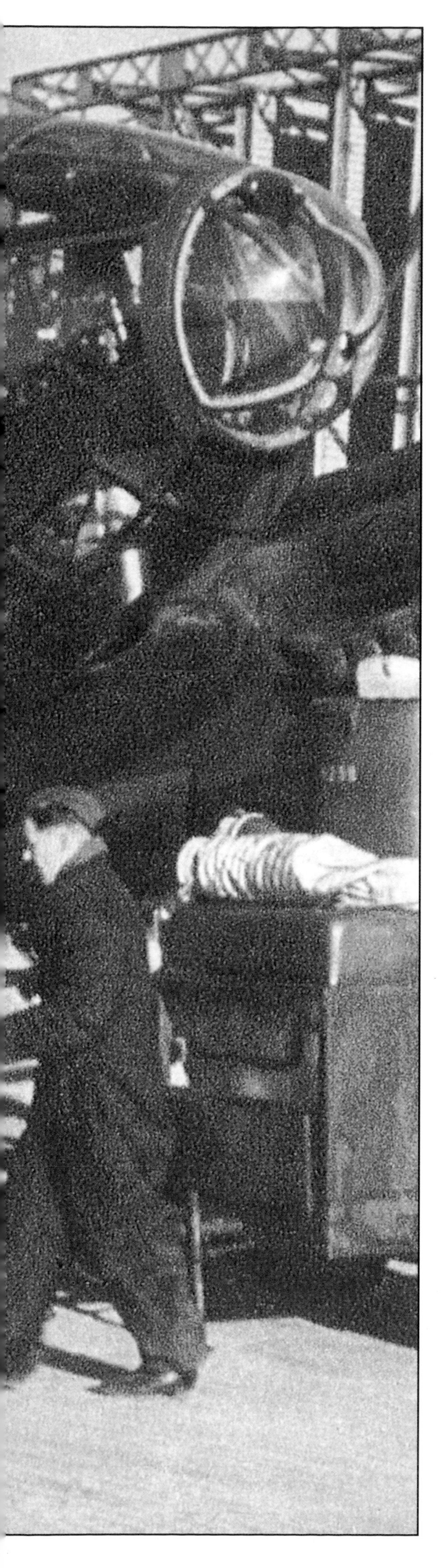

CHAPTER 3

BOMBERS OF WORLD WAR II

World War II gave fresh impetus to bomber design worldwide, and each year of the war saw new and improved aircraft in service, a process that culminated in the world's first operational jet bomber.

When World War II started in September 1939, Germany had the best equipped air force in the world. Although this air force had been maintained on a clandestine basis through the 1920s and early 1930s, and formally revealed only in 1935, considerable expansion and re-equipment had started as early as 1933. The new aircraft and tactics for the steadily growing air force were then thoroughly evaluated and modified through operational experience in the Spanish Civil War. The supremacy of German tactics was reflected bythe success of the 'Blitzkrieg' (lighting war) campaigns through Poland in September 1939 and then Denmark, Norway, the Netherlands, Belgium and France between April and June 1940.

One of the keys to Germany's initial successes was the Heinkel He 111 medium bomber. In 1934, the German air ministry issued to Heinkel and Junkers a requirement for an aeroplane that could, with minimum structural change, operate in two roles: 10-passenger transport with Deutsche Lufthansa and medium bomber with the still-secret Luftwaffe. The results of this effort were the He 111 and Ju 86. Heinkel's He 111 was a scaled-up and improved version of the He 70 Blitz. The He 111a (later He 111 V1) first prototype made its maiden flight in February 1935 with a powerplant of two BMW VI 6,0 Z Vee piston engines. There followed the He 111d (He 111 V4) civil prototype with a wing planform of semi-elliptical shape with reduced span but greater area, and the He 111c (He 111 V3) and He 111d (He 111 V4) military prototypes with provision for a defensive armament of three machine guns and a maximum bomb load of 2205 lb (1000 kg) stowed vertically in lower-fuselage weapons cells. The He 111 V3 was presented to the public as a civil transport, the weapons cell area being a four-person 'smoking compartment'. The He 111 handled well in the air, and its clean design meant that it could show a clean pair of heels to most current fighters.

LEFT: A German mechanic prepares a Heinkel He 111 for takeoff, as warm air is pushed round the engine. The Heinkel was a key type for the Luftwaffe in the early years of the war.

PRODUCTION ORDERS

An evaluation of the He 111 V3 and He 111 V4 confirmed their potential in the bomber role, and in late 1935 the German air ministry authorised a pre-production series of 10 He 111A-0 bombers with a powerplant of two BMW VI 6,0 Z engines each driving a three-blade variable pitch propeller. The first of these aircraft were delivered for trials in the spring of 1936, and proved a considerable disappointment, as the addition of full military equipment added considerable weight and drag. The handling of the pre-production aircraft was still good, but their performance was decidedly sluggish, as indicated by a maximum level speed of only 193 mph (310 km/h) with the ventral 'dustbin' machine gun installation retracted.

The He 111A lacked power because the German aircraft industry had failed to develop a modern Vee-type piston engine to replace the venerable BMW VI 6,0 and 7,3 series. In 1935, however, the better Daimler-Benz DB 600 inverted-Vee piston engine appeared, that was destined to become important not only in its own right, but also as the starting point for a series of increasingly powerful engines. Rated at a nominal 1000 hp (746 kW), the DB 600 was the answer to the

He 111's performance shortfall. Two engines were installed in the He 111 V5, the prototype for the He 111B series of bombers. The German air ministry had ordered a batch of He 111B-0 pre-production aircraft even before rejecting the He 111A, and the first of these aircraft were delivered in the autumn of 1936. The initial production He 111B-1 was tested operationally during the Spanish Civil War, and found to be an excellent type whose indifferent defensive armament was little needed, as the bomber was faster than most opposing fighters. Production of the He 111B series totalled some 300 aircraft.

The He 111C and He 111G were civil models, and the He 111D reached only prototype form with a powerplant of two DB 600Ga engines. Supplies of the DB 600 were not matching demand, however, and fighters had a higher priority for the engine than the He 111: a few He 111D-1 production aircraft were completed, but these were used only for trials. The He 111E-0 pre-production model that followed in January 1938 was a simple evolution of the He 111D with Jumo 211A-1 engines. Some 45 of these were soon deployed to Spain in further support of the Spanish Nationalists, and soon extended the already good reputation of the He 111B. Production of the He 111E model totalled some 190 aircraft.

The He 111F design had a simplified wing with structural changes and the elliptical shaping of the leading and trailing edges eliminated. The He 111F-0 pre-production model had a powerplant of two Jumo 211A-3 engines each rated at 1100 hp (820 kW) for take-off. Production was limited to 24 He 111F-1 bombers for the Turkish air force and 40 He 111F-4 bombers for the Luftwaffe.

By the summer of 1938 the delivery rate of the DB 600 had improved considerably, and Heinkel was instructed to develop a DB 600CG-powered version of the He 111F-4 as the He 111J for use as a torpedo bomber with two torpedoes carried externally. The He 111J-0 pre-production model thus lacked any provision for internal bombs, but the Luftwaffe changed its mind and demanded a conventional bombing capability. This resulted in the He 111J-1 production model, of which 90 were delivered during the summer of 1938 in parallel with the He 111F-4. By the summer of 1939 most of these early He 111 models had been withdrawn from first-line German service, although a number were used in their original bomber role during the Polish campaign of September 1939 and the Norwegian campaign of April 1940.

The He 111H was a close relative of the He 111P series, the two variants sharing a common airframe (revised and fully glazed forward fuselage with an unstepped cockpit, and a ventral gondola), but differed in their powerplant: the He 111P was designed for the Daimler-Benz DB 601 inverted-Vee piston engine while the He 111H was planned with the Junkers Jumo 211 inverted-Vee piston engine. The Luftwaffe placed great importance on this improved bomber model, as may be gauged from the fact that Heinkel and its licensees delivered some 400 of the type in the four months preceding the outbreak of World War II in September 1939; the He 111H therefore represented about half of the Luftwaffe's He 111 force at the start of hostilities.

THE OUTBREAK OF WAR

The He 111H-2 was introduced just as World War II was starting in September 1939 as an improved version of the He 111H-1 with a powerplant of two Jumo 211A-3 engines each rated at 1100 hp (820 kW) for take-off and, soon after the start of the production run, the defensive armament doubled from three to six 0.312 in (7.92 mm) MG 15 trainable machine guns. Introduced in November 1939, the He 111H-3 was a development of the He 111H-2 for the bombing and anti-ship roles with a powerplant of two Jumo 211D-1 engines each rated at 1200 hp (895 kW) for take-off and the gun armament bolstered by a 20 mm MG FF trainable forward-firing cannon in the ventral gondola. A bomb load of 4409 lb (2000 kg) was carried internally, and the weapons bay could alternatively be fitted with an auxiliary fuel tank. Deliveries of the He 111H-3 continued throughout 1940, and were complemented by the arrival of the He 111H-4, a development of the He 111H-3, initially with the same powerplant but later with two Jumo 211F-1 engines and an increased bomb load. The He 111H-5 was a variant of the He 111H-4 with two Jumo 211D-1 engines, provision for both halves of the bomb bay to carry auxiliary fuel tanks, and the disposable armament limited to 5511 lb (2500 kg) of weapons carried on two external hardpoints at a maximum take-off weight of 30985 lb (14055 kg).

He 111H-6 that entered production late in 1941 had a powerplant of two Jumo 211F-1 engines, a gun armament of one 20 mm (0.787 in) MG FF cannon and six 0.312 in (7.92 mm) MG 15 machine guns, in some aircraft a remotely controlled 0.312 in (7.92 mm) MG 17 fixed rearward-firing machine gun in the tailcone. It could also carry two 1686 lb (765 kg) LT F5b air-launched torpedoes under the fuselage. The He 111H-6 very quickly became the most extensively used version of the H series, for it was a delight to handle even at maximum take-off weight, was stable yet manoeuvrable, possessed adequate performance and defensive firepower, and was extremely versatile. It had been planned to phase the type out of production during 1942 in favour of the Heinkel He 177A Greif

BELOW: The medium bomber that served throughout World War II was the Heinkel He 111, seen here in the form of an He 111H-4 somewhere over the Mediterranean Sea.

Heinkel He 111H-16

Type: five-seat medium bomber
Country of origin: Germany
Powerplant: two 1350-hp (1007-kW) Junkers Jumo 211F-2 inverted-Vee piston engines
Performance: maximum level speed 252 mph (405 km/h; service ceiling 27,890 ft (8500 m); max range 1740 miles (2800 km)
Weights: empty 19,136 lb (8680 kg); max take-off 30,865 lb (14,000 kg)
Dimensions: wing span 74 ft 1.75 in (22.60 m); length 53 ft 9.5 in (16.40 m); height 13 ft 1.5 in (3.40 m)
Armament: one 20 mm MG FF cannon, up to six 0.312-in (7.92-mm) MG 15/MG 131/MG 81 machine guns, plus up to 5511 lb (2500 kg) of stores

heavy bomber and Junkers Ju 288 medium bomber, but the failure of both these types meant that He 111H-6 production was maintained. The He 111H-7 was a variant of the H-6 with minor equipment changes, and the 30 He 111H-8 were a development of the H-6 converted from He 111H-3 and H-5 standards with a balloon cable fender/cutter arrangement extending from a point ahead of the nose to both wing tips.

The He 111H-9 was a variant of the H-6 with minor equipment changes. The He 111H-10 was a development of the H-6 with a powerplant of two Jumo 211F-2 engines, balloon cable cutting devices in the wing leading edges, and the positions of the forward-firing 0.312 in (7.92 mm) machine gun and 20 mm (0.787 in) cannon reversed so that the MG FF cannon was in the nose and the MG 15 machine gun in the ventral gondola. Further development led to the He 111H-11 that was a development of the He 111H-10 with improvements to crew protection and defensive armament. The dorsal position was fully enclosed with toughened glass screens, and was provided with a 0.51 in (13 mm) MG 131 trainable rearward-firing machine gun in place of the original 0.312 in (7.92 mm) MG 15 weapon; the ventral defence was boosted by the replacement of the single 0.312 in (7.92 mm) MG 15 machine gun by two 0.312 in (7.92 mm) MG 81 weapons; and jettisonable armour plates were added over particularly vulnerable areas. Provision was also made for an improved offensive capability by the development of a carrier plate that could be added under the fuselage for five 551 lb (250 kg) SC-250 bombs.

INCREASING OBSOLESCENCE

The He 111H-11 proved successful within the limits of the airframe's increasing obsolescence, and the type's steadily worsening vulnerability to fighters was addressed by a number of front-line measures such as the replacement of the two 0.312 in (7.92 mm) MG 15 machine guns by two 0.312 in (7.92 mm) MG 81z two-barrel machine guns in the He 111H-11/R1 with the R1 Rüstsatz (field conversion set). The He 111H-11/R2 was another front-line conversion, in this instance with a glider-towing attachment. Appearing early in 1943 and lacking the ventral gondola, the He 111H-12 was planned as a specialised platform for the carriage and launch of two Henschel Hs 293A air-to-surface missiles. The H-14 was a pathfinder development of the He 111H-10 with special radio equipment for use by Kampfgeschwader (Bomber Group) 40 in its anti-shipping role over the eastern Atlantic, but 20 were modified before delivery to units on the Eastern Front as He 111H-14/R2 machines with the special radio equipment removed and a glider-towing attachment added.

If the He 111H-3 and He 111H-6 were regarded as the first and second definitive models of the H series, the He 111H-16 was the third model and in fact preceded a number of ostensibly earlier models. The H-16 was a development of the H-6 with a powerplant of two Jumo 211F-2 engines and the host of small but cumulatively important changes that had been introduced piecemeal on earlier variants. The defensive armament and armour were those of the He 111H-11, and provision was made for a number of different armament arrangements. Provision was also made for the addition of three Rüstsätze (field conversions sets) to provide the He 111H-16/R1 with an electrically operated dorsal turret carrying one 0.51 in (13 mm) MG 131 machine gun, the H-16/R2 with a boom-type glider towing attachment, and the H-16/R3 with additional armour protection to operate in the pathfinder role with a reduced weapon load. The He 111H-18 was a nocturnal pathfinder based on the He 111H-16/R3 but with the special radio equipment of the H-14. Although the He 111H had been planned as a bomber, the demands of the Eastern Front had meant that many of the aircraft had been pressed into alternative transport and glider-tug service during the first half of 1942. This capability was reflected later in the same year by the introduction of the He 111H-20, which was a development of the He 111H-16 optimised for adaptability in four main subvariants. The He 111H-21 introduced an uprated powerplant in the form of two Junkers Jumo 213E-1 inverted-Vee piston engines each rated at 1750 hp (1305 kW). The definitive model entered service in late summer 1944, but by then the days of the He 111's utility as a bomber were

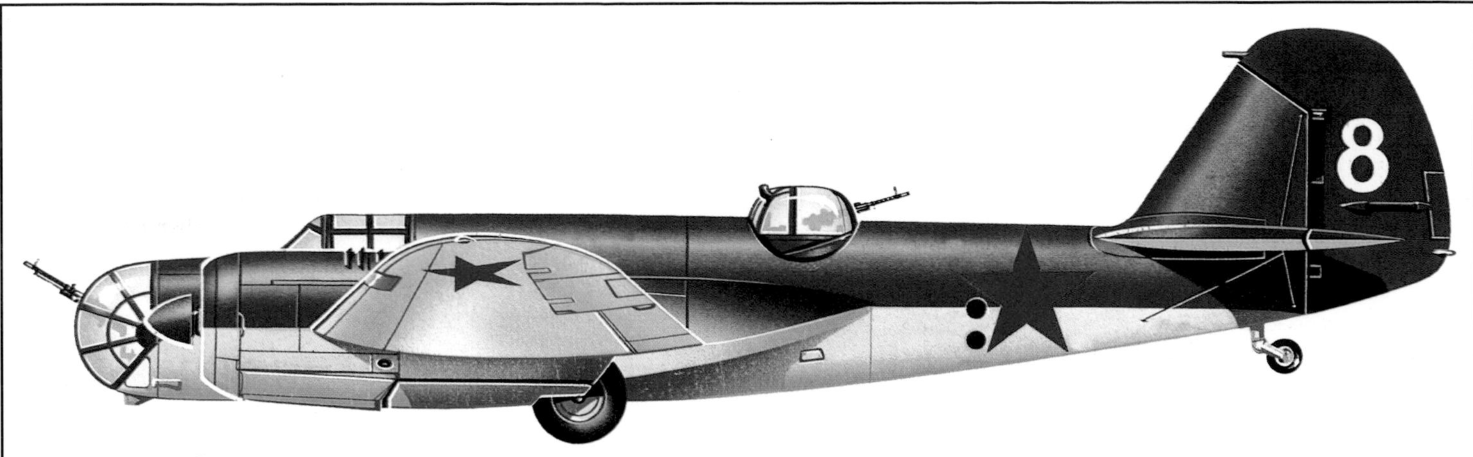

Tupolev SB-2

Type: three-seat light bomber
Country of origin: USSR
Powerplant: two 860-hp (641-kW) Klimov M-100A Vee piston engines
Performance: max level speed 244 mph (423 km/h); service ceiling 29,530 ft (9000 m); max range 777 miles (1250 km)
Weights: empty 8951 lb (4060 kg); max take-off 12,407 lb (5628 kg)
Dimensions: wing span 66 ft 8.5 in (20.33 m); length 41 ft 2.75 in (12.57 m); height 10 ft 8 in (3.25 m)
Armament: four 0.3 in (7.62 mm) ShKAS machine guns, up to 1323 lb (600 kg) of ordnance

past and most aircraft were adapted as airborne launch platforms for the Fieseler Fi 103 pilotless bomb better known by its Nazi designation of V-1.

SOVIET SUCCESS

The Tupolev SB-2 was almost certainly the most capable bomber in service anywhere in the world during the mid-1930s. In purely numerical terms it was the most important bomber in the world during the late 1930s, and was also the first 'modern' aeroplane of the stressed-skin type to enter production in the USSR. As far as the history of this important warplane is concerned, there is an amazing number of discrepancies for facts as basic as the date of the first flight, fuel capacity and overall length, and this account is at best a compromise trying to reconcile a number of differing information sources. Throughout the late 1920s and early 1930s the AGOS (Department of Aviation, Hydro-aviation and Experimental Construction), as the Tupolev design organisation within the TsAGI (Central Aerodynamics and Hydrodynamics Institute) was known, had made considerable strides in the evolution of basically all-metal aircraft of cantilever monoplane construction with increasingly clean lines. The SB-2 evolved via the ANT-40 (officially designated as the SB), which first flew in April 1934. An improved ANT-401 led to the production ANT-402 otherwise known as the SB-2IS (Izmeneniya Samolyet, or altered aeroplane), that introduced the Klimov M-100 (from 1940 VK-100) Vee piston engine, a licence-built version of the Hispano-Suiza 12Y rated at 750 hp (559 kW). However, the SB-2 production model introduced an enlarged wing to allow for the inevitable escalation of weight without degradation of field performance, a longer fuselage, strengthened main landing gear units, a structure revised for ease of production, and provision for the wheels to be replaced by skis for winter operations. The SB-2 entered service in 1935, and the production standard was altered soon after the start of deliveries by the introduction in early 1936 of the M-100A engine rated at 860 hp (641 kW) and driving a VISh-2 variable-pitch propeller for improved climb rate and ceiling. It was distinguishable from the initial variant by its more circular engine cowling and frontal radiator with a Venetian-blind shutter.

Built between October 1936 and January 1941, when production of the SB-2 series ended after the delivery of 6656 aircraft, the SB-2bis was the definitive fast bomber model, with the uprated powerplant of two Klimov M-103 Vee piston engines each rated at 960 hp (716 kW) and driving a three-blade VISh-22 metal constant-speed propeller and fitted with a more refined spinner. These engines were installed in revised nacelles, and had their radiators in a ventral tunnel installation in each nacelle. Other changes were: increased internal fuel tankage; an updated electrical system; an airframe restressed for operation at higher weights; under-wing provision for Der-19 bomb pods, 3.2 in (82 mm) RS-82 or 5.2 in (132 mm) RS-132 air-to-surface rockets, and 61.6 Imp gal (280 litre) long-range tanks; and, from a time in 1938, a revised ventral position incorporating a glazed gondola.

THE WHITLEY

In July 1934 the Air Ministry issued its B.3/34 requirement for a heavy bomber as one of the cornerstones of the British rearmament programme launched that year. The new aircraft would be a cantilever monoplane of basically all-metal construction, with advanced features such as an enclosed flightdeck, retractable main landing gear units, trailing-edge flaps on the inboard portions of its wings, a powerplant of two high-powered piston engines driving variable-pitch propellers, and an armament disposition that included internal bomb stowage and turreted defensive armament. The resulting Armstrong Whitworth A.W.38 design was ordered straight 'off the drawing board' in June 1935, with the order for an initial 80 aircraft placed in August. The prototype first flew on 17 March 1936 with a powerplant of two Armstrong Siddeley Tiger IX radial piston engines each rated at 795 hp (593 kW) and driving a three-blade de Havilland metal two-pitch propeller. In February 1937 a second prototype followed with the uprated powerplant of two Tiger XI radial engines, but by this time the first machine had undertaken its official trials and the first of 34 Whitley Mk I bombers were approaching completion.

The standard for this first operational model, which was dimensionally identical to the definitive Whitley Mk V except for its length of 69 ft 3 in (21.11 m), included a bomb load of 3360 lb (1524 kg) carried in two lower-fuselage weapons bays and small compartments in the wings, a defensive armament of just two 0.303 in (7.7 mm) Vickers 'K' trainable machine guns installed as single weapons in the power operated Nash and Thompson (Frazer-Nash) nose turret and Armstrong Whitworth A.W.38 tail turret.

From the 35th aircraft onwards, the production standard altered to the improved Whitley Mk II, of which 46 were delivered from January 1938 to complete the order for 80 aircraft. The Whitley Mk II introduced the Tiger VIII radial engine rated at 845 hp (630 kW) and fitted with a two-speed supercharger, the first such installation used on an operational RAF aeroplane. The Whitley Mk III (of which 80 were built from August 1938) was basically a development of the Mk II with improved offensive and defensive armament.

By the time the Whitley Mk III was under development, it had become clear that the basic design needed more power to overcome the steadily increasing weights of the recent models yet still provide an improvement in performance. The Tiger engine had reached the end of its useful development life, so it was decided to revise the Whitley with a powerplant of two Rolls-Royce Merlin Vee piston engines. Three Whitley Mk I conversions followed, with two Merlin II engines each rated at 1030 hp (768 kW) at 16000 ft (4875 m) and driving three-blade constant-speed Rotol propellers. The production version was the Whitley Mk IV with a powerplant of two Merlin IV engines each rated at 1030 hp (768 kW) for take-off, and 33 of this variant were built, of which the first flew in April 1939 for delivery in May. Other major changes were the improvement of the defensive armament by the replacement of the single 0.303 in (7.7 mm) machine gun in the manually operated tail turret by four 0.303 in (7.7 mm) Browning machine guns in a power-operated Frazer-Nash turret, and the improvement in offensive capability by the introduction of a better bombardier position in the nose behind a flat aiming panel.

With 1466 aircraft built, exceeding the combined production total of all other Whitley variants to a very considerable degree, the Whitley Mk V was basically an improved Whitley Mk IVA: the two vertical tail surfaces were revised with straight rather than curved leading edges, the rear fuselage was extended by 1 ft 3 in (0.38 m) to provide the rear gunner with larger fields of fire, inflatable rubber de-icing boots were added on the leading edges of the wings, and fuel capacity was further increased. Delivery of the Whitley Mk V was made from August 1940, and in May 1940, at the time of the German invasion of the Low Countries and France, the Whitley Mk V was one of five warplane types (the others being the Bristol Blenheim and Vickers Wellington bombers, and the Hawker Hurricane and Supermarine Spitfire fighters) that received the highest possible production priority in an attempt to boost the UK's offensive and defensive air capabilities. The last Whitley Mk V was delivered in June 1943. On the outbreak of war in September 1939, the relatively low speed of the Whitley meant that it was entrusted with night operations.

The Whitley was never especially successful as a night bomber, but did achieve a number of notable 'firsts': equal first to drop bombs on German soil, equal first to bomb Germany proper, first British bomber over Berlin (a leaflet raid), and first British bomber to attack Italy after that country's entry into the

BELOW: At the beginning of World War II, the most important night bomber in service with the Royal Air Force was the twin-engined Armstrong Whitworth Whitley.

war in June 1940. The Whitley Mk V was withdrawn from first-line bomber service in April 1942, although a few of the type were restored to first-line service in May 1942 to help boost numbers for the first 'thousand-bomber' raid on Köln.

BIRTH OF THE B-17

In the early summer of 1934, the US Army Air Corps released a requirement for a multi-engined medium bomber intended primarily for the coast-defence role. The requirement called for the ability to deliver a 2000 lb (907 kg) bomb load over a range of at least 1020 miles (1641 km) but preferably 2200 miles (3540 km) at a speed of at least 200 mph (322 km/h) but preferably 250 mph (402 km/h). Boeing had already developed its Models 214, 215 and 246 series of closely related monoplanes for limited use as the B-9 series of twin-engined experimental and service test bombers, and fully appreciated that the monoplane layout of these aircraft offered little scope for improvement in its twin-engined form given the relative lack of power available from contemporary radial piston engines, or those foreseeable in the immediate future. The design team therefore chose to construe the USAAC's multi-engined specification as meaning not necessarily just two engines as adopted by other contenders. The design team decided that a three-engined powerplant, with an engine in the nose, was impractical, and therefore agreed a four-engined design.

The design team began work in June 1934 on the Model 299, and construction of the prototype began in August of the same year as the start of a programme that was to produce one of the most important warplanes of all time. At the time it was designing the Model 299, Boeing was also at work on the considerably larger Model 294 (XBLR-1, later XB-15) bomber prototype, and the Model 299 can be regarded as an aerodynamic and structural cross between the Model 247 transport and Model 294 bomber. From the former came the basic structural design and from the latter the disposition of the four-engined powerplant, the circular-section fuselage, and the arrangement of the crew, weapons (both defensive and offensive) and other military equipment within the fuselage. In terms of size the Model 299 was about midway between the Model 247 and Model 294, and its span was only 8 ft 3 in (2.51 m) greater than that of its most significant rival, the military derivative of the twin-engined Douglas DC-3 transport that was designed as the DB-1 and developed into the B-18 Bolo bomber. The Model 299 prototype was a company-owned aeroplane, and first flew in July 1935 with a powerplant of four Pratt & Whitney R-1690-S1EG Hornet radial engines each rated at 750 hp (559 kW), a crew of eight (two pilots, bombardier, navigator/radio operator and four gunners), an offensive load of 4800 lb (2177 kg) with eight 600 lb (272 kg) bombs carried internally, and a defensive armament of five 0.3 in (7.62 mm) Browning trainable machine guns in a small nose turret and in four blister fairings (one dorsal, one ventral and two beam positions).

At this time, the USAAC had little funding and, thus lacking the ability to order the Model 299 into large-scale production, proceeded by ordering small batches, each introducing a significant improvement in capability over its predecessor. The 13 Y1B-17 service test aircraft were therefore followed by one example of the Y1B-17A, 39 examples of the B-17B, 38 examples of the B-17C and 42 examples of the B-17D, before the emergence of the first large-scale production variant, the B-17E, that resulted directly from the lessons of air operations over Europe in the opening campaigns of the war. The revised type was known to the manufacturer as the Model 299O, and its most important changes from the Model 299H (B-17C and B-17D) were a completely revised rear fuselage carrying larger tail surfaces, improved armour protection, a number of internal enhancements, and revised defensive armament. This last was particularly important: the waist positions were simplified, power-operated Sperry turrets each armed with two 0.5 in (12.7 mm) machine guns were added in the dorsal and ventral positions, and a manually operated tail turret had a further pair of 0.5 in (12.7 mm) machine guns. The first B-17E flew in September 1941, and the initial 112 aircraft off the production line featured a ventral turret that was remotely controlled from a periscopic sight in a Plexiglas blister located several feet farther to the rear; from the 113th aeroplane onwards, this installation was replaced by a Sperry ball turret accommodating a gunner. Other major changes included a powerplant of four R-1820-65 radial piston engines each rated at 1200 hp (895 kW).

FIRST B-17E DELIVERIES

The first B-17E bombers were delivered to the 7th Bombardment Group that joined the 19th Bombardment Group in the Pacific theatre from December 1941,

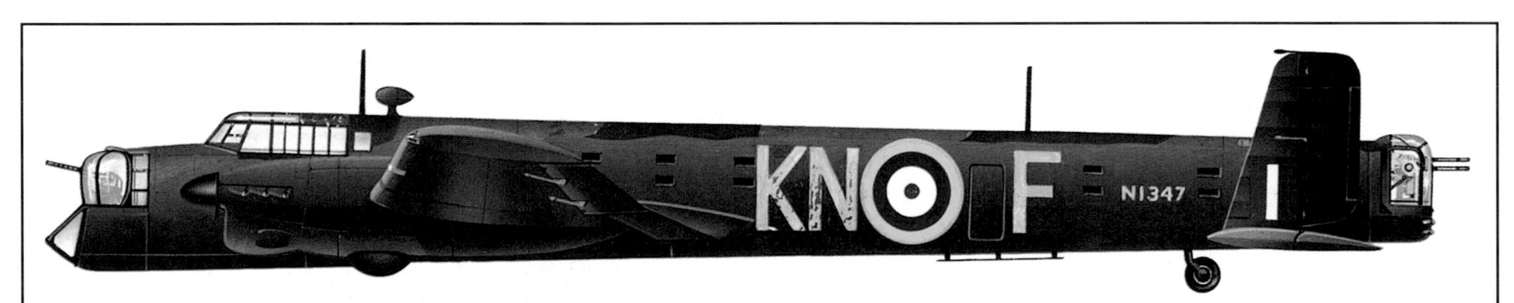

Armstrong Whitworth Whitley Mk V

Type: five-seat long-range night bomber
Country of origin: UK
Powerplant: two 1145-hp (854-kW) Rolls-Royce Merlin X piston engines
Performance: maximum level speed 230 mph (370 km/h); service ceiling 26,000 ft (7925 m); typical range 1650 miles (2655 km)
Weights: empty 19,350 lb (8777 kg); max take-off 33,500 lb (15,195 kg)
Dimensions: wing span 84 ft 0 in (25.39 m); length 70 ft 6 in (21.49 m); height 15 ft 0 in (4.57 m)
Armament: five 0.303 in (7.7 mm) Browning machine guns and up to 7000 lb (3175 kg) of ordnance

ABOVE: The mainstay of the US daylight bomber force, and operated by the 8th Army Air Force in England between 1942 and 1945, was the Boeing B-17 Flying Fortress.

and others of the 512 aircraft were allocated to the units that formed the first elements of the 8th Army Air Force in the UK from May 1942. The first British-based unit to become operational with the B-17E was the 97th Bombardment Group, which flew its first mission over Europe in August 1942. Other medium-range raids, mainly to targets in occupied North-West Europe, followed into the early part of 1943, but much of the European-based B-17E strength was diverted, from October 1942, to create the striking element of the new 12th Army Air Force that was to support the Anglo-American landing in Northwest Africa during November 1942 and the subsequent campaign up to the final elimination of the Axis forces from Africa by May 1943. Some 45 B-17E bombers were transferred to the RAF in late 1942 for use by Coastal Command designated as Fortress Mk IIA (the designation Fortress Mk I had been used for 20 B-17C aircraft) and, with the newer B-17F that had been delivered to the RAF earlier than the B-17E thus receiving the designation Fortress Mk II, served with four maritime and four meteorological reconnaissance squadrons.

The B-17F resulted from direct American operational experience, in this instance with the B-17D against the Japanese. The B-17F was externally distinguishable from the B-17E only by its single-piece blown rather than multi-piece built-up Plexiglas nose transparency, but the variant in fact incorporated more than 400 subtler but collectively very important changes that made the B-17F an altogether more formidable warplane. It was powered by four R-1820-97 radial piston engines each rated at 1200 hp (895 kW). Changes were added incrementally throughout the B-17F's production life, including improved armour protection, provision for external bomb racks under the wing, increasing the maximum possible bomb load to 20800 lb (9435 kg) for short-range missions, additional ball-and-socket machine gun mounts in the nose and the radio compartment for an extra three 0.5 in (12.7 mm) trainable machine guns, an electronic link between the Norden bomb sight and the autopilot, changed control settings, more photographic equipment, a revised oxygen system, upgraded main landing gear units allowing an increase in maximum take-off weight to 65,000 lb (29,484 kg) and eventually to 72,000 lb (32,659 kg), a dual braking system, self-sealing oil tanks, extra electrical power generation capability, dust filters over the carburettor air inlets, provision for 909.3 Imp gal (4133.7 litres) of auxiliary fuel in 'Tokyo tanks' installed in the wings, and paddle-blade propellers for the R-1820-97 radial piston engines but installed in revised nacelles to allow the full feathering of the wider-chord props.

The initial B-17F flew in May 1942, just two days after the delivery of the last B-17E, and was the first Flying Fortress to be built in the block system adopted by the USAAF in 1942 to differentiate minor improvements of standard introduced on the production line, but not meriting a change in the basic letter suffix. Production totalled 3405 aircraft in the form of 2300 from Boeing in 28 blocks, 605 from Douglas in 18 blocks, and 500 from Lockheed's Vega subsidiary in 11 blocks. The B-17F was allocated initially to the 8th Army Air Force in Europe, and flew the first American bombing mission against a target in Germany during January 1943. Thereafter the B-17F became the mainstay of the steadily increasing US daylight bombing effort, but operations from mid-1943 revealed that the Germans were becoming wise to American tactics and also to the defensive limitations of the B-17F. The crisis in this variant's career arrived in August and October 1943 with two major bombing efforts that resulted in very heavy American losses. The first was a raid by 376 aircraft on factories at Schweinfurt, Wiener Neustadt and Regensburg, and the second a raid by 291 aircraft on Schweinfurt. In each case the attacks lost some 60 aircraft as the Germans waited until the US escort fighters had turned back and then attacked the poorly coordinated bomber streams with a succession of fighters that attacked head-on against the bombers' most vulnerable defensive arc.

The final B-17G resulted directly from the experience of the US bomber crews in 1943, which revealed that the B-17F lacked adequate defence against head-on fighter attack. The primary change in the B-17G was therefore the introduction of a power-operated Bendix chin turret armed with two 0.5 in (12.7 mm) machine guns and controlled remotely from the glazed nose position that was now a more practical unit as it lost the one or two manually operated 0.5 in (12.7 mm) machine guns that had been fitted in the B-17F. These weapons had not enjoyed adequate fields of fire to be truly effective, and had also made movement in the nose position very difficult. Other changes effected successively in the B-17G were an improved navigator position, refinement of the bomb-control system, electric rather than hydraulic turbocharger control, improved turbochargers, an emergency oil supply for propeller feathering, improved cockpit instrumentation, a primitive form of electrical power boosting for the control column as a means of reducing pilot workload during heavily-laden formation flight, and further upgrading of the defensive armament. This last was effected by alterations to the waist and tail positions: the former were fitted with fixed windows that deflected the icy airflow that otherwise affected the two gunners, and then staggered longitudinally so that each of the two gunners could move freely without impeding the other; the latter became known as the 'Cheyenne turret' when modifications that reduced overall length by 5 in (0.127 m) increased the tail turret's field of fire by an appreciable degree and replaced the original ring-and-bead sight with a reflector sight. The single gun was later removed from the navigator's position, whose hatch mounting was deemed to provide inadequate fields of vision and fire.

The first B-17G was delivered in September 1943, and production lasted to April 1945, when the 8680th B-17G was delivered to end Flying Fortress production after the completion of 12,731 aircraft. The B-17G was the most prolific of all Flying Fortress variants: each of the three manufacturers produced the type in 23 blocks, deliveries from Boeing, Douglas and Vega amounting to 4035, 2395 and 2250 aircraft respectively.

THE FLYING PENCIL

Although Germany developed most of its warplanes of the early 1930s in the guise of civil aircraft, the Do 17 was virtually unique in being designed as a civil transport and only later being developed into a multi-role warplane. The first true military version, the Do 17 V4, was completed in the summer of 1935 and differed externally from its three civil predecessors mainly in its lack of cabin windows and the replacement of the single vertical surface by twin endplates to provide greater directional stability. Internally it had a radio operator's position in place of the passenger compartment, and a lower-fuselage weapons bay starting immediately to the rear of the front spar line. Two more prototypes, the Do 17 V5 and Do 17 V6, joined the military flight test programme during the autumn of 1935: the latter of these machines was virtually identical with the Do 17 V4, but the Do 17 V5 had a powerplant of two Hispano-Suiza 12Ybrs Vee piston engines each rated at 775 hp (578 kW) at sea level and 860 hp (641 kW) at 13125 ft (4000 m). No provision had been made for defensive armament in these early machines, for German tactical thinking of the day suggested that the Do 17 bomber would be too fast to intercept, but then more sanguine thinking intervened and the Do 17 V7 introduced a single defensive machine gun in a blister fairing above the fuselage, operated by the radio operator. This prototype also introduced a true bombardier nose position with a glazed hemispherical nose cap and glazed panels in the underside of the nose.

As final work on the prototypes was proceeding, Dornier had been preparing production lines at its Allmanweiler, Löwenthal and Manzell facilities for the large orders already placed for the two initial models, the Do 17E-1 bomber and Do 17F-1 reconnaissance aeroplane that were to be produced in parallel. The Do 17E-1 had the same defensive armament as the Do 17F-1, namely single 0.312 in (7.92 mm) MG 15 trainable rearward-firing machine guns in the dorsal and ventral hatch positions, and was also fully equipped for the bomber role, with a bomb sight in the glazed nose and bomb racks in the lower-fuselage weapons bay, which extended to the rear from a point in line with the wing main spar, for a standard disposable load of 1102 lb (500 kg). Dornier had also undertaken a major effort to 'productionise' the type, breaking the airframe down into component assemblies to help the type's production by different subcontractors.

Boeing B-17F Flying Fortres

Type: 10-seat heavy bomber
Country of origin: USA
Powerplant: four 1200-hp (895-kW) Wright R-1820-97 radial piston engines
Performance: maximum level speed 302 mph (486 km/h); service ceiling 35,600 ft (10,850 m); maximum range 3400 miles (5472 km)
Weights: empty 44,560 lb (20,212 kg); maximum take-off 72,000 lb (32,659 kg)
Dimensions: wing span 103 ft 9.4 in (31.63 m); length 74 ft 9 in (22.78 m) or 74 ft 4 in (22.66 m) with the 'Cheyenne' tail position; height 19 ft 1 in (5.82 m)
Armament: 13 0.5 in (12.7 mm) Browning M2 machine guns, plus up to 17,600 lb (7983 kg) of ordnance

The first Do 17E-1 bombers became available in early 1937, and the first units to equip with the type were the I Gruppen (wings) of Kampfgeschwadern (Bomber Groups) 153 and 155, followed later in the same year by II and III/KG 153 and by II and III/KG 155, the latter formation later becoming KG 158. The Luftwaffe considered the Do 17 a very important type, and in 1937 decided to send examples to Spain for operational evaluation in the Spanish Civil War.

DORNIER IMPROVEMENTS

Even before the first examples of the parallel Do 17E-1 bomber and Do 17F-1 reconnaissance series had left the production line, Dornier had embarked on a programme of long-term improvement for the basic design. The first step in this direction was represented by the Do 17 V8, which was also called Do 17M V1 with its much uprated powerplant of two Daimler-Benz DB 600A Vee piston engines each rated at 1000 hp (746 kW) for take-off and driving a three-blade VDM metal variable-pitch propeller for a maximum level speed of 264 mph (425 km/h). In 1937 this prototype was entered in the Military Aircraft Competition held at Zürich in Switzerland, and took first place in the Circuit of the Alps race, beating a number of fighters entered by other countries. German propaganda suggested that this was a perfectly standard bomber of the production line, which caused consternation amongst Europeans now becoming increasingly concerned about German military ambitions. There was no chance of the Do 17M V1 being the prototype of a production model, however, for supplies of the DB 600 engine were earmarked for fighter production. The Do 17M V1 did show how the Do 17's performance could be improved, however, and an uprated powerplant was adopted, in the form of two Bramo (from 1939 BMW-Bramo) 323A-1 Fafnir radial piston engines each rated at 900 hp (671 kW) for take-off and, with the aid of its two-speed supercharger, 1000 hp (746 kW) at 10170 ft (3100 m). The switch from a Vee engine to a radial engine presented no technical problem other than the comparatively simple design of new nacelles, and in the later stages of 1937 Dornier's production lines switched from the Do 17E and Do 17F to the Do 17M bomber and Do 17P reconnaissance aircraft.

It had been hoped that the Do 17M and Do 17P should be exact parallels of the Do 17E and Do 17F, but supplies of the Fafnir radial were inadequate for both the bomber and reconnaissance aircraft, and it was decided that the latter should have a powerplant based on another radial engine, the BMW 132N rated at 865 hp (645 kW) for take-off. Two Fafnir-powered prototypes were built as the Do 17 V13 (or Do 17M V1) and Do 17 V14 (or Do 17M V2) with a slightly upgraded defensive armament fit and a measure of local strengthening to balance the additional power. Experience in the opening phases of World War II soon showed that even with its additional power, the Do 17P could not show a clean pair of heels to the 'modern' monoplane fighters operated by France and the UK, and forward maintenance units often improved the defensive capability of surviving aircraft by the addition of another pair of MG 15 machine guns.

The new bomber variant, which entered service in 1938 as the Do 17M-1 , was dimensionally identical to the Do 17E-1 except for its height of 14 ft 11 in (4.55 m), but differed in details. As with the Do 17F-1, there remains no exact production figure for the Do 17P-1 within the total of 565 Do 17E, Do 17F, Do 17M and Do 17P aircraft. The type did not long survive in operational service as the altogether superior Do 17Z replaced it from the early months of 1939.

During the course of its operational evaluation of the Do 17 series in the Spanish Civil War, the Luftwaffe found that its early expectations for the type had been overly optimistic. The problem of performance shortfall was addressed with modest success in the higher-powered Do 17M and Do 17P bomber and reconnaissance developments of the Do 17E and Do 17F respectively, but the inadequate defensive armament required more drastic measures. Early in 1938, therefore, Dornier began work on a new four-man forward fuselage section optimised for operational efficiency rather than aerodynamic cleanliness.

CRAMPED CONDITIONS

The accommodation in the Do 17E/F and Do 17M/P series was notably cramped, and the new forward fuselage adopted a higher cockpit roof line which was completely glazed for better fields of vision. The bombardier position was also completely glazed with small flat panels, and this position was both deepened and extended aft to just forward of the wing leading edge: this provided a ventral step that allowed the incorporation of a defensive gun position with better fields of vision and fire than had been possible in the early variants. This new forward fuselage section was first used on the Do 17S high-speed reconnaissance model, of which only three Do 17S-0 evaluation aircraft were built with a powerplant of two DB 600G piston engines, the Do 17U pathfinder of which just 15 were built, and then on the definitive Do 17Z, which succeeded the Do 17U into production in the autumn of 1938. This version was basically similar to the Do 17S and Do 17U except for its reversion to a powerplant of two radial piston engines, as large-scale supplies of the DB 600 series of Vee piston engines were problematical given the fighter programme's higher priority. The selected radial was the Bramo 323A-1 Fafnir, and this was first installed in the Do 17Z-0 pre-production model that had a four-man crew with a defensive armament of three 0.312 in (7.92 mm) MG 15 machine guns in trainable windscreen, cockpit rear and ventral positions. A fourth gun of the same type was added in the nose position of the Do 17Z-1 production model that began to reach operational units in early 1939. Despite the additional drag of the new forward fuselage section, the Do 17Z-1 had performance basically similar to that of the Do 17M-1, except when fully loaded, where the additional weight of the new forward fuselage, additional crew member and extra gun degraded both speed and range to a degree that resulted in the decision to limit the maximum bomb load to 1102 lb (500 kg). The full bomb load was restored in the Do 17Z-2 that first flew early in 1939 with the uprated powerplant of two Bramo 323P Fafnir radial engines each rated at 1000 hp (746 kW). Carriage of the maximum bomb load meant a sacrifice of fuel capacity, however, and in fully loaded condition the Do 17Z-2 had a tactical radius of only 205 miles (330 km). The Do 17Z-3 was a reconnaissance

Boeing B-17G Flying Fortress

Type: 10-seat heavy bomber
Country of origin: USA
Powerplant: four 1200-hp (895-kW) Wright R-1820-97 radial engines
Performance: max level speed 302 mph (486 km/h); service ceiling 35,600 ft (10,850 m); max range 3400 miles (5472 km)
Weights: empty 44,560 lb (20,212 kg); max take-off 72,000 lb (32,659 kg)
Dimensions: wing span 103 ft 9.4 in (31.63 m); length 74 ft 9 in (22.78 m); height 19 ft 1 in (5.82 m)
Armament: 14 0.5 in (12.7 mm) Browning M2 machine guns, up to 17,600 lb (7983 kg) of ordnance

Dornier Do 17Z-2

Type: four-seat medium bomber
Country of origin: Germany
Powerplant: two 1000-hp (746-kW) BMW-Bramo 323P Fafnir radial piston engines
Performance: max level speed 255 mph (410 km/h); service ceiling 26,900 ft (8200 m); max range 932 miles (1500 km)
Weights: empty 12,958 lb (5715 kg); max take-off 19,481 lb (8837 kg)
Dimensions: wing span 59 ft 0.33 in (18.00 m); length 51 ft 9.67 in (15.80 m); height 14 ft 11.5 in (4.55 m)
Armament: up to eight 0.312 in (7.92 mm) MG 15 machine guns, plus up to 2205 lb (1000 kg) of ordnance

bomber derivative of the Do 17Z-2 with two Rb 20/30 automatic cameras and a maximum bomb load of 1102 lb (500 kg). The Do 17Z-3 was the last production version of the Do 17Z bomber, but two later variants appeared as a result of maintenance unit modifications. These were the Do 17Z-4 dual-control trainer and the Do 17Z-5 with inflatable flotation bags and live-saving gear for long over-water operations.

STALIN INTERVENES

First flown in February 1936, Russia's Ilyushin TsKB-26 was the prototype of a long-range medium bomber. It was powered by a pair of Gnome-Rhône 14K Mistral-Major radial piston engines each rated at 800 hp (597 kW), and was followed by the TsKB-20 second prototype with an enclosed cockpit, a light alloy rather than wooden semi-monocoque rear fuselage, and a powerplant of two Tumanskii M-85 radial piston engines each rated at 800 hp (597 kW) and derived from the Mistral-Major. At the express order of Iosif Stalin, the Soviet dictator, the Soviet air force was ordered to take the DB-3B production version of the TsKB-30 in preference to the generally superior Tupolev ANT-37 that was already being readied for production as the DB-2. Production began in February 1937, and eventually totalled 1528 aircraft up to 1940, in a series that included the basic DB-3B with a powerplant of two M-85 radial engines, (later replaced by improved M-86 units of the same basic rating and finally by M-87 units each rated at 950 hp (708 kW)), the DB-3M modernised model that appeared in 1938 with a simplified and more easily produced structure, and the DB-3T torpedo bomber version with provision for one 17.7 in (450 mm) 45-12-AN torpedo carried under the fuselage.

When production of the DB-3M had got into its stride during 1939, Ilyushin redesigned the structure to create the DB-3f (forsirovannyi, or intensive) variant that was considerably easier to produce and to maintain in the field. The powerplant was revised to two Tumanskii M-87B radial engines each rated at 950 hp (708 kW), driving three-blade VISh-23 metal variable-pitch propellers, installed in improved nacelles. The DB-3f made its first flight in January 1940, and entered production later in the year with a powerplant of two Tumanskii M-88 radial piston engines each rated at 1000 hp (746 kW). Towards the end of the year, the designation of the type was changed to Il-4, and production of 5256 aircraft was completed in 1944. Over the years changes were made to the engines and armament fit.

JAPANESE NELL

Although it was already obsolescent by 1941, the Mitsubishi G3M (later accorded the Allied reporting name 'Nell') belied this technical limitation by scoring a number of stunning successes in the opening phases of Japan's offensive onslaught, most notably the sinking of the HMS *Prince of Wales* and HMS *Repulse*, which thus became the first capital ships to be sunk at sea by aircraft alone. There was no adequate replacement for the type, however, and the G3M was therefore forced to soldier on into total obsolescence when it suffered very heavy losses to Allied fighters. During the 1930s, the Japanese navy established a land-based bomber force able to deliver a modest weapons load over very considerable ranges, and the bureau issued to Mitsubishi a requirement for such a bomber, which was designed by a team under the leadership of Sueo Honjo, Tomio Kubo and Nobuhiko Kusabake. Their Ka-9 design first flew in April 1934 with a powerplant of two Hiro Type 91 Vee piston engines each rated at 500 hp (373 kW). The Ka-9 revealed very good handling characteristics, including a high level of agility for an aeroplane of its size and configuration, as well as remarkable range. The Imperial Japanese navy air force was impressed by the capability of this proof-of-concept type, and in 1934 issued its definitive requirement for a land-based bomber able to deliver a weapons load of 1764 lb (800 kg) and carry a defensive armament of three 0.303 in (7.7 mm) trainable machine guns. The result was the Ka-15. Some 21 Ka-15 aircraft were built for prototype and development trials, and in June 1936 the type was put into production with a powerplant of two Kinsei 3 radial engines each rated at 910 hp (679 kW). The variant entered service with the full and short designations Navy Type 96 Attack Bomber Model 11 and G3M1 respectively, of which 34 examples were built.

In all 343 Mitsubishi-built aircraft were delivered for service with the full designation Navy Type 99 Attack Bomber Model 21. The G3M2 variant differed from the G3M1 in minor internal details as well as its powerplant of two Kinsei 41 or Kinsei 42 radial engines, each rated at

1075 hp (802 kW) for take-off and 990 hp (738 kW) at 13715 ft (4180 m), and supplied with fuel from a slightly increased internal capacity. Later aircraft, in the form of 238 delivered by Mitsubishi and an uncertain number by Nakajima from a production run of 412 G3M2 and G3M3 aircraft, differed from the earlier machines in being completed to the Navy Type 99 Attack Bomber Model 22 standard, with the modestly improved Kinsei 45 engine and the defensive armament somewhat revised: the retractable dorsal and ventral turret were eliminated, the former being replaced by a turtleback fairing fitted with a 20 mm (0.787 in) Type 99 Model 1 trainable cannon, and provision was made for three more 0.303 in (7.7 mm) Type 92 trainable machine guns in two lateral-firing beam blister positions and a lateral-firing cockpit side position.

ITALIAN SPARROWHAWK

Arguably one of the finest torpedo bombers of World War II despite its technical obsolescence, the Savoia-Marchetti SM.79 Sparviero (sparrow-hawk) was a cantilever low-wing monoplane of mixed construction with tailwheel landing gear that included main units which retracted rearward into the underside of the nacelles for the two wing-mounted units of the tri-motor powerplant arrangement. The type first flew late in 1934 as a civil transport prototype, with accommodation for eight passengers and a powerplant of three Alfa Romeo 126 RC.34 radial piston engines, each rated at 780 hp (582 kW), but the capabilities of the type were sufficiently impressive for the Italian air force to adopt the type as a reconnaissance bomber. The first model was the SM.79-I reconnaissance bomber, and this saw considerable and effective service with the Italian expeditionary force supporting the Nationalist insurgents against the Republican government forces in the Spanish Civil War . The SM.79-II was the torpedo bomber version of the SM.79-I with provision for two 17.7 in (450 mm) torpedoes in the form of either a Silurificio Whitehead weapon with a 375 lb (170 kg) warhead or a Silurificio Italiano weapon with a 353 lb (160 kg) warhead, although these were replaced from December 1941 by a torpedo with a 441 lb (200 kg) warhead. The SM.79-II generally had a powerplant of three Piaggio P.XI RC.40 radial piston engines each rated at 1000 hp (746 kW) or, in a smaller number of aircraft, three Fiat A.80 RC.41 radial piston engines each rated at 1030 hp (768 kW) or three Alfa Romeo 135 RC.32 radial piston engines each rated at 1350 hp (1007 kW).

The SM.79-III Sparviero was an improved version of the SM.79-II with the ventral gondola removed, the gun armament revised by the replacement of the 0.5 in (12.7 mm) fixed forward-firing machine gun above the flightdeck by a 20 mm (0.787 in) cannon, better propellers fitted, the exhaust manifold pipes lengthened, and more modern radio equipment installed.

RIGHT: The definitive Dornier Do 17 twin-engined bomber was the Do 17Z, seen here in the form of a Do 17Z-2 of Kampfgeschwader 2 over the Ionian Sea off the coast of Greece.

HANDLEY PAGE HAMPDEN

When the Air Ministry issued its B.9/32 requirement for a modern twin-engined medium bomber, it received design proposals from Handley Page and Vickers for aircraft that were to mature as the Hampden and Wellington respectively. The H.P.52 design from Handley Page envisaged a cantilever mid-wing monoplane of essentially all-metal construction, based on a pod-and-boom type of fuselage of exceptional slenderness. This design's maximum external width of only 3 ft 0 in (0.91 m) kept drag to a minimum and therefore boosted performance, but had two principal failings: it limited the defensive armament to manually operated machine guns rather than the turreted weapons that were installed in the Wellington, and made it impossible for the crew to change position in flight, which meant that a dead or badly injured pilot could not be pulled from his seat and replaced by another member of the crew. The Air Ministry ordered a single H.P.52 prototype, and this made its maiden flight on 21 June 1936. An order for 180 Hampden Mk I production aircraft was placed in August 1936, and the first of these aircraft flew in May 1938, allowing deliveries to No 49 Squadron to began in the following September.

Production eventually totalled 1432 aircraft delivered by the parent company (502 machines) and English Electric (770) in the UK as well as a further 160 by a Canadian production line run by the Canadian Associated Aircraft Ltd. The Hampden Mk I equipped the whole of No 5 Group of the Royal Air Force's Bomber Command which, on the outbreak of World War II, had ten Hampden squadrons comprising eight first-line and two reserve units; eventually a total of 15 squadrons operated the Hampden and its Hereford half-brother. The Hampden was initially operated in the reconnaissance role but was soon committed to daylight bombing. Early operations in this latter role soon confirmed that the Hampden was highly vulnerable to fighter attack, and the type was soon relegated to the night bombing and minelaying roles. The Hampden remained in service with Bomber Command up to September 1942, but from April most surviving aircraft were gradually transferred to RAF Coastal Command, where 157 of them were adapted as torpedo bombers with

the designation Hampden TB.Mk I. These aircraft were retired late in 1943.

First flown on 1 July 1937 with a powerplant of two Napier Dagger VIII H-type piston engines each rated at 955 hp (712 kW), the Hereford was known to its parent company as the H.P.53 and was identical to the Hampden in all but its powerplant. The first Hereford Mk I flew in May 1939 and the type entered service with a powerplant of two Dagger VIII engines uprated to 1000 hp (746 kW). Experience showed that the Dagger was unreliable and possessed a high-pitched exhaust note that was decidedly uncomfortable for the crew, and the type was used mainly for training after a very short first-line career in partnership with the Hampden.

The Vickers Wellington was one of the most important warplanes in the British inventory at the beginning of World War II, and it bore the brunt of the British bomber effort until large numbers of four-engined heavy bombers became available. Even then, however, the type did not disappear from service as it found an important second career in the maritime reconnaissance, transport and training roles until after the end of the war. Total production was 11,461 aircraft from three factories, the last machine not being delivered until October 1945 – the largest number of any British bomber type ever placed in production. The origins of the Wellington can be traced to the Air Ministry's release of its B.9/32 requirement for an advanced twin-engined bomber, and Vickers decided at this stage that the type of light alloy geodetic structure designed by Dr. Barnes Wallis for the R.100 airship and already proved on its Wellesley general-purpose bomber would be ideal for a sturdy structure that would be capable of sustaining very considerable combat damage. The Air Ministry contracted for a single prototype of the Type 271 design which eventually emerged with an empty weight of 11,508 lb (5220 kg) rather than the figure of 6300 lb (2858 kg) that had first been specified. The escalation in empty weight allowed the creation of an immensely strong airframe fitted with two engines of sufficient power to provide good performance.

From 1933 onward the Air Ministry started an upward revision of the Type 271's maximum take-off weight and weapons load, and by November 1935 had reached the position of considering the deployment of the type at a maximum take-off weight of 30,500 lb

Ilyushin Il-4

Type: four-seat medium bomber
Country of origin: USSR
Powerplant: two 1100-hp (820-kW) Tumanskii M-88B piston engines
Performance: maximum level speed 261 mph (420 km/h); service ceiling 30,840 ft (9400 m); max range 2361 miles (3800 km)
Weights: empty 12,787 lb (5800 kg); max take-off 22,707 lb (10,300 kg)
Dimensions: wing span 70 ft 4.5 in (21.44 m); length 48 ft 7 in (14.80 m); height 13 ft 5.5 in (4.10 m)
Armament: two 0.3 in (7.62 mm) ShKAS and one 0.5 in (12.7 mm) Beresin UBT machine guns, plus up to 5952 lb (2700 kg) of bombs

(13,835 kg), a weight that was made feasible only by earlier demands of Vickers to be permitted to design a heavier and therefore stronger structure. In August 1936 the Air Ministry placed an initial order with Vickers for 180 Wellington Mk I medium bombers, and in the following year contracted with Gloster for another 200 aircraft (100 examples each of the Wellington Mks I and II with a powerplant of two Bristol Pegasus radial and Rolls-Royce Merlin Vee piston engines respectively), and then with Armstrong Whitworth for a further 64 aircraft.

WELLINGTON DEVELOPMENT

The Type 271 was originally offered with a powerplant of two air-cooled radial or liquid-cooled Vee piston engines, the decisions for the former falling on the Bristol Mercury in preference to the Armstrong Siddeley Tiger, and for the latter on the Rolls-Royce Goshawk, which was essentially a development of the Kestrel with evaporative cooling. The Air Ministry initially preferred the Goshawk I, and by this stage the basic requirement had been modified to include nose, dorsal and tail gun positions with protection against the wind, and power operation to secure the high rates of traverse that would be required to track fighters attacking at high crossing speeds. Vickers had meanwhile modified its original concept from a high to a mid-wing layout to provide the pilots with better fields of vision for formation flying, and introduced a number of aerodynamic changes to provide better handling characteristics. By the middle of 1934, Vickers was becoming concerned that the escalation of empty weight, caused by its own improvements and the incorporation of revised Air Ministry requirements, was overtaking the power likely to become available from the Goshawk engine, which was itself troubled in development. In August 1934 they approached the Air Ministry with the suggestion that the Goshawk should be replaced by either of two Bristol radial piston engines, namely the Perseus or Pegasus, for a higher power/weight ratio and thus improved single-engined flight capability and better performance in level speed, climb and ceiling. The Air Ministry accepted Vickers' reasoning, and ordered that the prototype be completed with a powerplant of two Pegasus radial engines each driving a three-blade propeller of the variable-pitch type, enlarged internal fuel capacity to provide a range of 1500 miles (3414 km) at 213 mph (343 km/h) at 15000 ft (4570 m), and manually-operated nose and tail defensive gun positions of Vickers design.

The prototype made its first flight on 15 June 1936 with a powerplant of two Bristol Pegasus X radial piston engines each rated at 915 hp (682 kW). The name Crecy had originally been selected for the new bomber in June 1936, but by September 1936 this had been changed to Wellington, which was notionally in keeping with the Air Ministry's policy of naming bombers after British towns but more fortuitously maintained a link with its Vickers' predecessor, the Wellesley that bore the family name of the dukes of Wellington. The prototype was lost in a fatal crash during April 1937, but its success up to that time had confirmed to the company and the Air Ministry that the new type was potentially an excellent bomber. Thus the already placed production orders were confirmed, and the final configuration for the production standard was discussed by the company and the Air Ministry.

The result of these discussions included a powerplant of two Pegasus XVIII radial engines, with provision for the installation of Pegasus XX radial engines if there were delays in the finalisation of the Pegasus XVIII. The defensive scheme modified to six 0.303 in (7.7 mm) Browning machine guns in power-operated turrets of Vickers design but fitted with Frazer-Nash control units and installed in the nose, retractable ventral and tail positions. The new standard was embodied in the B.29/36 specification that was issued in February 1937 to cover the Wellington Mk I initial production version.

The Wellington Mk I was in most respects a new design. Preceded by the Type 285 pre-production prototype that first flew on 23 December 1937, the initial production model was the Type 290 of which 183 were eventually built for service as the Wellington Mk I with a powerplant of two Pegasus XVIII radial engines each rated at 1050 hp (783 kW) and a defensive armament that included single (later two) 0.303 in (7.7 mm) machine guns in the nose and ventral 'dustbin' turrets and two 0.303 in (7.7 mm) machine guns in the tail turret.

WELLINGTON IN SERVICE

The Wellington Mk I entered service with No 9 Squadron in October 1938, and by the outbreak of World War II in September 1939 this unit had been joined by nine squadrons to make up Bomber Command's main medium bomber capability. Such was the faith attached to the type's strength, performance and defensive firepower that daylight operations were considered feasible. The fallacy of this supposition was revealed in December 1939, when 24 Wellington bombers were intercepted over the Heligoland Bight by Messerschmitt Bf 109 single-engined and Bf 110 twin-engined fighters, which shot down 12 of the bombers and severely damaged another three. The Wellington was immediately switched to the night bomber role, in which its vulnerability to beam attacks was significantly reduced.

Before this time it had been decided that the first two variants of the Wellington to be built in substantial numbers would be the Wellington Mk II with a powerplant of two Rolls-Royce Merlin X Vee piston engines and the Wellington Mk III with a powerplant of two Bristol Hercules III radial piston engines. A delay was inevitable before these two variants could enter production and to fill this gap improved versions of the Wellington Mk I were evolved. The Wellington Mk IA, of which 187 were delivered, was in fact based on the Wellington Mk II with its trio of Frazer-Nash turrets each carrying two 0.303 in (7.7 mm) Browning trainable machine guns. The Wellington Mk IA entered service at about the time of the outbreak of World War II in September 1939. The Wellington Mk IC was the most important bomber version available in the early part of the war, and reflected all the lessons that had been learned with the Wellington Mks I and IA in the first months of combat. Built to the extent of 2685 aircraft, the variant had the airframe and systems improvements introduced in the Wellington Mk IA, but differed in having the ventral 'dustbin' gun position replaced by two 0.303 in (7.7 mm) Vickers 'K' machine guns in two beam positions or two 0.303 in (7.7 mm) Browning machine guns in a position slightly farther to the rear.

The 400 Wellington Mk IIs were essentially similar to the Wellington Mk IA, described above even though in fact it was the Wellington Mk IA that was derived from the forthcoming Wellington Mk II, except for its powerplant of two Rolls-Royce Merlin X inverted-Vee piston engines each rated at 1145 hp (854 kW). The first example made its maiden flight in March 1939 as the Type 298 prototype, and the Wellington Mk II otherwise differed from the Wellington Mk IC in details such as its offensive armament of 4000 lb (1814 kg) often comprising a single 4000 lb (1814 kg) 'blockbuster' bomb whose carriage was pioneered in this model. Designed in parallel with the Wellington Mk II and built to the extent of 1517 aircraft, the Wellington Mk III was essentially similar to the Wellington Mk IA except for its powerplant of two Bristol Hercules XI radial piston engines each rated at 1425 hp (1062.5 kW) and a Frazer-Nash F.N.20A tail turret with four 0.303 in (7.7 mm) Browning trainable machine guns. The prototype made its maiden flight in May 1939 with a powerplant of two Hercules HEISM radial engines each fitted with a two-stage supercharger and driving a three-blade de Havilland propeller of the constant-speed type, but the powerplant failed to live up to expectations. This was a considerable blow for Bomber Command, which had wanted early delivery of the Wellington Mk III as its primary bomber pending the advent of four-engined bombers such as the Short Stirling. At the request of the Air Ministry, Vickers completed a second prototype with a powerplant of two Hercules III radial engines each driving a three-blade Rotol propeller of the constant-speed type. The Hercules III was currently the most powerful variant of the Hercules family in production, and in a 'power egg' form this engine was adopted as standard for the Wellington Mk III, whose delayed entry into production did in fact have some compensations as it allowed the incorporation of better armour protection, self-sealing fuel tanks, balloon cable-cutters in the wing leading edges and, in order that the aircraft could be operated by bomber squadrons in North Africa and the Middle East, provision for long-range fuel tanks and sand/dust filters over the carburettor air inlets. Early operations

Mitsubishi G3M2

Type: seven-seat medium bomber
Country of origin: Japan
Powerplant: two 1075-hp (801.5-kW) Mitsubishi Kinsei 43 radial piston engines
Performance: max level speed 232 mph (373 km/h); service ceiling 29,950 ft (9130 m); max range 2722 miles (4380 km)
Weights: empty 10,936 lb (4965 kg); max take-off 17,637 lb (8000 kg)
Dimensions: wing span 82 ft 0.25 in (25.00 m); length 53 ft 11.625 in (16.45 m); height 12 ft 1 in (3.685 m)
Armament: one 20 mm Type 99 Model 1cannon, up to three 0.303 in (7.7 mm) Type 92 machine guns, plus up to 1764 lb (800 kg) of ordnance

had also revealed the Wellington Mk I's inadequate defence against beam and tail attacks. The former problem had already been addressed by the replacement of the overweight and tactically limited Frazer-Nash F.N.21A ventral turret by two beam-mounted machine guns, but the latter demanded a more comprehensive solution in the form of a tail turret with one 20 mm (0.787 in) cannon or four 0.303 in (7.7 mm) machine guns. It was the latter that was adopted in the form of the Frazer-Nash F.N.20A turret, but for lack of these units the first Wellington Mk III bombers were delivered with the two-gun Frazer-Nash F.N.4 turret. This evolution meant that the Wellington Mk III finally entered service with an empty weight of 21160 lb (9598 kg) and maximum take-off weight of 34500 lb (15649 kg). During this time the maximum take-off weight had escalated in steps via 30000 and 33000 lb (13608 and 14969 kg). The Wellington B.Mk III reached operational units in 1942, and was the most important bomber in Bomber Command's inventory until it was overtaken in 1943 by the new four-engined bombers.

Built to the extent of 3803 aircraft, the Wellington B.Mk X was the final major bomber variant to enter production and was also the model built in the largest numbers. It was basically similar to the Wellington B.Mk III with the exception of its powerplant, which comprised a pair of Hercules VI or XVI radial engines each rated at 1675 hp (1249 kW), and its structure built of light alloy rather than mild steel for additional strength (and thus performance) without any increase in structural weight. The first Wellington B.Mk X was flown in July 1942, and from a time early in 1943 entered service with 20 operational squadrons as well as 25 operational conversion units. The Wellington B.Mk X fulfilled exactly the same task as the Wellington B.Mk III with the improved survivability offered by higher all-round performance, and although supplanted in the primary night bomber role over northern Europe from mid-1943, remained in bomber service for some while longer in the Middle East, Mediterranean and Burmese campaigns.

CANT DESIGNS

The Cantieri Navali de Monfalcone was a shipbuilding company in the northeastern Italian port of Trieste that decided in 1923 to expand into the aircraft manufacturing business, and therefore established CANT (Cantiere Navale Triestino) for the design and manufacture of water-based aircraft for civil as well as military use. In 1931 the CANT company was reorganised as the Cantieri Riuniti dell'Adriatico, and it is for this reason that aircraft produced after this time are sometimes known as CRDA (CANT) designs.

The first of the firm's significant landplane designs to reach the hardware stage was the Z.1007 medium bomber which, with the Savoia-Marchetti SM.79 Sparviero, was destined to be the most important Italian bomber of World War II. The first prototype made its maiden flight in March 1937 with a powerplant of three Isotta-Fraschini Asso XI R2C.40 Vee piston engines each rated at 825 hp (615 kW) at 13125 ft (4000 m) and driving a two-blade wooden propeller of the fixed-pitch type. The original props were replaced by three-blade constant-speed Piaggio metal ones and the ventral

ABOVE: The most successful Italian bomber of World War II was the Savoia-Marchetti SM.79 Sparviero, which operated in level bomber and, notably, torpedo bomber forms.

radiators were revised to improve cooling and eliminate an airflow problem. Successful evaluation of the prototype in this revised form led to an order for 34 pre-production bombers that retained the Asso XI engines in a revised arrangement with annular radiators. These Z.1007 aircraft were issued to the 221o Gruppo in 1939, and were used only for operational development of the bomber and not for any real service task. The Italian air force had already decided that while the Z.1007 was adequate, it really needed additional size and power to become an effective bomber. This had led to work on a larger, heavier and more powerful model, which was the first to receive the name Alcione (kingfisher).

The first of eight pre-production aircraft flew in 1938 with a powerplant of three Piaggio P.XI RC.40 radial engines each rated at 1000 hp (746 kW) at 13125 ft (4000 m), and the success of these aircraft led to the placing of major orders for aircraft to be built by CANT and also by IMAM (Meridionali). The aircraft were built in nine series, and while the first three (Z.1007bis Serie I Alcione to Z.1007bis Serie III Alcione) retained the original type of tail unit with a single vertical surface, the later six (Z.1007bis Serie IV Alcione to Z.1007bis Serie IX Alcione) introduced a revised tail unit: this had been designed to provide the defensive gunners with improved rearward fields of fire, and comprised a sharply dihedralled tailplane carrying endplate vertical surfaces of ovoid shape. The revised tail unit affected neither performance nor handling, and aircraft of the single- or twin-tailed types were often found in service with the same unit. Some 87 aircraft had been delivered by the time of Italy's entry into World War II in June 1940, and these served with the 16o and 47o Stormi da Bombardamento Terrestre. Later the Alcione served with an eventual five stormi da bombardamento terrestre, seven gruppi da bombardamento terrestre, and two squadriglie da bombardamento terrestre that operated mainly from bases in metropolitan Italy, Sicily, Sardinia and Greece, although limited deployments were made to the southern USSR and the southern coast of the English Channel for operations against the Soviets and British respectively.

The Z.1007ter was the final development of the Z.1007 concept. It entered production late in 1942, and was a derivative of the Z.1007bis with the uprated powerplant of three Piaggio P.XIX RC.45 radial piston engines each rated at 1175 hp (876 kW) at 16405 ft (5000 m). Total production of the Z.1007bis and Z.1007ter amounted to 526 aircraft of which the last 25 were delivered after the armistice of September 1943 in which Italy changed sides to the Allied cause but was then riven in two by German occupation, with Fascist support, of the areas not already occupied by the Allies. The Z.1007 series was then used by each side to the end of World War II. A few aircraft remained operational to 1948 in second-line tasks.

THE JUNKERS JU 88

Rivalling the de Havilland Mosquito for the accolade of most versatile aeroplane of World War II , the Ju 88 was arguably the most important German warplane of its period and was used in a host of roles ranging from basic bombing to pilotless attack via torpedo and dive bombing, heavy attack, night fighting and reconnaissance. Yet the full potential of the machine was not even the subject of wishful thinking when the German air ministry issued its 1935 requirement for a three-seat fast bomber that could deliver a maximum bomb load of 1764 lb (800 kg) at a maximum level speed of 311 mph (500 km/h). The requirement was issued to Focke-Wulf, Henschel, Junkers and Messerschmitt. Focke-Wulf was not interested, Henschel and Junkers started work on new designs, and Messerschmitt prepared the Bf 162 derivative of its Bf 110 heavy fighter design. Junkers felt that the requirement would result in considerable orders for the winning design and expended great effort in the evolution of a far-sighted design embodying the full spectrum of advanced features that had emerged in the last few years. The company had already decided that it lacked the experience to design an advanced monoplane of the modern stressed-skin type and accordingly hired two American engineers, W. H. Evers and A. Gassner, who had considerable experience with this type of structural medium. Work began in January 1936 and was initially concentrated on two related types, namely the Ju 85 and Ju 88 with twin and single vertical tail surfaces respectively. The German air ministry decided that the latter offered greater promise and ordered an end to work on the Ju 85. The construction of three Ju 88 prototypes began in May 1936, and the Ju 88 V1 first prototype made its maiden flight in December 1936 with a powerplant of two Daimler-Benz DB 600Aa piston engines each rated at 1000 hp (746 kW) for take-off.

The Ju 88 V2 second prototype was very similar to the first machine, but the Ju 88 V3 third prototype switched to a different powerplant in the form of two Junkers Jumo 211A inverted-Vee piston engines each rated at 1000 hp (746 kW) for take-off, and also introduced full military equipment as well as a cockpit with a raised roof. The potential of the Ju 88 had by now been recognised and, even before any competitive evaluation against the Henschel Hs 127 and Messerschmitt Bf 162, it had been ordered into production. The German air ministry decided that the Ju 88 should have a four-man crew, improved defensive armament and the ability to undertake the dive-bomber role, and this resulted in the construction of the Ju 88 V4 fourth prototype with dive brakes under the outer wing panels, the 'solid' nose replaced by an approximately hemispherical arrangement of flat glazed panels, and a small gondola added under the nose with provision at its rear for a single 0.312 in (7.92 mm) MG 15 trainable rearward-firing machine gun for ventral defence.

There followed another six prototypes for record-breaking and development

Savoia-Marchetti SM.79-I Sparviero

Type: five-seat medium bomber
Country of origin: Italy
Powerplant: three 780-hp (582-kW) Alfa Romeo 126 RC.34 radial piston engines
Performance: max level speed 267 mph (430 km/h); service ceiling 21,325 ft (6500 m); max range 2050 miles (3300 km)
Weights: empty 14,991 lb (6800 kg); max take-off 23,104 lb (10,480 kg)
Dimensions: wing span 69 ft 2.67 in (21.20 m); length 51 ft 3.125 in (15.62 m); height 14 ft 5.25 in (4.40 m)
Armament: five 0.5 in (12.7 mm) Breda-SAFAT machine guns, plus up to 2756 lb (1250 kg) of stores

purposes, and then ten examples of the Ju 88A-0 pre-production model. The first of these pre-production aircraft was delivered in March 1939 to the specially created Erprobungskommando 88 intended to explore the new bomber's capabilities and develop the appropriate operational techniques. This unit provided the core of I/Kampfgeschwader (Bomber Group) 25 (soon redesignated as I/KG 30), which was the first Gruppe to receive the new Ju 88A-1 in August 1939, just a few days before the outbreak of World War II. The Ju 88A-1 flew its first operational sortie in the closing days of September 1939, and from that time onward began to emerge as one of the most formidable German warplanes of World War II. The Ju 88A-1 was powered by two Jumo 211B-1/G-1 engines each rated at 1200 hp (895 kW) for take-off. The standard internal bomb load was 3086 lb (1400 kg) in the form of 28 110 lb (50 kg) SC-50 bombs, and this bay was supplemented by four hardpoints, each rated at 1102 lb (500 kg), under the wing inboard of the engine nacelles. The maximum weapon load for short-range missions was thus 5291 lb (2400 kg). The defensive armament was originally three 0.312 in (7.92 mm) MG 15 machine guns but operations soon revealed the inadequacy of the arrangement, which was boosted on the production line by the addition of a second MG 15 in the rear of the cockpit, and in the field by two MG 15 lateral-firing weapons in the sides of the cockpit glazing.

ROCKET-ASSISTED JU 88

The Ju 88A-2 was the Ju 88A-1 derivative with attachment points for RATO units, which were designed for descent to the ground under parachutes after use. The Ju 88A-3 was the conversion trainer version of the Ju 88A-1 with dual controls, dual throttles and a measure of instrument duplication. The Ju 88A-4 was the first definitive model, and a development of the Ju 88A-1 with the wing extended slightly in span and area, inset rather than trailing ailerons with metal rather than fabric skinning, strengthened main landing gear units, and the uprated powerplant of two Jumo 211J-1/2 inverted-Vee piston engines each rated at 1340 hp (999 kW) – although early aircraft were completed with a powerplant of two Jumo 211F-1 engines each rated at 1340 hp (999 kW). Early aircraft also had the same defensive armament as the improved Ju 88A-1, in the form of five 0.312 in (7.92 mm) MG 15 machine guns, but the definitive version of the Ju 88A-4 switched to superior 0.312 in (7.92 mm) MG 81 weapons that were often replaced by 0.51 in (13 mm) MG 131 machine guns. The Ju 88A-4 was the starting point for most further developments of the Ju 88A series, although the number sequence of their designator suffixes should not be construed as the order in which the specific subvariants appeared.

As there were delays in the final development of the Jumo 211J engine for the Ju 88A-4, the revised wing was fitted to the Ju 88A-1 airframe to create the Ju 88A-5 interim type which also had the strengthened main landing gear units and introduced two hardpoints, each rated at 551 lb (250 kg), under the outer wing panels. The variant appeared in the summer of 1940, and proved itself the most capable of the German bombers operating in the Battle of Britain. The Ju 88A-6 was a development of the Ju 88A-5 intended to clear the way for any main bomber force by cutting the cables of balloon barrages. This was achieved by the addition of a large forward-mounted fender that terminated at each wing tip in a cable-cutting device. The Ju 88A-7 was the variant of the Ju 88A-5 for the dual-control conversion trainer role. The Ju 88A-8 was a development of the Ju 88A-4 with balloon cable cutters built into the wing leading edges and the crew reduced to three. The Ju 88A-9, A-10 and A-11 were the tropicalised versions of the Ju 88A-1, A-5 and A-4 respectively with sand filters, desert survival equipment and cockpit sun blinds, and Ju 88A-4 aircraft adapted to the same standard by field maintenance units received the designation Ju 88A-4/Trop. The Ju 88A-12 was the Ju 88A-4 adapted on the production line to dual-control trainer standard with the dive brakes, undernose gondola and all armament removed. The Ju 88A-13 designation was applied to a number of Ju 88A-4 bombers rebuilt for the low-level attack role with the dive brakes and bomb sight removed, additional armour worked into the airframe to protect the crew, engines and fuel supply, provision made for a disposable load of 1102 lb (500 kg) of fragmentation bomblets, and fixed forward-firing armament provided in the form of up to 16 0.312 in (7.92 mm) MG 17 machine guns in pods carried on the underwing hardpoints. The Ju 88A-14 was an improved version of the Ju 88A-4 with increased armour protection, balloon cable cutters in the wing leading edges and, in some aircraft, a 20 mm (0.787 in) MG FF forward-firing cannon in the forward part of the undernose gondola for improved firepower in the anti-ship role. The Ju 88A-15 was a development of the Ju 88A-4 with an enlarged weapons bay of wooden construction for the carriage of a 6614 lb (3000 kg) weapon load, the crew reduced to three, the undernose gondola removed, and the defensive armament restricted to two 0.312 in (7.92 mm) MG 15 machine guns. The Ju 88A-16 was the dual-control trainer version of the Ju 88A-14 with the undernose gondola and all armament capability removed. The Ju 88A-17 was a development of the Ju 88A-4 for the torpedo bombing role with the

BELOW: The Martin Baltimore was a development of the concept first embodied in the Martin Maryland, and this American warplane was used by the British and their allies.

four ETC racks inboard of the engine nacelles replaced by two PVC racks each capable of carrying one 1686 lb (765 kg) LT F5b torpedo and the forward fuselage revised to carry on its starboard side a large bulged fairing accommodating the gear to adjust the guidance mechanism of the torpedoes before release. The crew was reduced to three, and many of the aircraft were stripped of their undernose gondolas. The production model was preceded in 1942 by a number of field conversions of the same type, aircraft thus modified receiving the revised designation Ju 88A-4/Torp.

The Ju 88A served with the Luftwaffe throughout the war, with a number of Germany's allies from early in 1943, and in captured form with the French air force from 1944 into the early years of the post-war period. The number of aircraft built is no longer known, but certainly exceeded 7000 aircraft.

FINE FRENCH BOMBER

The finest bomber developed by the French aero industry in the period leading up to World War II, the Lioré-et-Olivier LeO 451 was also an aesthetic masterpiece. The type resulted from a French air ministry requirement of November 1934 for an advanced four-seat day bomber able to deliver a 2646 lb (1200 kg) bomb load over a radius of 435 miles (700 km) with performance high enough to reduce the chances of fighter interception and defensive armament potent enough to deal with any such attacks that might nonetheless materialise. The four designs submitted to meet this requirement were the Amiot 341, Latécoère Laté 570, Lioré-et-Olivier LeO 45 and Romano R-120, and the most advanced of these in aerodynamic terms was without doubt the LeO 45 designed as a cantilever monoplane of very clean lines and essentially all-metal construction with fabric-covered control surfaces. The LeO 45.01, first of two prototypes, made its maiden flight in January 1937, and shortly after this the Lioré-et-Olivier company was overtaken by the wholesale nationalisation of the French aero industry that had been decided in 1936, and now became part of the Société Nationale de Constructions Aéronautiques du Sud-Est. Trials revealed good performance and generally adequate handling that was improved by modification of the vertical tail surfaces and the introduction of larger rudders, but also confirmed the unreliability of the powerplant, which comprised two Hispano-Suiza 14AA-8/9 radial piston engines each rated at 1078 hp (804 kW). Despite its lack of reliability, this powerplant was specified for the LeO 45B.4 initial production model, of which 20 were ordered in January 1938 in the Bombardement quattre-place (four-seat bomber) category. In the late summer of 1938 the LeO 45.01 was transformed into the LeO 451.01 with a powerplant of two Gnome-Rhône 14N-20/21 radial piston engines each rated at 1,030 hp (768 kW) for take-off. The revised prototype made its new maiden flight in October 1938 and revealed much improved reliability. The original order for 20 aircraft had meanwhile been doubled to 40, and was now revised to cover the LeO 451B.4 as the initial production model, of which a further 100 examples were soon ordered.

ABOVE: The Vickers Wellington was an effective medium bomber up to 1942, but was then used as a maritime reconnaissance bomber right up to the end of World War II.

LEO 451 AT WAR

The first of these aircraft flew in March 1939, and the French air force was soon operating an experimental flight of several LeO 451 bombers. Between the beginning of 1939 and the outbreak of World War II in September 1939, the French Government placed contracts for a further 602 LeO 451 bombers. Soon after the outbreak of war the French Government placed additional orders for a total of 1255 aircraft including the basic LeO 451 with a powerplant of two Gnome-Rhône 14N-48/49 radial engines each rated at 1140 hp (850 kW) for take-off and 1035 hp (772 kW) at 15750 ft (400 m) and driving a three-blade Ratier metal propeller of the constant-speed type, the LeO 454 with a powerplant of two SIGMA (Bristol) Hercules II radial piston engines, the LeO 455 with a powerplant of two Gnome-Rhône 14R-0/1 radial piston engines each rated at 1375 hp (1025 kW) at 8530 ft (2600 m) and 1230 hp (917 kW) at 16405 ft (5000 m), the LeO 456 version of the LeO 451 for the French naval air arm with different equipment and 0.295 in (7.5 mm) Darne rather than MAC 1934 machine guns, and the LeO 458 with a powerplant of two Wright GR-2600-A5B Cyclone 14 radial piston engines each rated at 1600 hp (1193 kW) for take-off and 1400 hp (1044 kW) at 10000 ft (3050 m). Early in 1940, additional orders were placed for a further 528 aircraft of the LeO 451, LeO 451M (previously LeO 456) and LeO 458.

In the event only 452 of these aircraft, all but one of them standard LeO 451 bombers, had been completed by the time of France's defeat by Germany in June 1940, and many of these had been destroyed on the ground by German air attack before they could be delivered to the French air force. Germany agreed that the Vichy regime ruling the unoccupied part of France could order an additional 225 aircraft of the basic LeO 451 type for its air force, and the first of these machines made its maiden flight in April 1942. All in-service aircraft were gradually upgraded with an improved SAMM AB-74 dorsal mounting that added two 0.295 in (7.5 mm) MAC 1934 machine guns with 750 rounds per gun to the 20 mm (0.787 in) cannon. Some 130 aircraft from this order had been delivered before the Germans overran Vichy France during November 1942 in the aftermath of the Allied landings in French Northwest Africa, and in the process seized a large number of LeO 451 bombers of which they pressed about 50 into their own service as LeO 451T transports; others were transferred to the Italian air force. Many of the Vichy French aircraft were stationed overseas, however, and suffered heavy losses on the ground to Allied air attacks. The survivors were allocated to the Free French forces for use as bombers and, from 1944, as high-speed communications aircraft and, in the case of 12 aircraft, LeO 451E.2 glider tugs.

THE MITSUBISHI KI-21

The best bomber available to the Japanese in significant numbers in the course of the Pacific War of World War II, the Mitsubishi Ki-21 was yet another example of the fallacy of Japan's insistence on high speed and long range achieved only by sacrificing protection, defensive firepower and offensive warload. The type resulted from a February 1936 requirement for a modern bomber to replace both the Mitsubishi Ki-20 (Army Type 92 Heavy Bomber) and the Mitsubishi Ki-1 (Army Type 93 Heavy Bomber). The first of eight prototype and service trials aircraft was completed in a remarkably short time and made its maiden flight in December 1936 with a powerplant of two Mitsubishi Ha-6 radial piston engines each rated at 825 hp (615 kW) and driving a three-blade metal propeller of the variable-pitch type. The type was ordered into production from the summer of 1938 with the short and full designations Ki-21-Ia and Army Type 97 Heavy Bomber Model 1A respectively with a powerplant of two Nakajima Ha-5 Kai (Army Type 97) radial piston engines each rated at 950 hp (708 kW) for take-off and 1080 hp (805 kW) at 13125 ft (4000 m) with fuel supplied from an internal capacity of 579.6 Imp gal (2635 litres). The armament comprised just three 0.303 in (7.7 mm) Type 89 machine guns in single-gun nose, dorsal and ventral positions, and a bomb load of up to 2205 lb (1000 kg) of bombs that was generally limited to 1653 lb (750 kg) on all but the shortest-range missions.

The Ki-21-Ia was dimensionally identical to the later Ki-21-IIb variant. Production totalled 143 aircraft between March 1938 and 1939, before production switched to 120 examples of the Ki-21-Ib (Army Type 97 Heavy Bomber Model 1B)

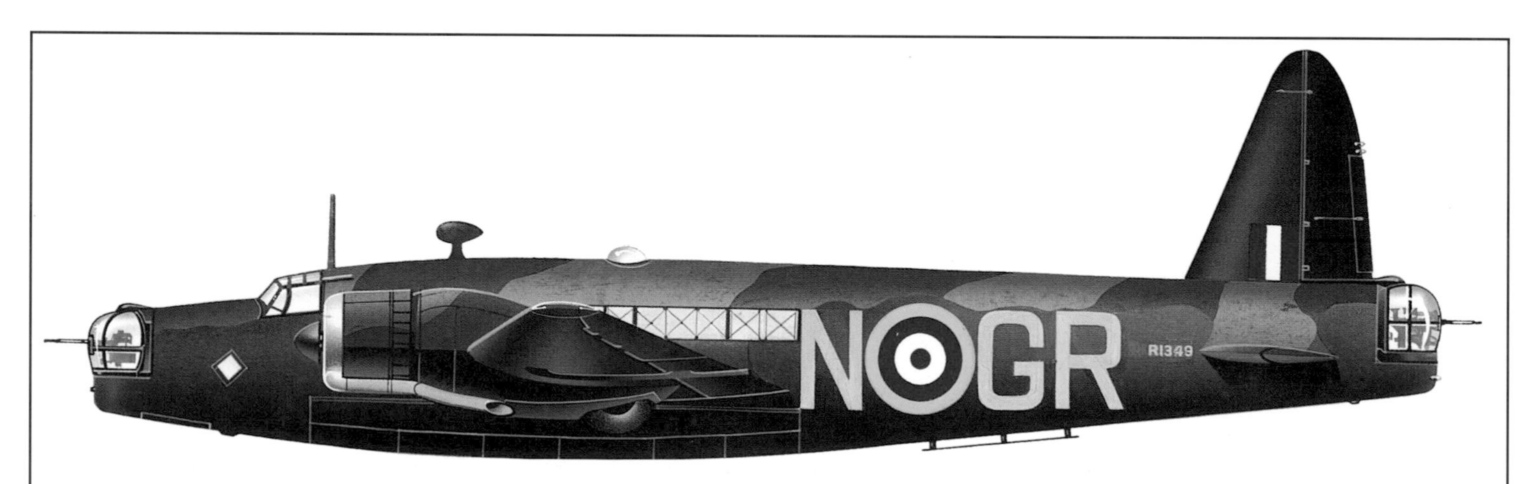

Vickers Wellington Mk IC

Type: six-seat medium bomber
Country of origin: UK
Powerplant: two 1000-hp (746-kW) Bristol Pegasus XVIII piston engines
Performance: max level speed 235 mph (378 km/h); service ceiling 18,000 ft (5485 m); maximum range 2550 miles (4104 km)
Weights: empty 18,556 lb (8417 kg); max take-off 28,500 lb (12,928 kg)
Dimensions: wing span 86 ft 2 in (26.26 m); length 64 ft 7 in (19.68 m); height 17 ft 5 in (5.31 m)
Armament: four 0.303 in (7.7 mm) Browning, one 0.303 in (7.7 mm) Vickers 'K' machine guns, plus up to 4500 lb (2041 kg) of ordnance

CANT Z.1007bis Alcione

Type: five-seat medium bomber
Country of origin: Italy
Powerplant: three 1000-hp (746-kW) Piaggio P.XI R2C.40 piston engines
Performance: maximum level speed 290 mph (466 km/h); service ceiling 26,900 ft (8200 m); typical range 1087 miles (1750 km)
Weights: empty 20715 lb (9396 kg); max take-off 30,029 lb (13,621 kg)
Dimensions: wing span 81 ft 4.33 in (24.80 m); length 60 ft 2.5 in (18.35 m); height 17 ft 1.5 in (5.22 m)
Armament: one 0.5 in (12.7 mm) Scotti four Breda-SAFAT machine guns, plus up to 2646 lb (1200 kg) of ordnance

that were delivered up to 1940 with an enlarged weapons bay and the defensive armament increased to five guns by the addition of one 0.303 in (7.7 mm) Type 89 machine gun in a tail position and one 0.303 in (7.7 mm) Type 89 machine gun in either of two beam positions.

The Ki-21-Ic (Army Type 97 Heavy Bomber Model 1C), of which 160 examples were delivered in 1940, differed from the Ki-21-Ib in its increased fuel capacity and the addition of two lateral-firing machine guns. Between August 1938 and February 1941, Nakajima delivered a total of 351 Ki-21-Ia, Ki-21-Ib and Ki-21-Ic bombers to supplement the parent company's delivery of 423 aircraft for a Ki-21-I total of 774 machines. The Ki-21-II variant introduced a more potent powerplant, and production amounted to 1278 Mitsubishi-built aircraft between December 1940 and September 1944. The first 590 machines were delivered in Ki-21-IIa (Army Type 97 Heavy Bomber Model 2A) form with the same armament as the preceding Model 1C, while the last 668 aircraft were completed to the improved Ki-21-IIb (Army Type 97 Heavy Bomber Model 2B) standard with a number of refinements including a dorsal turret carrying one 0.5 in (12.7 mm) Type 1 trainable machine gun, and increased internal fuel capacity. The Ki-21 was known to the Allies in World War II by the reporting name 'Sally' except in its Ki-21-IIb form that had the name 'Gwen'.

NEW AMIOT DESIGN

Having produced the extraordinarily ungraceful Amiot 143 during the late 1920s, in the early 1930s the Amiot design team then acquired an equally extraordinary flair for graceful design and evolved the beautiful Amiot 341 long-range mailplane as an all-metal type with a circular-section fuselage into which the shoulder-set cantilever wing was carefully faired for minimum drag. It was clear from the start that the Amiot 341 was also under development for a more martial task than mail delivery, however, for the prototype was fitted with hydraulically operated weapons bay doors. The Amiot 341 was first revealed at the 1936 Paris Salon de l'Aéronautique, and in December 1937 the Amiot 340.01 bomber prototype made its maiden flight with a powerplant of two Gnome-Rhône 14N-0/1 radial piston engines each rated at 920 hp (686 kW) at 12140 ft (3700 m) and installed under close-fitting cowlings of the NACA type to reduce drag. The aeroplane had a heavily framed bombardier nose, a raised cockpit under a heavily framed canopy that provided the pilot with good fields of vision, a plain tail unit with a single vertical surface, and tailwheel landing gear that included single-wheel main units that retracted rearward and upward into the two wing-mounted engine nacelles. Initial trials were highly encouraging, but the French air ministry decided that the type should be revised with four rather than three-seat accommodation and a number of other changes designed to enhance its operational utility. As a first step, the aeroplane was re-engined with a pair of Gnome-Rhône 14N-20/21 radial engines each rated at 1020 hp (761 kW), and the accommodation was revised to allow the carriage of a fourth crew member operating a 0.295 in (7.5 mm) MAC 1934 trainable rearward-firing machine gun installed in a ventral hatch position immediately behind the weapons bay. Further revision with a dihedralled tailplane carrying ovoid endplate vertical surfaces turned the prototype into the Amiot 351.01, and in this modified form the aeroplane first flew in January 1939.

The Amiot design team was working on the basic structure to create a single type that could be built with any of several different powerplants; such as the Amiot 350 with two Hispano-Suiza 12Y-28/29 Vee piston engines, the Amiot 351 with two Gnome-Rhône 14N-38/39 radial engines, the Amiot 352 with two Hispano-Suiza 12Y-50/51 Vee engines, the Amiot 353 with two Rolls-Royce Merlin III Vee engines, the Amiot 354 with two Gnome-Rhône 14N-48/49 radial piston engine or the Amiot 356 with two Merlin X engines.

The French air force decided not to procure the Amiot 350, so the first production variant was the Amiot 351B.4, and the first example of this was completed in the summer of 1939 for service trials that began in November of the same year, some two months after the beginning of World War II. This machine was joined a few days later by the first example of the Amiot 354B.4 , which was identical to the Amiot 351B.4 in all details save its powerplant and tail unit, itself an interchangeable assembly. The first production orders for the Amiot 350 series had been placed in 1938 and called for 30, 60 and 40 examples of the Amiot 351, Amiot 353 and Amiot 354 respectively, and during 1939 additional contracts had been signed for 30, 100 and 35 examples of the Amiot 351, Amiot 353 and Amiot 356 respectively. Almost immediately after the start of World War II in September 1939, the French air ministry had increased these orders dramatically, with further contracts for 30, 560 and five Amiot 351, Amiot 352 and Amiot 356 aircraft respectively, thereby increasing its Amiot 350 series total to 890 aircraft.

As the production programme began to develop momentum, the French air force decided not to have a certain number of the aircraft completed in four-seat reconnaissance form, as originally intended, but instead to concentrate exclusively on the bomber variant. However, by the beginning of April 1940, the air force had received only 21 aircraft out of the 285 that had been scheduled for delivery. By the start of the following month deliveries amounted to 37 aircraft, and by the end of the same month the French air force had received a total of 57 aircraft (17 Amiot 351 and 40 Amiot 354 bombers). It was too late for France,

however, for the German invasion had started in May and France was to succumb before the end of June 1940.

THE DORNIER DO 215

In 1937 the German air ministry issued a requirement for a long-range warplane of considerably versatility but optimised for the heavy bombing role and capable of undertaking both level and diving attacks. Dornier responded with a design that was, in basic conceptual terms a scaled-up version of the successful Do 17 bomber in its full-development form as the Do 215, with a deepened forward fuselage section accommodating all four members of the crew in the fashion that was becoming standard for German bombers. On one side of the coin this eased the problems of crew members trying to change places, simplified communication between the crew members and promoted morale. However, on the other side of the coin, this practice greatly increased the chances of the whole crew being killed or wounded in a single burst of fire hitting the cockpit area. Impressed with the basic design presented by Dornier in the summer of 1937, the German air ministry allocated the designation Do 217 and ordered the completion of the detailed design and the construction of prototypes.

The Do 217 V1 first prototype made its maiden flight in August 1938 with a powerplant of two Daimler-Benz DB 601A inverted-Vee piston engines each rated at 1075 hp (801.5 kW). Another seven prototypes followed before there appeared two batches of pre-production aircraft, of which the first comprised eight Do 217A-0 long-range reconnaissance machines. These aircraft were delivered in the spring of 1940 to the Aufklärungsgruppe (reconnaissance wing) of the Luftwaffe high command and used in the winter of 1940-41 for clandestine reconnaissance of the western USSR in preparation for the German invasion of that country in June 1941. Preceded by a Do 217C V1 prototype with a powerplant of two Jumo 211A engines, the four Do 217C-0 pre-production bombers had a powerplant of two DB 601A engines and introduced much improved armament. The offensive load was 6614 lb (3000 kg).

By the spring of 1940 the Do 217 programme was concentrated on the much improved Do 217E, and no further production of the Do 217C series was contemplated. The five Do 217C aircraft (one prototype and four pre-production aircraft) were thereafter used as equipment and engine test beds. Resulting from the decision to adopt the considerably uprated powerplant of two BMW 801MA radial engines, each rated at 1580 hp (1178 kW) and driving a three-blade Schwarz wooden propeller of the variable-pitch type, the Do 217 V9 prototype made its maiden flight in January 1940 and introduced a considerably revised fuselage that had been made considerably deeper along its full length. The central and rear sections were divided into lower and upper sections, the former now accommodating a longer weapons bay that extended to a point not far short of the retractable tailwheel and was covered by three-section doors, and the latter with the additional bracing required to support the weapons bay and its load, as well as an additional fuel tank and stowage for a dinghy. The weapons bay proper was 14 ft 10 in (4.52 m) long and had a rearward extension, 5 ft 8 in (1.73 m) long, to allow the carriage of a torpedo. The Do 217E was placed in production during the early months of 1940. The designations Do 217F and Do 217G were reserved for models that did not proceed past the project stage, and the Do 217H designation was applied to a single Do 217E-1 converted with a powerplant of two DB 601 inverted-Vee piston engines fitted with turbochargers for high-altitude trials.

The next variant to enter production was therefore the Do 217K-1 , which started its flight trials in March 1942. The primary changes in this model were a completely revised forward fuselage that eliminated the pilot's stepped windscreen to allow the incorporation of a rounded and more extensively glazed forward fuselage, a change in the powerplant from two BMW 801C radial piston engines to BMW 801D engines each rated at 1700 hp (1268 kW) for take-off and 1440 hp (1074 kW) at 18,700 ft (5700 m), and a revised defensive gun armament. This last comprised one 0.51 in (13 mm) MG 131 trainable rearward-firing machine gun in the electrically operated dorsal turret, one 0.51 in (13 mm) MG 131 trainable rearward-firing machine gun in the ventral step position, one 0.312 in (7.92 mm) MG 81z trainable forward-firing machine gun (paired MG 81 weapons) in the nose position, and two or later four 0.312 in (7.92 mm) MG 81 trainable lateral-firing machine guns in the cockpit side windows. The type was evaluated in the form of the Do 217K V1, Do 217K V2 and Do 217K V3 prototypes, of which the first was tested with a single

LEFT: The Ju 88 was an amazingly adaptable and 'developable' warplane that in its primary bomber form was adapted for the carriage of ever increasing bomb loads.

vertical tail surface and the third was later used as the launch aeroplane for the DFS 228 experimental high-altitude reconnaissance glider. The Do 217K-1 entered production in the early summer of 1942, and entered service in the autumn of the same year with Kampfgeschwader (Bomber Group) 2 in the night bomber role. The Do 217K-1 was the first variant of the Do 217 series to enter production with the R25 tail fitting for a brake parachute, and others of these Rüstsätze (field conversion kits) could be applied to this and later variants adopting such a kit were indicated by adding the relevant designator as a suffix to the primary designation.

THE FRITZ-X GUIDED BOMB

Entering service in December 1942, the Do 217K-2 was a development of the Do 217K-1 for the use of the FX-1400 Fritz-X guided bomb, a stand-off weapon designed to provide a heavyweight capability against capital ships and other major vessels. This variant was fitted with the FuG 203a Kehl I guidance transmitter system (associated with the FuG 230a Strassburg receiver in the weapon), carried two weapon adapters under its inner wing panels, introduced extended outer wing panels that increased span to 81 ft 4.33 in (24.80 m) with an area of 721.218 sq ft (67.00 m2), was fitted as standard with the R17 forward weapons bay kit for 255.2 Imp gal (1160 litres) of auxiliary fuel, and carried two R19 kits in the tailcone for four 0.312 in (7.92 mm) MG 81 machine guns in two MG 81z pairs that could be supplemented by another two pairs of MG 81z machine guns in the rear of each engine nacelle for a fixed rearward-firing battery of six machine guns controlled by the pilot via a periscopic sight. The Do 217K-2 first used the Fritz-X operationally in August 1943 over the Mediterranean, sinking the Italian battleship *Roma* as she was steaming to Malta after the Italian armistice with the Allies, and was later supplemented by the Do 217K-3 that differed only in having the FuG-203c/d Kehl IV guidance transmitter allowing it to control either the Fritz-X guided bomb or Henschel Hs 293A anti-ship missile.

In the spring of 1943 Dornier flew the Do 217L V1 and Do 217 V2 prototypes with a rearranged cockpit and defensive armament scheme, but the Do 217L did not enter production, so the next (and indeed final) development of the Do 217 in its pure bomber form was the Do 217M that was built in parallel with the Do 217K. The variant resulted from fears that construction of the BMW 801 radial engine would fail to match demand, and Dornier therefore evolved the Do 217M as a derivative of the Do 217K with a powerplant of two Daimler-Benz DB 603A inverted-Vee piston engines, each rated at 1750 hp (1305 kW), for performance and capabilities basically similar to those of the Do 217K-1. The sole model to enter operational service was the Do 217M-1, for developed versions were postponed and later cancelled so that Do 217 production could be concentrated on the Do 217N night-fighter derivative.

The final development of the Do 217 series in its bomber form was the Do 217P, which was a high-altitude reconnaissance bomber that resulted from a Dornier programme launched in 1941. The Do 217P was basically the Do 217E-2 revised with a four-man pressurised cockpit and the HZ-Anlage powerplant. This latter comprised two DB 603B inverted-Vee piston engines installed in the wing-mounted nacelles and supercharged by a DB 605T in a semi-exposed installation under the rear fuselage and driving a two-stage compressor. The whole system offered 3500 hp (2610 kW) for take-off and 2880 hp (2147 kW) at 45110 ft (13750 m). Production of the Do 217 bomber was discontinued in June 1944 after the delivery of 1541 aircraft.

THE HALIFAX

Although overshadowed by the superb Avro Lancaster which it partnered throughout much of World War II in Royal Air Force Bomber Command, the Handley Page H.P.57 Halifax was still a magnificent warplane that deserves greater attention than it has generally received. The early Halifax bombers were not quite as 'right' as the early Lancasters, and it took considerable effort and time to eliminate all its initial problems. The Halifax then matured as an exceptional bomber that in its late-war variants was faster than the Lancaster and could carry a roughly equivalent weapon load, even though it was not as fuel economical and lacked the Lancaster's rate of climb and agility. The

Junkers Ju 88A-4

Type: four-seat medium bomber
Country of origin: Germany
Powerplant: two 1340-hp (999-kW) Junkers Jumo 211J-1/2 inverted-Vee piston engines
Performance: maximum level speed 292 mph (470 km/h) at 17,390 ft (5300 m); service ceiling 26,900 ft (8200 m); maximum range 1696 miles (2730 km)
Weights; empty 21,737 lb (9860 kg); max take-off 30,865 lb (14,000 kg)
Dimensions: wing span 65 ft 7.5 in (20.00 m); length 47 ft 2.75 in (14.40 m); height 15 ft 11 in (4.85 m)
Armament: between five and nine 0.312 in (7.92 mm) MG 81 and 0.51 in (13 mm) MG 131 machine guns, up to 5511 lb (2500 kg) of stores

origins of the Halifax can be traced to the Air Ministry's B.1/35 requirement for a twin-engined bomber to succeed the Vickers Wellington. The Handley Page design team planned the H.P.55 as a mid-wing type with a powerplant of two Bristol Hercules radial or Rolls-Royce Merlin inverted-Vee piston engines, and the Air Ministry ordered a single prototype in October 1935. Then came the P.13/36 requirement for a somewhat faster medium bomber, and the company decided to recast the H.P.55 as the H.P.56 with the wing reduced in span from 95 ft 0 in (28.96 m) to 90 ft 0 in (27.43 m) and carrying the twin-engined powerplant. The company suggested to the Air Ministry that the development of the H.P.56 should be undertaken in two stages, the first with a powerplant of two Hercules radial engines and the second with the considerably more potent arrangement of two Rolls-Royce Vulture X-type piston engines. Given the pace and scope of the German rearmament programme, however, the Air Ministry wanted to proceed as rapidly as possible and in April 1937 placed a contract for two H.P.56 prototypes, each with a powerplant of two Vulture engines. In theory this H.P.56 package offered the promise of an excellent warplane, but in practice Handley Page became increasingly concerned about the Vulture engine, which was proving very troublesome in development. The company therefore approached the Air Ministry with the suggestion that the H.P.56 be revised as the H.P.57 with a longer-span wing carrying a powerplant of four Merlin engines. The Air Ministry gave its approval for the change in September 1937 and the H.P.57 began to take shape with a wing enlarged in span to 98 ft 10 in (20.12 m) and carrying outer panels that still carried large Handley Page automatic leading-edge slats but were tapered on both the leading and trailing edges rather than on just the leading edge, as had been the case with the H.P.56.

Work on the completion of the first type was pushed ahead as rapidly as possible, and this machine made its maiden flight on 25 October 1939 (less than two months after the outbreak of World War II) with a powerplant of four Merlin IX engines each driving a three-blade propeller of the constant-speed type, but no armament. The second prototype followed on 17 August 1940, with the same powerplant driving different Rotol propellers with densified wood blades, and this machine also had full armament but no leading-edge slats. By this time production was already under way, the Air Ministry having ordered the H.P.57 into production late in 1938 and allocated the name Halifax early in the following year. Production on a very large scale was envisaged, with initial aircraft coming from the English Electric line that was currently delivering the Handley Page Hampden medium bomber, and then being supplemented by deliveries from an industrial grouping that eventually included the Rootes Group, the Fairey Aviation Co Ltd and

ABOVE: After World War II surviving German aircraft like these Ju 88s were disarmed and disabled, to await scrapping at bases such as this at Flensburg in northern Germany.

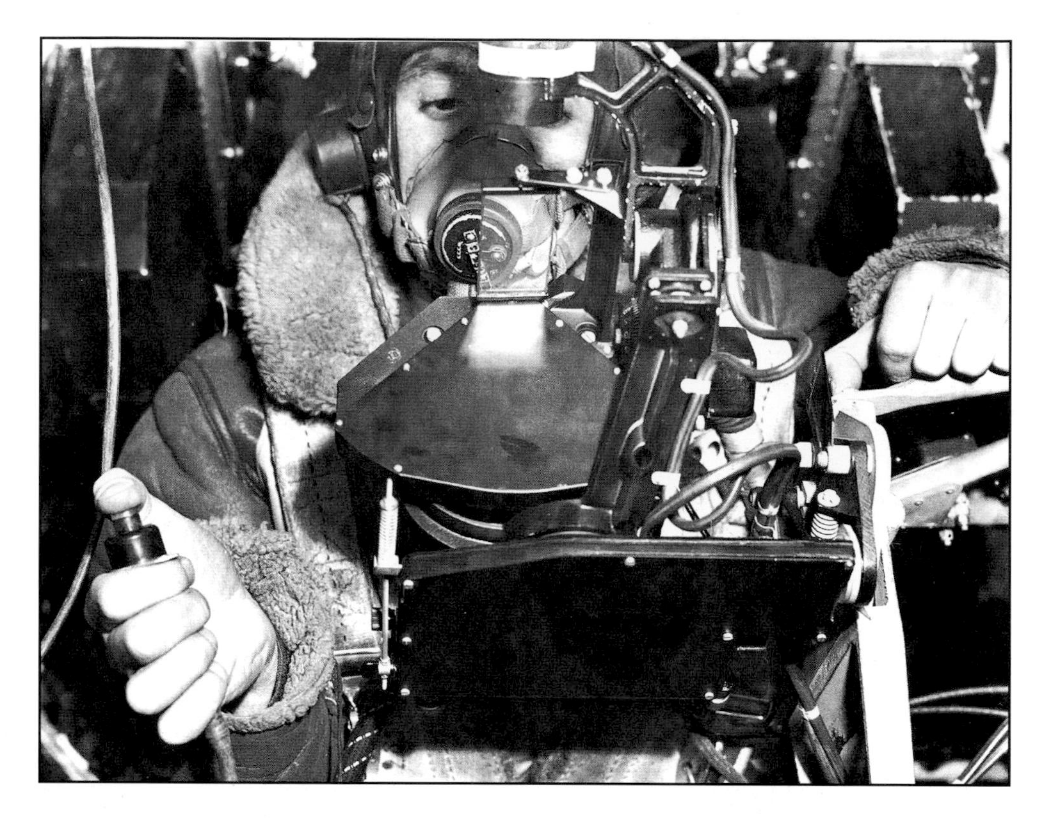

■ **ABOVE: As World War II continued, bombers were fitted with ever more sophisticated equipment including, most importantly, advanced bomb sights, like this British example.**

the London Aircraft Production Group. The Halifax Mk I entered service in November 1940 as the industrial machine began to gather production pace, and the first of an eventual 36 RAF Bomber Command squadrons to receive the type was No 35 Squadron, which flew its first mission in March 1941.

Deliveries of the Halifax Mk I totalled 84 aircraft in three subvariants: the Halifax Mk I Series 1 had a powerplant of four Merlin X engines and was stressed for a maximum take-off weight of 58,000 lb (26,309 kg), the Halifax Mk I Series 2 had a powerplant of four Merlin X engines and was stressed for a maximum take-off weight of 60,000 lb (27,216 kg), and the Halifax Mk I Series 3 had a powerplant of four Merlin X or Merlin XX engines and had increased fuel capacity.

THE HALIFAX B.MK II

Built to the extent of 1977 aircraft and receiving the revised designation Halifax B.Mk II in 1942, the Halifax Mk II was the first large-scale production model and was, in essence, a development of the Halifax Mk I Series 3 with a powerplant of four Merlin XX or Merlin 22 engines each rated at 1390 hp (1036 kW) and fitted with a much improved supercharger. The initial production model was the Halifax B.Mk II Series 1 that had a powerplant of four Merlin XXS engines and also introduced a power-operated Boulton Paul dorsal turret armed with two 0.303 in (7.7 mm) Browning trainable machine guns. Despite the extra power offered by the uprated powerplant, the weight and drag of the new turret seriously affected performance and it was decided that performance was of greater importance. This led to the Halifax B.Mk II Series 1 (Special) that omitted both the new dorsal turret and also the original nose turret. Most of the aircraft were also stripped of their flame-damper exhausts as crews felt that the 20 mph (32 km/h) additional cruising speed and higher ceiling were more useful than the damping of exhaust flames that were only visible within a range of a few hundreds of feet. These changes considerably improved performance, which was further boosted by the adoption of Merlin 22 engines each rated at 1390 hp (1036 kW) in the Halifax B.Mk II Series 1A that reintroduced a power-operated dorsal turret in the form of a low-drag Boulton Paul unit with four 0.303 in (7.7 mm) Browning machine guns, and a moulded Perspex nose fairing fitted with one 0.303 in (7.7 mm) Browning or Vickers 'K' forward-firing machine gun. This increased the overall length to 71 ft 7 in (21.82 m) but improved the line of the forward fuselage and thereby increased speed.

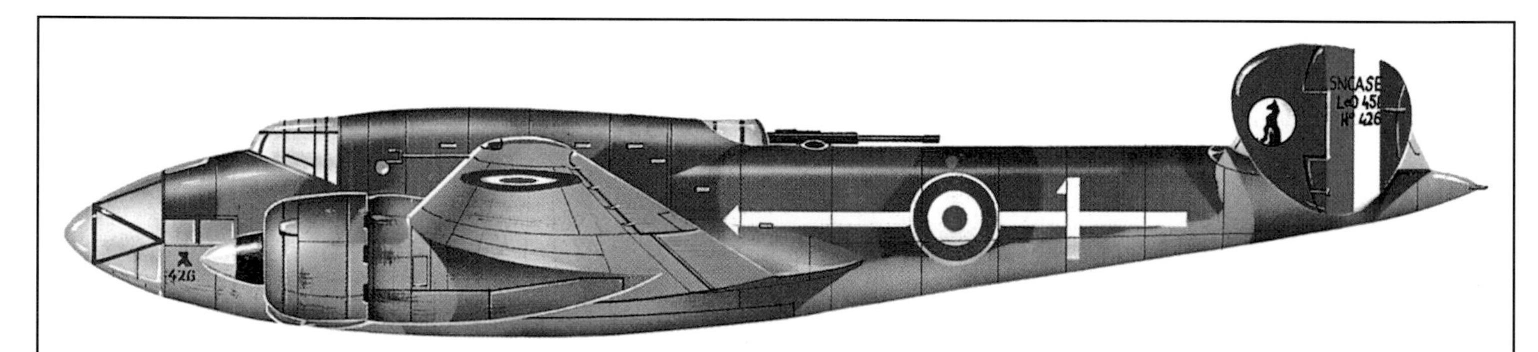

Lioré-et-Olivier LeO 451B.4

Type: four-seat medium bomber
Country of origin: France
Powerplant: two 1140-hp (850-kW) Gnome-Rhône 14N-48/49 radial piston engines
Performance: maximum level speed 307 mph (495 km/h; service ceiling 29,530 ft (9000 m); max range 1802 miles (2900 km)
Weights: empty 17,229 lb (7815 kg); normal take-off 25,133 lb (11,400 kg)
Dimensions; wing span 73 ft 10.5 in (22.52 m); length 56 ft 4 in (17.17 m); height 17 ft 2.25 in
Armament: machine guns, cannon, up to 4409 lb (2000 kg) of stores

In October 1942, however, Handley Page revised a Halifax B.Mk II 'hack' with a powerplant of four Bristol Hercules radial piston engines as the prototype of the radial-engined H.P.61 series, and this change wrought a considerable alteration in the type: performance was generally improved in every regard except range. The type's handling characteristics, which had never been more than acceptable, were also improved. The success of this re-engining led to the introduction of the Halifax B.Mk III production model, of which the first flew in July 1943 with a powerplant of four Hercules XVI engines each rated at 1615 hp (1204 kW) and driving a three blade de Havilland metal propeller of the constant-speed type and installed without a spinner but with long flame-damper exhausts. Other changes included provision for H_2S nav/attack radar and a ventral blister position carrying one 0.5 in (12. mm) Browning trainable rearward-firing machine gun. The Halifax B.Mk III was a marked improvement over the previous models, and in this form the bomber was now allowed to operate against targets that had hitherto been regarded as too difficult for it. Production of the Halifax B.Mk III totalled 2091 machines, and the rapidly accelerating availability of this model allowed the removal of all Merlin-engined models from operations over Germany.

The next variant to enter production was the Halifax B.Mk V that was a development of the Halifax B.Mk II with the original Messier landing gear units and hydraulic system replaced by Dowty units. Most of the aircraft were fitted with four-blade propellers, and production totalled 904 aircraft from Fairey and Rootes. The type was built in Halifax B.Mk V Series 1 , Halifax B.Mk V Series 1 (Special) and Halifax B.Mk V Series 1A subvariants, basically equivalent to their Halifax B.Mk II half-brothers, but significant numbers were converted to the airborne forces, maritime reconnaissance and meteorological reconnaissance roles. First flown in October 1944 and built to the extent of 557 aircraft delivered by Handley Page and English Electric, the Halifax B.Mk VI was an improved version of the Halifax B.Mk IV intended for operations against the Japanese in South-East Asia and therefore fitted with Hercules 100 radial engines each rated at 1800 hp (1342 kW), fuel-injection carburettors with filters, and a revised fuel system that was both enlarged and pressurised. A number of the aircraft were later converted to other roles. With production of the Hercules 100 radial engine lagging behind that of the Halifax B.Mk VI airframe, a final 193 aircraft were completed to the Halifax B.Mk VII standard with Hercules XVI engines, and these machines were used by French and Polish squadrons.

ABOVE: Parachute fragmentation bombs are dropped from a US 5th Air Force aircraft onto a heavily camouflaged Mitsubishi Ki-21, known as a 'Sally' by the Allies.

THE MITSUBISHI G4M

The Mitsubishi G4M originated in a 1937 requirement of the Imperial Japanese navy air force for a successor to the G3M. The task of designing the improved type was entrusted by Mitsubishi to a team under the leadership of Kiro Honjo, who quickly decided that the requirement could not be met with the Imperial Japanese navy air force's preferred power of 2000 hp (1491 kW) provided by two engines. He opted for two examples of the new Mitsubishi MK4 Kasei radial piston engine rated at 1500 hp (1118 kW). The resulting aeroplane was very clean in aerodynamic terms and the first of two prototypes made its maiden flight in October 1939 with a powerplant of two MK4A Kasei 11 radial engines each rated at 1530 hp (1141 kW). The aeroplane was ordered into production as the G4M1 for service as the Navy Type 1 Attack Bomber Model 11. Deliveries amounted to

1200 aircraft with internal provision for 1764 lb (800 kg) of bombs or one torpedo, and a defensive armament of one 0.303 in (7.7 mm) Type 92 forward-firing machine gun in the nose position, one 0.303 in (7.7 mm) Type 92 rearward-firing machine gun in the dorsal blister position, two 0.303 in (7.7 mm) Type 92 lateral-firing machine guns in two beam blister positions, and one 20 mm (0.787 in) Type 99 Model 1 rearward-firing cannon in the tail position. The early aircraft were completed to this basic standard with a powerplant of two MK4A Kasei 11 radial engines, but later Navy Type 1 Attack Bomber Model 12 aircraft switched to the uprated powerplant of two MK4E Kasei 15 radial engines each rated at 1530 hp (1141 kW) for take-off and 1280 hp (954 kW) at 19685 ft (6000 m).

There followed 1154 aircraft completed to the improved G4M2 standard, with a powerplant of two MK4P Kasei 21 radial engines each rated at 1800 hp (1342 kW), a new wing of laminar-flow section, a horizontal tail surface of greater area, rounded tips on the wing and tailplane, a revised bombardier's position for improved nocturnal capability, provision for a single 0.303 in (7.7 mm) Type 92 trainable lateral-firing machine gun firing through a small port on either side of the nose, the replacement of the dorsal blister position by a power-operated turret armed with a 20 mm (0.787 in) Type 99 Model 1 cannon, provision for a fuselage-mounted tank accommodating 349.75 Imp gal (1590 litres) of auxiliary fuel and, from the 65th aeroplane onwards, doors for the weapons bay. This improved variant entered service as the Navy Type 1 Attack Bomber Model 22. Later variants were the Navy Type 1 Attack Bomber Model 22A with the lateral-firing machine guns in the beam positions replaced by 20 mm (0.787 in) Type 99 Model 1 cannon, and the Navy Type 1 Attack Bomber Model 22B with the all four cannon altered to Type 99 Model 2 weapons.

For lack of a replacement, due late in 1943 in the form of the Mitsubishi G7M Taizan, the G4M2 had to be kept in production and this led to the G4M2a model with bulged weapons bay doors allowing a bombload of up to 2205 lb (1000 kg) and with a powerplant of two MK4T Kasei 25 radial engines each rated at 1825 hp (1361 kW) for take-off and 1540 hp (1148 kW) at 18045 ft (5500 m), and each driving a four-blade Sumitomo (VDM) metal propeller of the constant-speed type.

The G4M2a was operated by the Imperial Japanese navy air force in four variants as the Navy Type 1 Attack Bomber Model 24, with the same defensive armament as the Model 22, the Navy Type 1 Attack Bomber Model 24A and Navy Type 1 Attack Bomber Model 24B, with the same defensive armament as the Model 22A and Model 22B respectively, and the Navy Type 1 Attack Bomber Model 24C with the nose armament supplemented by one 0.51 in (13 mm) Type 2 trainable machine gun and, in late examples, air-to-surface search radar.

THE SHORT STIRLING

The first four-engined heavy bomber to enter service with Bomber Command of the Royal Air Force during World War II, the Short Stirling was also the only British four-engined bomber to enter service having been designed as such. Despite the fact that it was designed from the start as a four-engined bomber, however, the Stirling can be described as only a workmanlike rather than inspired aeroplane. This resulted not so much from any failing in the basic design, but in the Air Ministry's insistence in its B.12/36 requirement that the winning design should have a wing capable of fitting into the standard RAF hangar, which could accommodate aircraft with a span of 100 ft 0 in (30.48 m) or less, and should be capable of carrying 500 lb (227 kg) bombs. The former meant that the Stirling suffered from a high wing loading and was thus unable to climb above 12000 ft (3660 m) with a full weapons load. On the other side of the operational coin, however, the Stirling was monumentally sturdy and could return to base even after suffering very heavy damage. The B.12/36 requirement called for a four-engined strategic bomber that could be designed, developed and placed in production with the utmost speed. The Air Ministry received design submissions from Armstrong Whitworth, Short and Supermarine, and ordered prototypes of the Short and Supermarine types. Short initially proposed a design with good high-altitude performance provided by a wing spanning 112 ft 0 in

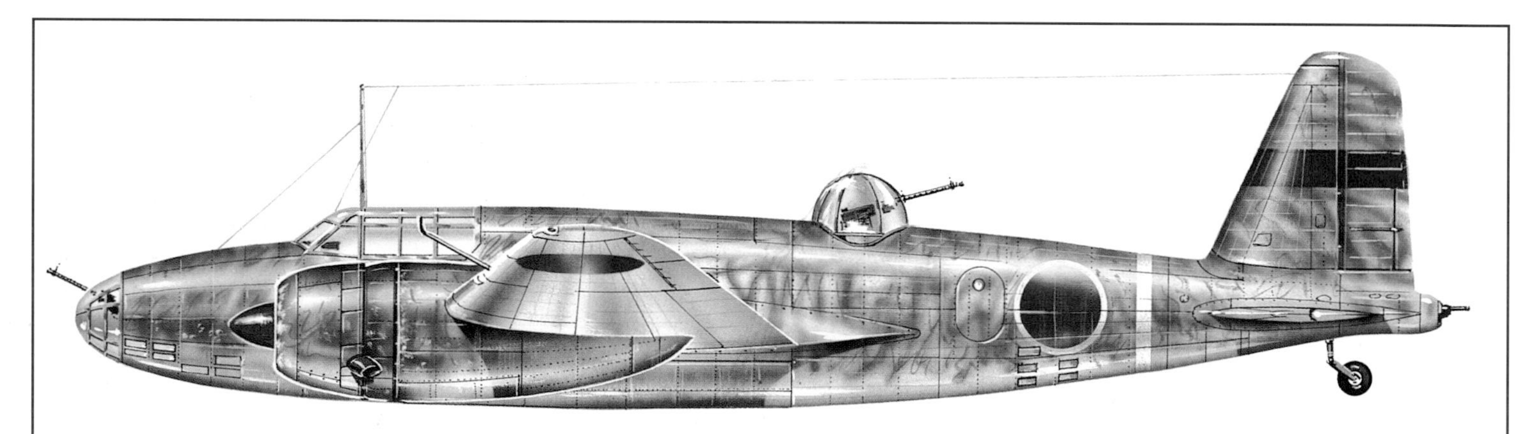

Mitsubishi Ki-21-IIb

Type: seven-seat heavy bomber
Country of origin: Japan
Powerplant: two 1500-hp (1118-kW) Mitsubishi Ha-101 (Army Type 100) radial piston engines
Performance: maximum level speed 302 mph (486 km/h) at 15,485 ft (4720 m); service ceiling 32,810 ft (10,000 m); maximum range 1678 miles (2700 km)
Weights: empty 13,382 lb (6070 kg); max take-off 23,391 lb (10,610 kg)
Dimensions: wing span 73 ft 9.75 in (22.50 m); length 52 ft 6 in (16.00 m); height 15 ft 11 in (4.85 m)
Armament: one 0.5 in (12.7 mm) Type 1 machine gun, five 0.303 in (7.7 mm) Type 89 machine guns, plus up to 2205 lb (1000 kg) of ordnance

(34.14 m) and based in structural and aerodynamic terms on that of its Sunderland maritime reconnaissance flying boat, but it was at this stage that the Air Ministry demanded the ability to fit into the standard hangar. The Short design team had therefore to revise its concept with a wing of reduced span and greater chord. The Air Ministry, faced with steadily more depressing intelligence information about the extent and speed of German rearmament in the later 1930s, agreed to this degradation of capability, ordered two prototypes of this S.29 design and revealed the fact that it would start to order production aircraft even before the prototypes had flown.

Construction of the two S.29 prototypes continued into the early part of 1939. The first of these made its maiden flight on 14 May 1939, being written off as it landed. The main landing gear units were redesigned, and the second prototype made a successful first flight on 3 December 1939. Production was already under way, and the first Stirling Mk I bomber made its initial flight in May 1940. The first production aircraft were of the Stirling Mk I Series 1 type with a powerplant of four Bristol Hercules II radial piston engines each rated at 1375 hp (1025 kW) for take-off and installed in fully monocoque nacelles; next came the Stirling Mk I Series 2 with a powerplant of four Hercules XI radial engines with Short-designed engine mountings of welded steel tube; finally there appeared the definitive Stirling Mk I Series 3 with Hercules XI radial engines in Bristol-designed nacelles. The Hercules XI radial engine was rated at 1590 hp (1185.5 kW) for take-off and 1020 hp (760.5 kW) for cruising at optimum altitude, and drove a three-blade constant-speed propeller.

Deliveries of the Stirling Mk I began in August 1940, and deliveries of this initial model totalled 756. The first service aircraft were delivered to No 7 Squadron in August 1940, and the Stirling Mk I entered operational service in February 1941. Aircraft in service at the end of 1942 received the revised designation Stirling B.Mk I . The Stirling Mk II, which was to have been built in Canada to an initial total of 140 aircraft, was in fact produced only in the form of two prototypes with a powerplant of four Wright GR-2600-A5B Cyclone 14 radial piston engines each rated at 1600 hp (1193 kW) for take-off. Built to the extent of 875 aircraft for service from 1943, the Stirling B.Mk III was a version of the Stirling Mk I Series 3 with a Frazer-Nash F.N.50 dorsal turret (as used on the Avro Lancaster and generating less drag than the F.N.7 unit), a powerplant of four Hercules XVI radial engines each rated at 1635 hp (1219 kW) for take-off, provision for greater fuel capacity, and a revised interior configuration with fewer windows in the rear fuselage. The Stirling B.Mk III soon replaced the Stirling B.Mk I in the existing four Stirling squadrons, and was also issued to nine other squadrons. The Stirling was later relegated to the airborne forces and transport roles.

Produced in a large number of variants for a host of tasks, both operational and training, the Liberator was built in greater numbers (18,431 machines in all) than any other warplane of American design during World War II and was delivered in greater quantities than any other bomber in aviation history. These would be remarkable facts in their own rights, but are made doubly so by the fact that the Liberator was a four-engined machine. The origins of the type can be traced to January 1939 when Reuben H. Fleet and Isaac M. 'Mac' Laddon, respectively chairman and chief designer of the Consolidated Aircraft Corporation, approached the US Army Air Corps with an offer to design and build a bomber superior to the Boeing B-17. The corporation felt it was able to offer a machine superior to the Boeing bomber after itself being approached by the USAAC to become a second source for B-17 production, and Consolidated engineers who had travelled from San Diego in California to the Boeing facility at Seattle in Washington returned with the suggestion that a considerably better aeroplane could be designed on the basis of the high-aspect-ratio wing evolved by Laddon, on the basis of the concept patented by David R. Davis, for the Model 28 flying boat that had entered production as the PBY for the US Navy. The USAAC was impressed with the Consolidated proposal and by the end of January 1939 had inspected a Consolidated mock-up. The service then issued a competitive requirement to Martin and Sikorsky, but this was nothing more than a formality as it gave the other two 'contenders' a mere three weeks to create their proposals. In February 1940, the Consolidated Model 32 design was approved, and in March a single XB-24 prototype was ordered for delivery by the end of the year, later orders in the same year adding seven YB-24 service test aircraft and 38 B-24A initial production bombers.

ABOVE: In the late 1930s French designers switched with apparent ease from slab-sided monstrosities to superbly elegant bombers, such as the Amiot 351.

PROTOTYPE LIBERATOR

Consolidated made rapid progress with the completion of the detail design and the construction of the prototype, which emerged for its first flight in December 1939 as a large shoulder-wing monoplane of all-metal construction with fabric-covered control surfaces. The prototype was powered by four Pratt & Whitney R-1830-33 radial piston engines each rated at 1200 hp (895 kW) and driving a three-blade Hamilton Standard Hydromatic metal propeller of the constant-speed type. Its defensive armament comprised six 0.3 in (7.62 mm) Browning machine guns in manually operated single-gun nose, dorsal, ventral, tail and two beam positions. Trials revealed that the XB-24 handled well in the air and possessed excellent range, but also that its speed fell somewhat short of the required figure. The aeroplane was therefore adapted to XB-24B standard with a powerplant of four R-1830-41 turbocharged engines, and this model was accepted by the USAAC in August 1940.

Meanwhile the Model 32 had attracted considerable export interest, initially from France where strenuous efforts were being made to bolster the country's air capabilities in the opening phases of World War II. In April 1940, the month before the German invasion of France, the French purchasing mission in the USA ordered 175 examples of the LB-30MF version, the core designation indicating that this was the 30th design in Consolidated's Land Bomber series, and the suffix standing for Mission Français (French mission). France accepted defeat in June 1940 before any of the aircraft could be delivered, and the UK took over 135 of the aircraft ordered by France, adding the name Liberator (already used by Consolidated) to the basic LB-30 designation. The changes demanded by the British were considerable and concerned mostly with improving the defensive capability of the aircraft. The changes included self-sealing fuel tanks, armour protection for the crew, and power-operated nose and tail turrets. Delivery of these aircraft was scheduled for a time after the completion of the USAAC's B-24A order, but such was the pressure being exerted on the British that they were able to negotiate an exchange of priorities, so that they received six of the seven YB-24 machines for service as LB-30A unarmed transport aircraft for use on the North Atlantic Return Ferry Service. There followed 20 examples of the LB-30B that entered service in March 1941 as Liberator Mk I aircraft with No 120 Squadron of the Royal Air Force's Coastal Command. These aircraft were fitted with early air-to-surface search radar, and their armament comprised six 0.303 in (7.7 mm) trainable machine guns and a ventral tray carrying four or six 20 mm (0.787 in) fixed forward-firing cannon to provide a significant punch in the war against the German U-boats that had previously been able to operate on the surface in the mid-Atlantic region. Thereafter the British received large numbers of later Liberator variants for the bombing, maritime patrol and transport roles.

In the USA the one XB-24 prototype and seven YB-24 service test aircraft were followed by nine B-24A and nine B-24C production aircraft, used mainly for the development of the powerplant and defensive armament, before the advent of the first large-scale production version. This was the B-24D, of which 2728 examples were delivered from the Consolidated line and a further ten from the Douglas line. The delivery of aircraft from Douglas is evidence of the importance now attached to the Liberator by the USAAF. Consolidated had built two new production facilities at Lindbergh Field in San Diego and at Fort Worth in Texas, and the efforts of these two centres was increasingly supplemented by the work of the Douglas facility at Tulsa in Oklahoma, of Ford at Willow Run in Michigan, where components were also produced for other production centres, and of North American at Dallas in Texas. Delivered from January 1942, the B-24D had a powerplant of four R-1830-43 or -65 radial engines each rated at 1200 hp (895 kW) at optimum altitude and supplied with fuel from an internal capacity increased from a standard capacity of 1968.5 Imp gal (8948.7 litres) in early aircraft with a maximum take-off weight of 55,000 lb (24,948 kg) with a defensive armament of seven machine guns to a maximum of 3009.3 Imp gal (13,680.4 litres) in later aircraft with a maximum take-off weight of 64,000 lb (29,030 kg) with a defensive armament of ten machine guns.

Of these aircraft, 272 were completed with a ventral turret (a Bendix unit in 179 aircraft and a Sperry unit in the other 93 aircraft) increasing the variant's defensive armament from seven or eight to ten 0.5 in (12.7 mm) Browning trainable machine guns; the offensive load was also increased to a maximum of 8800 lb (3992 kg) in the form of eight 1100 lb (499 kg) bombs. The other primary details of the late-production B-24D, where different from the B-24J, included a length of 66 ft 4 in (20.22 m), height of 17 ft 11 in (5.46 m), empty weight of 32,605 lb (14,790 kg), normal take-off weight of 60,000 lb (27,216 kg), maximum level speed of 303 mph (488 km/h) at 25,000 ft (7620 m), cruising speed of 200 mph (322 km/h) at optimum altitude, maximum range of 3500 miles (5633 km), typical range of 2300 miles (3701 km) with a 5000 lb (2268 kg) bomb load, climb to 20,000 ft (6095 m) in 22 minutes 0 seconds, and service ceiling of 32,000 ft (9755 m).

ABOVE: The Dornier Do 217 was an enlarged and more powerfully engined development of the Do 17Z, designed for use in the hitherto neglected heavy bomber role.

THE B24E

The B-24E was a development of the B-24E with different propeller blades, and production amounted to 801 aircraft. Delivered from September 1942, the 167 Douglas-built aircraft had a powerplant of four R-1830-43 radial engines, while the 634 Ford-built aircraft had a powerplant of four R-1830-65 radial engines. The type was delayed in production, primarily by the conflict between Ford's vehicle and aircraft interests, and was obsolescent even as it entered service. The type was therefore used mostly for training within the continental USA.

The 430 examples of the B-24G were built by North American to a standard basically similar to that of the B-24D with the R-1830-43 radial engine but with provision for a power-operated Emerson nose turret, carrying two 0.5 in (12.7 mm) Browning trainable forward-firing machine guns, in an effort to counter the type of head-on attack that German and Japanese fighters had found to be the most successful tactic against the early Liberators. Early aircraft had no ventral turret, but a Briggs-Sperry ball turret was reintroduced later in the production run at the same time as the powerplant was revised to four R-1830-65 radial engines.

Built by Consolidated, Douglas and Ford, the B-24H was introduced in June 1943 as a type basically similar to the late-production B-24G and therefore equipped with an Emerson nose turret and the retractable Sperry ventral ball turret that had been introduced on some later B-24D bombers. The first B-24H warplanes had a powerplant of four R-1830-43 radial engines that was replaced by a quartet of R-1830-65 radial engines in later machines, which also had improved beam positions with improved fairings that improved the airflow and also made life more comfortable for the two waist gunners. The total of 3100 such aircraft was delivered from Fort Worth (738 machines), Tulsa (582 machines) and Willow Run (1780 machines).

With a total of 6678 delivered from all five factories in the Liberator production group, the B-24J was the most extensively built variant of the whole series, and was in essence an improved B-24H with hydraulically operated Consolidated-designed but Motor Products-built nose and tail turrets, a Martin dorsal turret, a Briggs-Sperry ventral turret, a new C-1 autopilot, a new M-series bomb sight, and other equipment changes, including electronic turbocharger regulators. Delivered to the extent of 1667 aircraft (1250 from Willow Run and 417 from Lindbergh Field), the B-24L was a development of the B-24J with a new lightweight tail position designed by Consolidated with two manually operated 0.5 in (12.7 mm) Browning trainable rearward-firing machine guns. The last variant of the Liberator to be built in quantity (2593 aircraft in all, with 916 and 1677 respectively from Lindbergh Field and Willow Run), the B-24M was a development of the B-24L with a light Motor Products tail turret. The type was dimensionally identical with the B-24J, but differed in details such as its empty weight of 36,000 lb (16,330 kg), maximum take-off weight of 64,500 lb (29,257 kg), and maximum speed of 300 mph (483 km/h) at 30,000 ft (9145 m).

THE MOSQUITO

The de Havilland Mosquito remains one of the most beautiful and successful warplanes ever built, and is rivalled only by the equally great Junkers Ju 88 as the most versatile warplane ever placed in service. This is all the more remarkable as the type was designed without official support in a company effort to prove the basic fallacy of the official 'line' in the design of successive generations of British bombers. No matter which category of bomber was envisaged, namely a light day bomber, a medium day/night bomber or a heavy night bomber, the Air Ministry requirement was based on the premise that any successor type must inevitably carry a heavier offensive load, embark a larger

BELOW: Partnering the Avro Lancaster through most of the British night bomber offensive in World War II was the Handley Page Halifax, another four-engined type.

crew, deliver its weapons over a longer range, and be fitted with a more effective defensive armament than its predecessor. The result was an escalation of weight and thus the maintenance or improvement of performance only by the installation of ever more potent engines with considerably greater specific fuel consumption. Moreover, even before this stage was reached in service, the increasing weight, size and complexity of bombers in each class had already made serious demands during production on constructional man hours and on the strategic light alloys that had become the standard structural medium for advanced warplanes. At this stage in the mid-1930s de Havilland was renowned for its training, sporting and racing aircraft rather than warplanes, but was thus able to look at the development of modern bombers with an eye that was not prejudiced by direct involvement. Thus, when it received the P.13/36 requirement that was eventually to lead to bombers such as the Avro Manchester, Avro Lancaster and Handley Page Halifax, the company worked initially on adaptations of its existing designs, most notably the all-wood D.H.91 Albatross and all-metal D.H.95 Flamingo transports. By mid-1938, de Havilland had decided that in the short term the best solution to the official specification was a version of the Albatross with a powerplant of two Rolls-Royce Merlin inverted-Vee piston engines: in its recommendation to the Air Ministry, de Havilland strongly emphasised the current lack of metal-working capability in industries that were already hard pressed by the demands of the current rearmament programme, and forecast that there would soon be a glut of wood-working capability of the type needed for the construction of wooden aircraft. De Havilland now proposed a bomber that was not only of wooden construction but also of radically different concept. This was based on the notion that a bomber with very high speed and a considerable operating altitude would not require defensive armament as it would be all but impossible for enemy fighters or anti-aircraft artillery to intercept it. This meant that the crew could be restricted to a mere two men in an airframe small and light enough that a powerplant of two of the current generation of piston engines would guarantee the required performance. Another feature of the de Havilland proposal concerned gun armament. The company was still convinced that speed and ceiling obviated the need for defensive guns, but was equally sure that cannon armament should be installed in place of some or all of the disposable weapons load to provide part of the offensive armament in fighter-bomber and escort fighter versions. The company also opined that the D.H.98 could easily be turned into a highly effective photo-reconnaissance aeroplane.

CONVINCING THE MINISTRY

The Air Ministry found much of merit in the de Havilland design proposal, but was deeply sceptical of the proposed warplane's lack of armament. The company was thus bombarded with requests for the enlargement of the airframe to allow the accommodation of a gunner to operate either a dorsal turret or remotely controlled gun barbettes. Ultimately it was only the support of Air Chief Marshal Sir Wilfrid Freeman, the Air Member for Development, that kept the de Havilland proposal alive in its original form. The Air Ministry was not altogether convinced that the company's performance estimates were realistic, but decided that even its own downgraded version of the estimates suggested the prospect of exceptional performance. In December 1939, therefore, the Air Ministry decided to order a single D.H.98 prototype: no specific role was fixed for the prototype, but the contract included the B.1/40 specification so bombing was clearly considered the primary role. As the contract was being prepared for the prototype D.H.98, to which the official name Mosquito was later allocated by the Air Ministry at de Havilland's suggestion, the Air Ministry appreciated the lack of foresight implicit in an order for just one prototype, and finally contracted for 50 aircraft to be completed in reconnaissance-bomber form. De Havilland received the order in March 1940. Even as work on the prototype was beginning, the future of the Mosquito seemed once again to be in jeopardy as Germany invaded the Netherlands, Belgium and France, overrunning the former two during May and defeating the latter by the end of June. This left the UK as Germany's sole opponent in the war and Lord Beaverbrook, the Minister of Aircraft Production, decided that the country's aircraft production resources should be concentrated on accelerated deliveries of the five types of warplane that could best serve the Royal Air Force's immediate needs, at a time when German invasion was thought imminent.

Handley Page Halifax B.Mk III

Type: seven-seat heavy bomber
Country of origin: UK
Powerplant: four 1615-hp (1204-kW) Bristol Hercules VI or XVI radial piston engines
Performance: maximum level speed 282 mph (454 km/h) at 13,500 ft (4115 m; service ceiling 24,000 ft (7315 m); typical range 1985 miles (3194 km)
Weights: empty 42,500 lb (19,278 kg); max take-off 65,000 lb (29,484 kg)
Dimensions: wing span 98 ft 8 in (30.07 m), later 103 ft 8 in (31.59 m); length 71 ft 4 in (21.74 m); height 20 ft 1 in (6.12 m
Armament: nine 0.303 in (7.7 mm) Vickers 'K' machine guns, plus up to 14,500 lb (6577 kg) of ordnance

Mitsubishi G4M1 Model 11

Type: seven-seat medium bomber
Country of origin: Japan
Powerplant: two 530-hp (1141-kW) Mitsubishi MK4A Kasei 11 radial piston engines
Performance; maximum level speed 266 mph (428 km/h); max range 3749 miles (6033 km)
Weights: empty 14,991 lb (6800 kg); max take-off 20,944 lb (9500 kg)
Dimensions: wing span 82 ft 0.25 in (25.00 m); length 65 ft 7.25 in (20.00 m); height 19 ft 8.25 in (6.00 m)
Armament: one 20 mm Type 99 Model 1 cannon, two 0.303 in (7.7 mm) Type 92 machine guns, plus up to 1764 lb (800 kg) of stores

DUNKIRK

Thus the prototype and 49 production aircraft were cancelled and then reinstated on three separate occasions in the dark weeks after the Dunkirk evacuation of May and June 1940. With the programme finally confirmed, the gates began to open on a more ambitious career for the Mosquito, and in July 1940 de Havilland was ordered to complete one of the 50 aircraft as a fighter prototype. The final amendment of the contract settled the final proportions of the initial 50 aircraft as three prototypes (one each in the bomber, fighter and photo-reconnaissance configurations) and 47 pre-production aircraft (10, 28 and 9 aircraft in the bomber, fighter and photo-reconnaissance configurations respectively). This started a production effort that finally witnessed the construction of 7757 aircraft (6411 in the UK by an eventual three de Havilland factories as well as the Standard Motor Co Ltd, Percival Aircraft Ltd. and Airspeed Ltd, 212 in Australia and 1034 in Canada). The first prototype was completed late in 1940 and made its first flight on 25 November of that year, less than 12 months after the start of design work. This was a prodigious achievement in itself, but all the more remarkable was the excellent performance and handling displayed by the prototype in its early trials, which astounded all who saw the new type.

The first bomber prototype was the eighth Mosquito to be built, and this was completed for a first flight on 8 September 1941. Only three weeks later it was followed to the Aircraft & Armament Experimental Establishment at Boscombe Down by the first of nine Mosquito B.Mk IV Series 1 bombers off the production line. These aircraft had the original form of engine nacelle that ended just forward of the trailing edge, but the following 291 aircraft were completed to the Mosquito B.Mk IV Series 2 standard with lengthened nacelles and provision for two flush-fitting underwing drop tanks. There should have been 300 of the type, but nine were completed to different standards and, in the event, another 27 were later converted into photo-reconnaissance aircraft. As these aircraft were beginning to enter service with No 105 Squadron, initially in the training role, the prototype was being modified to an improved standard as prototype for the proposed Mosquito B.Mk V that was built only in prototype form with underwing hardpoints for the carriage of two 500 lb (227 kg) bombs. The debut of the Mosquito Mk IV was seriously delayed by the slow delivery of Mosquito B.Mk IV Series 2 aircraft, which were completed only after urgent demands for fighters and photo-reconnaissance aircraft had been satisfied.

Thus the Mosquito B.Mk IV Series 1 had entered service with No 105 Squadron in November 1941 as noted above, but deliveries of the Mosquito B.Mk IV Series 2 began only in April of the following year. Issue to operational units followed in May of the same year, and on the last day of that month four Mosquito B.Mk IV Series 1 bombers were used for the Mosquito bomber's first operational sorties, namely nuisance raids in the aftermath of the first 1000-bomber raid, Operation 'Millennium', which had been flown against Köln on the previous night. There followed a number of other small-scale operations, but the Mosquito B.Mk IV Series 2 was not notably successful at this early stage of its career. This was partially the result of continued teething problems but more significantly of the fact that the right tactics had yet to be evolved for the type. Thus these early sorties experimented with high-level attack, low-level attack and even shallow dive-bombing attack. Success started to come as the Mosquito came to be used for pinpoint low-level attacks, usually at dawn or dusk, on important targets, and then for pathfinder missions. Here an important aid was the 'Oboe' system, which allowed the aeroplane to follow signals from two transmitting stations in the UK to reach its designated bombing position without any reference to the ground being overflown. Another later addition in a number of Mosquito B.Mk IV bombers was H_2S bombing radar, which presented the navigator/bombardier with an image of the ground being overflown and thus greatly improved bombing accuracy. This system became operational in January 1944. The operational efficiency of the Mosquito was considerably enhanced by such navigation and bombing aids, and so too was the destructive effect of the bombers' raids when provision was made for the carriage of a 4000 lb (1814 kg) thin-walled bomb, a high-capacity weapon often called a 'cookie'. De Havilland had become convinced as early as April 1943 that such a weapon could be carried by the Mosquito, and the resulting programme saw the adoption of a slightly deeper lower line for the fuselage, revised and slightly bulged bomb bay doors, a small fairing immediately to the rear of the bomb bay, and a single-point suspension system in the bomb bay. The first such aeroplane flew in July 1943, and the Mosquito B.Mk IV (Special) was cleared for operations in January 1944. Some 20 conversions to this standard were effected.

ABOVE: The Mitsubishi G4M was created for long missions over the Pacific, but was so lightly built and so lacking in defensive features that it was easy prey for US fighters.

CANADIAN MOSQUITO

Plans for Canadian production of the Mosquito were considered as early as 1940, the obvious manufacturer being de Havilland Aircraft of Canada Ltd, using a version of the Merlin engine made in the USA as the Packard V-1650. In July 1941 the Air Ministry placed an order for 400 Canadian-built Mosquitoes. Production started with 25 examples of the Mosquito B.Mk VII, which was in effect the Mosquito B.Mk IV Series 2. The aircraft were built using a large measure of British-supplied components, and the first of these aircraft made its maiden flight in September 1942, with a powerplant of two Packard Merlin 31 engines, each rated at 1460 hp (1089 kW). These aircraft were retained in North America for development work and the training of Mosquito crews, and therefore saw no operational service.

As the Mosquito B.Mk IV was launching the type's operational career, development of the Mosquito bomber was continuing. The first step in this direction had been the introduction of two underwing hardpoints each able to carry one 500 lb (227 kg) bomb, as noted above, and this paved the way for the development of a universal wing with two hardpoints each able to carry one 500 lb (227 kg) bomb or one 100 Imp gal (454.6 litre) drop tank. However, maintenance of performance now demanded the adoption of a Merlin variant with a two-stage supercharger to boost speed and, just as importantly, raise operational altitude to the points at which interception by German fighters would become virtually impossible. In June 1942 the Mosquito bomber prototype made its first flight with Merlin 61 engines each incorporating a two-stage supercharger, and four months later these engines were replaced by Merlin 77 units to increase maximum level speed to 437 mph (703 km/h) at optimum altitude. A second Mosquito bomber prototype had meanwhile made its debut, and this introduced a pressure cabin that made a service ceiling of 40,000 ft (12,190 m) feasible for Mosquito bombers. This cabin had not been developed to production standard by the time the next variant of the Mosquito bomber was ready for production, and was therefore omitted in the Mosquito B.Mk IX, of which a mere 54 examples were built. The first Mosquito B.Mk IX flew in March 1943 with a powerplant of two Merlin 72/73 engines each rated at 1680 hp (1253 kW) at 8500 ft (2590 m) in 'M' gear and 1460 hp (1089 kW) at 21,000 ft (6400 m) in 'S' gear, although these were replaced in later aircraft by Merlin 76/77 engines each rated at 1710 hp (1275 kW) at 11,000 ft (3355 m) in 'M' gear and 1475 hp (1100 kW) at 23,000 ft (7010 m) in 'S' gear; the maximum fuel capacity was 697 Imp gal (3168.6 litres) declining to 497 Imp gal (2259.4 litres) with a useful disposable load. The standard bomb load of this variant was 3000 lb (1361 kg) in the form of six 500 lb (227 kg) weapons carried as four in the weapon bay and two under the wings and, although its dimensions remained identical to those of the Mosquito B.Mk IV, the Mosquito B.Mk IX otherwise differed in details such as its empty weight of 14,644 lb (6643 kg), maximum take-off weight of 23,745 lb (10,771 kg) later increased to 24,865 lb (11,279 kg) as equipment was added or 26,001 lb (11,794 kg) with the H2S Mk VI navigation and bombing radar that was added in some pathfinder aircraft. Less than 20 Mosquito B.Mk IX bombers were converted to carry a single 4000 lb (1814 kg) 'cookie', and these machines received the designation Mosquito B.Mk IX (Special).

The longitudinal stability problem of Mosquito bombers converted for the 'cookie' bomb was overcome with a longer rear fuselage in the Mosquito B.Mk XVI which, with the exception of the first 12 aircraft, was therefore built with capability for the 4000 lb (1814 kg) 'cookie' in a bulged weapon bay. The other major change in this variant was the introduction of a pressurised cockpit, although the pressure differential of only 2 lb/sq in (0.14 kg/cm2) produced a decrease of only 10,000 ft (3050 m) or so in apparent altitude, which meant that crews still had to wear oxygen masks above an altitude of 25000 ft (7620 m). The first Mosquito B.Mk XVI with the bulged weapon bay flew on the very first day of 1944, and the variant entered operational service in the following month. The Mosquito B.Mk XVI was powered by the same Merlin 72/73 or Merlin 76/77 engines as the Mosquito B.Mk IX, and its other details included a maximum fuel capacity of 860 Imp gal (3909.6 litres) declining to 539 Imp gal (2450.3 litres) with a disposable load of four 500 lb (227 kg) bombs as well as two 100 Imp gal (454.6 litre) drop tanks or to 497 Imp gal (2259.4 litres) with a disposable load of one 4000 lb (1814 kg) bomb and two 50 Imp gal (227.3 litre) drop tanks, span of 54 ft 2 in (16.51 m) with an area of 454.00 sq ft (42.18 m2), length of 44 ft 6 in (13.56 m), height of 15 ft 3 in (4.65 m) with the tail down, empty weight of 15,500 lb (7031 kg), normal take-off weight of 23,000 lb (10,442 kg), maximum take-off weight of 25,917 lb (11,766 kg), maximum level speed of 415 mph (668 km/h) at 28,000 ft (8535 m) declining to 400 mph (644 km/h) at 15,000 ft (4570 m), cruising speed of 358 mph (576 km/h) at optimum altitude, typical range of 1795 miles (2888 km) with a 2000 lb (907 kg) bomb load or 1370 miles (2204 km) with a 4000 lb (1814 kg) bomb load, maximum rate of climb at sea level of 2800 ft (853 m) per minute, climb to 15,000 ft (4570 m) in 7 minutes 30 seconds, and service ceiling of 37,000 ft (11,280 m). Production of the Mosquito B.Mk XVI totalled 1200 aircraft and this was naturally the type that equipped the largest number of Mosquito bombers squadrons. These eventually totalled 15 Bomber Command, three Mediterranean and one special duties squadrons in World War II, and four squadrons of the post-war British Air Force of Occupation in Germany.

The Mosquito B.Mk XX was one of the main Canadian-built versions, and was basically similar to the Mosquito B.Mk IV Series II apart from its use of American equipment and the powerplant of two Merlin 31 or Merlin 33 engines, and production totalled 245 aircraft delivered by mid-1944. The Mosquito B.Mk 25 was numerically the most important of the Canadian-built bomber variants, production totalling 400 aircraft delivered from July 1944. This model differed from the Mosquito B.Mk XX only in its powerplant, which comprised two Packard-built Merlin 225 engines.

FINAL VARIANT

First flown in March 1945, the Mosquito B.Mk 35 was a derivative of the Mosquito B.Mk XVI, with a powerplant of two Merlin 113A/114A engines, each rated at 1690 hp (1260 kW). Production of this final British-built bomber variant had reached some 60 aircraft by the time of VE-Day in May 1945, but none of these aircraft had entered service. Production eventually totalled 122 aircraft, all delivered by August 1946. The type remained in post-war service as a fast bomber, the last two units being Nos 109 and 139 Squadrons operating in the pathfinder role with this variant of the Mosquito until July 1952 and June 1953 respectively, when the squadrons' Mosquitoes were finally retired in favour of the turbojet-powered English Electric Canberra B.Mk 2 light bomber. The most important details of the Mosquito B.Mk 35 included a span of 54 ft 2 in (16.51 m) with an area of 454.00 sq ft (42.18 m2), length of 40 ft 6 in (12.34 m), height of 15 ft 3 in (4.65 m) with the tail down, empty weight of 14,635 lb (6638 kg), normal take-off weight of 23,000 lb (10,433 kg), maximum take-off weight of 25,200 lb (11,431 kg) with a 4000 lb (1814 kg) bomb, maximum level speed of 415 mph (668 km/h) at 28,000 ft (8535 m), cruising speed of 276 mph (444 km/h) at optimum altitude, maximum range of 1955 miles (3146 km), maximum rate of climb at sea level of 2700 ft (823 m) per minute, and service ceiling of 42,000 ft (12,800 m).

THE MARAUDER

Evolved in parallel with the North American B-25 Mitchell to provide the USAAC and its USAAF successor with a medium bomber type optimised for the attack role, with good performance and agility at low and medium altitude, the Martin B-26 Marauder was one of the most important tactical warplanes operated by the USA and its allies in the course of World War II. The type was difficult for an inexperienced pilot to handle as a result of its high wing loading and high landing speed, but once mastered was an excellent warplane that achieved very good results at very low loss rate. During 1938, Martin was one of four companies working on designs of a light bomber to a USAAC requirement, and although this Model 167 did not win any USAAC contract, it was produced in quantity to meet orders from France and the UK, the latter designating the type as the Maryland. The Model 167 paved the way for the Model 187, which was also bought by the UK for service as the Baltimore. Production of these two types totalled some 1800 aircraft. The origin of the B-26 can be traced back to January 1939, when the USAAC launched a design competition for five-crew medium bombers conforming to a requirement, with full details circulated in March of the same year and demanding the submission of all design proposals by July. The result was the Model 179 design that was offered to the USAAC in July 1939 and in the resulting design competition scored higher than any of its rivals. This led to the issue of an August 1939 contract for 201 examples of the new bomber with the designation B-26, the designation B-25 having been accorded earlier to the Model 179's only serious rival, the North American NA-62, based on the NA-40 private-venture prototype and therefore at a more advanced stage. The initial order for the

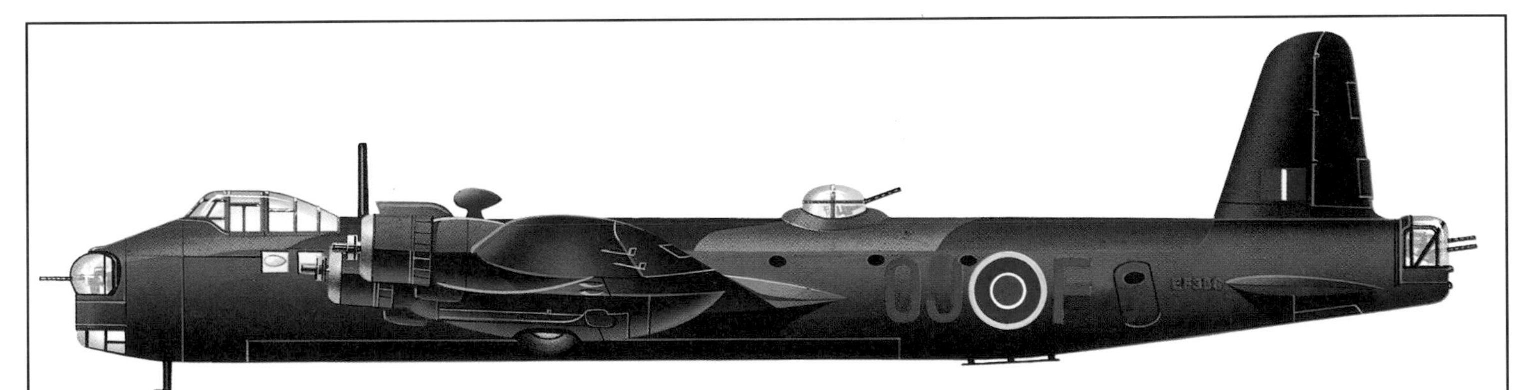

Short Stirling B.Mk III

Type: seven-seat heavy bomber
Country of origin: UK
Powerplant: four 1650-hp (1230-kW) Bristol Hercules XVI radial piston engines
Performance: maximum level speed 270 mph (434 km/h) at 14,500 ft (4420 m); service ceiling 17,000 ft (5180 m); typical range 2010 miles (3235 km)
Weights; empty 46,900 lb (21,274 kg); max take-off 70,000 lb (31,752 kg)
Dimensions: wing span 99 ft 1 in (30.20 m); length 87 ft 3 in (26.59 m); height 22 ft 9 in (6.93 m)
Armament: eight 0.303 in (7.7 mm) Browning machine guns , plus up to 14,000 lb (6350 kg) of ordnance

B-25, placed at the same time as that for the B-26, was 184 aircraft.

The Model 179 was in no way unconventional in its design, but was nonetheless radical in its combination of features such as its shoulder-set cantilever wing, single large vertical tail surface and tricycle landing gear, all of which were well proven by 1939, with other aspects such as fuselage of circular section that offered low drag for its volume and a wing of small size and comparatively low aspect ratio. The volume of the fuselage was dictated by the need to carry sufficient crew, fixed armament, disposable armament and fuel to meet the requirement, but its circular cross section made production more difficult as it required the creation of double-curvature skin panels. The small wing was selected for its low drag and thus its promise of high speed, despite the fact that its inevitably high loading would result in poor field performance in terms of a long take-off run and a high landing speed. At a maximum figure of 53 lb/sq ft (2.23 kg/m2), the B-26 had the highest wing loading of any aeroplane accepted for USAAC service up to that time, and with its powerplant of two Pratt & Whitney R-2800 radial piston engines, each rated at 1850 hp (1379.5 kW) and installed in very large wing-mounted nacelles, the B-26 would inevitably be a 'hot ship' and thus more liable than most to a high accident rate when it was first introduced to service.

DEFENSIVE ARMAMENT

As originally schemed, the Model 179 had a defensive armament of single 0.3 in (7.62 mm) Browning machine guns in the nose and tail (the former on a ball mounting) and twin 0.5 in (12.7 mm) Browning machine guns in a dorsal turret. Developed specifically for this application, this Martin Model 250CE turret was electrically powered and was the first powered dorsal turret installed on an American bomber. Provision was also made for one more 0.5 in (12.7 mm) Browning machine gun in a ventral hatch position to the rear of the weapons bays. The maximum bomb load was in theory 5800 lb (2631 kg) but in practice 4000 lb (1814 kg) to ensure that a tactically useful range could be achieved.

Oddly enough, given the fact of the new bomber's high wing loading and consequent likelihood of tricky take-off and landing performance, the USAAC did not specify either a prototype or even a service trials machine, and the first aeroplane was therefore a B-26 that made its maiden flight on 25 November 1940 with a powerplant of two R-1800-5 radial engines supplied with fuel from an internal capacity of 784.4 Imp gal (3565.8 litres) including a main supply of 582.9 Imp gal (2649.8 litres) in self-sealing tanks and an auxiliary supply of 201.5 Imp gal (916.12 litres) in unprotected tanks. The second machine was completed in February 1941, the month in which the USAAC began to accept the type, but it was already becoming evident that the original performance estimates could not be achieved as a result of the inevitable weight escalation resulting from a host of factors including the addition of more operational equipment. In September 1940 the USAAC had placed additional contracts for another 930 examples of the new Martin bomber in the form of 139 B-26A machines and 791 B-26B machines. Improvements planned for the B-26A included self-sealing fuel tanks in place of the bag tanks previously intended, which made the B-26A the first USAAC aeroplane fitted only with self-sealing tanks, as well as about 555 lb (252 kg) of armour for the protection of the crew and vital equipment items. Even before the first B-26 had been completed, the USAAC decided that these features should be adopted as standard on the earlier aircraft. As a result the empty weight rose to 21,375 lb (9696 kg) and the maximum weight to 28,340 lb (12,855 kg) for the maintenance of the estimated payload/range performance, but the escalation of weight inevitably meant the degradation of other aspects of the flight performance: the maximum level speed fell to 315 mph (507 km/h) at 15,000 ft (4570 m) but, more importantly for a type which had yet to enter service in the hands of pilots accustomed to slower bombers with far better field performance, the approach and landing speeds went up.

The importance attached to the new medium bomber was so great, however, that the USAAC decided to accept the B-26 as it was, and the first unit to receive the B-26 was the 22nd Bomb Group at Langley Field, Virginia, where it converted from the Douglas B-18. Early difficulties included a series of nosewheel failures during landings heavier than intended because of trimming problems in the absence of much equipment, and accidents resulting from the tendency of the Curtiss Electric propeller to go into fine pitch and cause engine overspeeding at take-off. The B-26's accident rate was therefore very high by the standards of the day, although it is worth noting that by the later stages of World War II the US 9th Army Air Force recorded that the

LEFT: A heavy bomber, soon relegated to more successful use as a transport and glider tug, was the Short Stirling, the UK's first four-engined bomber of World War II.

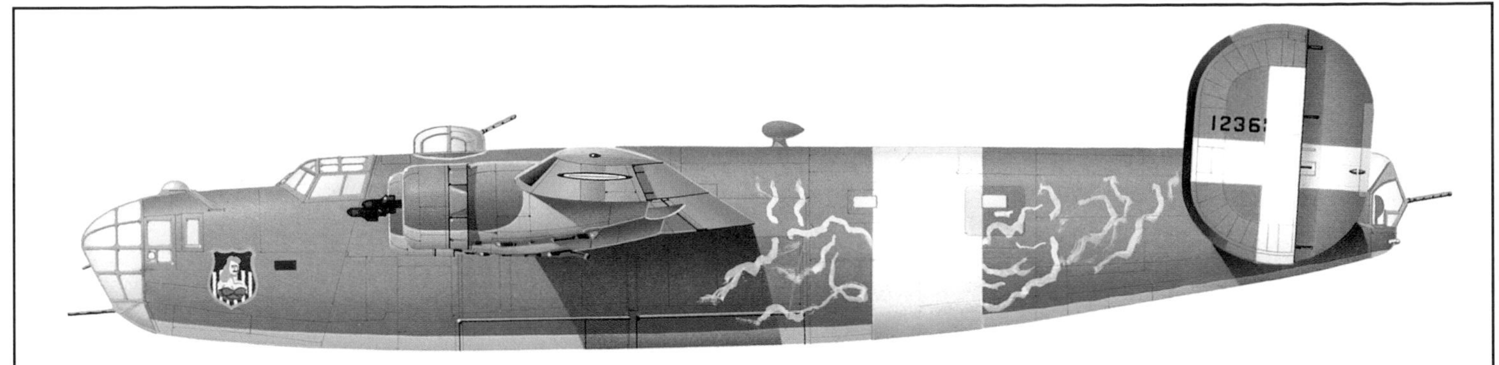

Consolidated B-24J Liberator

Type: 10-seat heavy bomber
Country of origin: USA
Powerplant: four 1200-hp (895-kW) Pratt & Whitney R-1830-65 radial piston engines
Performance: maximum level speed 300 mph (483 km/h); service ceiling 30,000 ft (9145 m); max range 3300 miles (5311 km)
Weights: empty 36,500 lb (16,556 kg); max take-off 65,000 lb (29,484 kg)
Dimensions: wing span 110 ft 0 in (33.53 m); length 67 ft 2 in (20.47 m); height 18 ft 0 in (5.49 m)
Armament: 10 0.5 in (12.7 mm) Browning M2 machine guns, plus up to 12,000 lb (5443 kg) of stores

B-26 (officially named as the Marauder in October 1941) had the lowest operational loss rate of any warplane operated in the European theatre. Ways in which the B-26 could be improved were already being developed even as production of the new bomber was beginning, and these factory-installed improvements were complemented in the field by other changes dictated by continuous assessment and then, in many cases, incorporated on later production aircraft.

MARAUDER PRODUCTION

Production of the B-26 totalled 201 aircraft to a standard of which the other most salient details included a span of 65 ft 0 in (18.81 m) with an area of 602.00 sq ft (55.93 m2), length of 56 ft 0 in (17.07 m), height of 19 ft 10 in (6.05 m), empty weight of 21,375 lb (9696 kg), maximum take-off weight of 32,000 lb (14,515 kg), maximum level speed of 315 mph (507 km/h) at 15,000 ft (4570 m), cruising speed of 265 mph (426.5 km/h) at 15,000 ft (4570 m), typical range of 1000 miles (1609 km), climb to 15,000 ft (4570 m) in 12 minutes 30 seconds, and service ceiling of 25,000 ft (7620 m).

Built to the extent of 139 aircraft, the B-26A was a simple development of the B-26 with a 24 rather than 12-volt electrical system, fittings for two more 208.2 Imp gal (946.4 litre) auxiliary fuel tanks in the rear weapons bay, and the armament revised by the replacement of the 0.3 in (7.62 mm) machine guns in the nose and tail positions by 0.5 in (12.7 mm) weapons. This last had resulted from a field modification made on many B-26 aircraft, and the modification of the rear fuselage required by this alteration resulted in an overall length of 58 ft 3 in (17.75 m). The first 30 examples of the B-26A had the same R-2800-5 engines as the B-26, but the subsequent 109 aircraft changed to the identically rated R-2800-9 or -39 to create the B-26A-1 Marauder subvariant. Another change was the introduction of shackles under the fuselage for the carriage of one 2000 lb (907 kg) torpedo of 22 in (559 mm) calibre so that the B-26B and basically similar B-26C could operate in the anti-ship role. When the torpedo was carried the internal bomb load was two 1600 lb (726 kg) bombs. It was with the B-26A that the 22nd Bomb Group (Medium) opened the new bomber's account when it became operational in Australia during April 1942. With additional fuel in the rear weapons bay, the aircraft were used to deliver small but accurately placed bomb tonnages on the positions that the Japanese were beginning to consolidate on the northern shore of New Guinea. The B-26A also saw service at this time as a torpedo bomber during the Battle of Midway (June 1942) and as an anti-ship type in the hands of the 73rd and 77th Bomb Squadrons operating in the Aleutian Islands.

The aircraft completed to the second order placed in September 1940 comprised the initial 791 examples of the B-26B, of which total production eventually amounted to 1883 aircraft. The B-26B was this the first genuinely 'mass production' variant, which was in fact produced in a number of subvariants identified by their block numbers. The primary changes characterising the B-26B were the introduction of a stepped tail position with two manually operated 0.5 in (12.7 mm) Browning machine guns, and the provision for one manually operated 0.3 in (7.62 mm) Browning machine gun firing through the rear crew entrance hatch for enhanced rearward defence. A number of internal modifications were also effected as a means of improving the comfort and thus the operational capability of the crew, and the propeller spinners were removed.

The R-2800-5 engines were retained in the 81 examples of the basic B-26B and 225 examples of the virtually identical B-26B-1 Marauder, but in the 96 aircraft of the B-26B-2 Marauder block, these engines were replaced by two R-2800-41 radial units, each rated at 1920 hp (1431.5 kW) for take-off, 1490 hp (1111 kW) at 14,300 ft (4360 m) and 1550 hp (1156 kW) at 7100 ft (2165 m). Similar ratings applied to the R-2800-43 engine introduced in the 27 examples of the B-26B-3 Marauder and all subsequent Marauder bombers. The 211 examples of the B-26B-4 Marauder pioneered a lengthened nosewheel leg to increase the effective wing incidence and thus shorten the take-off run, and also to facilitate the task of pilots converting from aircraft with tailwheel landing gear. This modification required the addition of a bulged fairing under the fuselage, partially overlapping the forward edge of the nosewheel doors. In the last 141 aircraft of this block, the ventral machine gun was replaced by two 0.5 in (12.7 mm) Browning trainable lateral-firing machine guns with 240 rounds per gun in the lower sides of the rear fuselage. The

ABOVE: Partnering the B-17 but with somewhat greater range, the Consolidated B-24 Liberator was made in larger numbers than any other US aircraft of World War II.

aircraft of the B-26B-2, B-26B-3 and B-26B-4 blocks were otherwise similar to each other and conformed to a standard whose details included a span of 65 ft 0 in (18.81 m) with an area of 602.00 sq ft (55.93 m^2), length of 58 ft 3 in (17.75 m), height of 19 ft 10 in (6.05 m), empty weight of 23,500 lb (10,660 kg), maximum take-off weight of 35,000 lb (15876 kg), maximum level speed of 298 mph (479.5 km/h) at 15,000 ft (4570 m) declining to 281 mph (452 km/h) at sea level, cruising speed of 294 mph (473 km/h) at 15,000 ft (4570 m), ferry range of 2000 miles (3218.5 km), typical range of 900 miles (1448.5 km) with a 1500 lb (680 kg) bomb load, maximum rate of climb at sea level of 1500 ft (457 m) per minute, and service ceiling of more than 20,000 ft (6095 m).

The 150 aircraft of the B-26B-10 Marauder block completed the initial contract for the B-26B variant, and introduced a major alteration in the form of a wing increased in span by 6 ft 0 in (1.83 m) and in area by 56.00 sq ft (5.20 m^2), and a vertical tail surface increased in height and area. A larger wing of this type had featured in some of the earliest design proposals, but had initially been rejected in an effort to ensure that the new bomber had the lowest possible drag and thus the highest possible speed. The development of the B-26B out of the B-26A had inevitably resulted in further weight escalation, as indicated by the acceptance of a maximum take-off weight of 34,000 lb (15,422 kg) with further increase inevitable, and it was now decided that the increased degradation of handling characteristics resulting from still further increases in the wing loading was a matter that needed urgent attention even if the remedy did result in a loss of performance. The enlarged wing entailed a reduction in the maximum level speed of the B-26B-10 by 16 mph (26 km/h) at 15,000 ft (4570 m), but most Marauder crews thought that this was a minimal price to pay for the concomitant reduction in landing speed and required runway lengths. An early field modification had added a second nose gun on some B-26 bombers, and this feature became standard on the B-26B-10 in the form of a 0.5 in (12.7 mm) Browning fixed forward-firing machine gun with 200 rounds on the lower starboard side of the nose. Another improvement in the armament, reflecting the fact that the Marauder was increasingly operated in the low-level attack role, which offered ground targets of opportunity such as anti-aircraft guns, was the addition of four 0.5 in (12.7 mm) Browning fixed forward-firing machine guns, with between 200 and 250 rounds per gun in packages scabbed onto the sides of the forward fuselage. This provided the Marauder with the potent forward armament of six 0.5 in (12.7 mm) Browning machine guns in addition to the six other 0.5 in (12.7 mm) Browning weapons installed as two weapons in the two waist positions, the dorsal turret, and the tail position. The aircraft of the B-26B-10 block were completed to standard with details including a span of 71 ft 0 in (21.64 m) with an area of 658.00 sq ft (23.97 m^2), length of 58 ft 3 in (17.75 m), height of 19 ft 10 in (6.05 m), empty weight of 24,500 lb (11,113 kg), normal take-off weight of 37,000 lb (16,783 kg), maximum take-off weight of 38,200 lb (17,328 kg), maximum level speed of 282 mph (454 km/h) at 15,000 ft (4570 m) declining to 270 mph (434.5 km/h) at sea level, cruising speed of 273 mph (439.5 km/h) at 15,000 ft (4570 m), ferry range of 2600 miles (4184 km) with four auxiliary tanks, typical range of 1050 miles (1690 km) with a 4000 lb (1815 kg) bomb load, maximum rate of climb at sea level of 1300 ft (396 m) per minute, and service ceiling of more than 15,000 ft (4570 m). The 100 examples of the B-26B-15 Marauder were identical to the B-26B-10 in all important respects, while the 100 aircraft of the B-26B-20 Marauder block had the original type of manually operated tail gun position replaced by a power-operated Martin-Bell turret, still armed with two 0.5 in (12.7 mm) Browning machine guns, and this installation reduced the overall length by 2 ft 2 in (0.66 m). Further evolution of the B-26B resulted in blocks that differed only marginally from each other, and these were the B-26B-25 (100 aircraft), B-26B-30 (100 aircraft), B-26B-35 (100 aircraft), B-26B-40 (101 aircraft), B-26B-45 (91 aircraft), B-26B-50 (200 aircraft) and B-26B-55 (200 aircraft).

FURTHER PRODUCTION ORDERS

Even as the early variants of the Marauder were being produced and placed in service, orders for the type were climbing steadily. During 1941, for example, Martin received orders for an additional 1700 aircraft. This scale of production was beyond the capabilities of the company's plant at Baltimore, so a second production line was created at a plant located at Omaha, Nebraska. This was owned by the US government but operated by Martin, and it was decided that 1200 of the 1700 aircraft ordered under 1941 contracts should be built here to a standard comparable to that of the Baltimore-built B-26B but with the revised designation B-26C. In 1942 orders were placed for a further 1600 aircraft, and the split for these aircraft was 600 B-26B and 1000 B-26C machines, although in the event only 385 of the B-26C machines were completed and the remaining 615 cancelled as the Omaha plant was switched to production of the Boeing B-29 Superfortress strategic heavy bomber. Deliveries from Omaha started in August 1942 and ended in April 1944. The later B-26B and B-26C batches dispensed with the single fixed forward-firing machine gun in the nose, reducing the gun armament to 11 0.5 in (12.7 mm) weapons with 4200 rounds of ammunition, and at the same time the rear weapons bay was sealed. This limited the number of small bombs that could be carried, which was a matter of little significance, but it also meant that the aircraft were limited to two, rather than four, auxiliary tanks. Production at Omaha comprised the B-26C-5 (115 aircraft), B-26C-6 (60 aircraft), B-26C-10 (60 aircraft), B-26C-15 (90 aircraft), B-26C-20 (175 aircraft), B-26C-25 (199 aircraft), B-26C-30 (177 aircraft) and B-26C-45 (334 aircraft).

The final contracts for production of the Marauder, all to be completed at the Baltimore plant, were for 300 examples of the B-26F ordered in 1943, and for 950 examples of the B-26G ordered in 1943 and 1944. The B-26F was a development of the B-26B and B-26C with the same powerplant of two R-2800-43 radial engines, but offered a significant improvement in handling, especially at low level, through a 3.5º increase in the wing's angle of incidence, the introduction of sharp leading edges on the ailerons, and the reduction of the rudder's chord. The change in the angle of incidence also allowed a small increase in the capacity of the fuel tanks in the wing, and all torpedo capability was removed. The maximum bomb load of the B-26F was therefore 4000 lb (1814 kg) in the form of two 2000 lb (907 kg) or four 1000 lb

BELOW: Rivalling the Ju 88 in versatility, the de Havilland Mosquito was a superb light bomber offering performance so high that no defensive armament was needed.

(454 kg) bombs, or 3000 lb (1361 kg) in the form of six 500 lb (227 kg) bombs. The B-26F was built in three 100-aircraft blocks as the B-26F-1, B-26F-2 and B-26F-6. The B-26G was identical to the B-26F in all except its use of standardised 'AN' (Army/Navy) fittings in place of the B-26F's 'AF' (Air Force) fittings. The B-26G was built in eight blocks as the B-26G-1 (100 aircraft), B-26G-5 (200 aircraft), B-26G-10 (125 aircraft), B-26G-11 (75 aircraft), B-26G-15 (140 aircraft), B-26G-20 (60 aircraft), B-26G-21 (75 aircraft) and B-26G-25 (118 aircraft). The last of these aircraft made its first flight on 18 April 1945, ending production of the Marauder series after the completion of 5266 aircraft.

TOKYO BOMBER

One of the most important tactical warplanes operated by the Allies in World War II, with 9816 examples built, the Mitchell was a classic medium bomber that generally operated in the land attack role but was also a potent anti-ship warplane. Its origins can be found in 1938, when North American gambled that the US Army Air Corps' circular proposal of January for a three-seat twin-engined attack bomber would soon lead to a full requirement for a medium attack bomber that would eventually be built in very large numbers, and therefore started work as a private venture on its NA-40 design. This was based on an all-metal structure, combining a semi-monocoque fuselage and cantilever stressed-skin flying surfaces. The NA-40 prototype made its maiden flight in January 1939, and in that month the USAAC announced a requirement for a new attack bomber. The requirement called for design submissions to be made by July 1939, and North American decided to revise the NA-40 into the NA-40B (otherwise NA-40-2) with a powerplant of two Wright GR-2600-A71 Cyclone 14 radial piston engines each rated at 1500 hp (1118 kW) for take-off and 1275 hp (951 kW) at 12,000 ft (3660 m) and driving a three-blade Hamilton Standard metal constant-speed propeller. North American delivered the NA-40B for trials in March 1939, but the aeroplane was lost in an accident only two weeks later. The type ordered to satisfy the attack bomber requirement was the Douglas Model 7 that was ordered as the A-20.

The NA-40B had impressed the USAAC, however, and when the service issued a March 1939 circular proposal for a five-seat medium bomber North American was well placed to respond with its NA-62 design evolved from the NA-40B. The various submissions were evaluated from July 1939, and the USAAC then contracted with North American for 'off the drawing board' production of 184 B-25 aircraft of the NA-62 type that was basically the NA-40B with a wider fuselage that allowed a doubling of the weapons load to 3600 lb (1633 kg), the wing moved down to the mid-set position that permitted the upper line of the fuselage to be straightened, the powerplant changed to two R-2600-9 radial engines each rated at 1700 hp (1267.5 kW) for take-off and 1350 hp (1007 kW) at 13000 ft (3960 m) and supplied with fuel from an internal capacity of 759.4 Imp gal (3452.3 litres), the crew increased from three to five, and the defensive armament altered to one 0.5 in (12.7 mm) Browning rearward-firing machine gun operated by a prone gunner in the tail, two 0.3 in (7.62 mm) Browning lateral-firing machine guns in single-gun beam positions operated by waist gunners, and one 0.3 in (7.62 mm) Browning forward-firing machine gun in any of three nose positions operated by the bombardier. The B-25 initial production model was used as a service trials type, and 24 NA-62 aircraft were delivered from February 1941 after a first flight in August 1940. The type revealed a lack of directional stability, and from the tenth aeroplane onward was delivered with the flat outer wing panels that gave the Mitchell its final and highly distinctive gull-wing appearance.

Production of the B-25A, which was delivered from May 1941, amounted to 40 aircraft and received the company designation NA-62A as they incorporated changes suggested by the nature of the air war over Europe. These changes included protective armour for the crew, and a revised fuel system that comprised four self-sealing tanks in the wings for 577.9 Imp gal (2627.1 litres) of fuel that could be supplemented by an additional 348.1 Imp gal (1582.3 litres) of fuel in a droppable tank carried in the weapons bay. The B-25A had a length of 54 ft 1 in (16.485 m), empty weight of 17,870 lb (8105 kg), normal take-off weight of 25,322 lb (11,486 kg), maximum take-off weight of 27,100 lb (12,293 kg), maximum level speed of 315 mph (507 km/h) at 15,000 ft (4570 m), typical range of 1350 miles (2172.5 km) with a 3000 lb (1361 kg) bomb load, climb to 15,000 ft (4570 m) in 8 minutes 24 seconds, and service ceiling of 27000 ft (8230 m). The aircraft entered service in the early summer of 1941 with the 34th, 37th and 95th Bombardment Squadrons and attached 89th Reconnaissance Squadron of the 17th Bombardment Group (Medium). In December 1941 it was a B-25A of the 17th BG that was during the war thought to have drawn the type's first blood when it claimed the sinking of a Japanese

de Mosquito B.Mk IV Srs 2

Type: two-seat fast bomber
Country of origin: UK
Powerplant: two 1280-hp (954-kW) Rolls-Royce Merlin 21 or 23 Vee piston engines
Performance: max level speed 380 mph (611.5 km/h); service ceiling 34000 ft (10,360 m); max range 2040 miles (3283 km)
Weights: empty 13,400 lb (6078 kg); max take-off 22,380 lb
Dimensions: wing span 54 ft 2 in (16.51 m); length 41 ft 2 in (12.55 m), tail up; height 17 ft 5 in (5.31 in)
Armament: up to 2000 lb (907 kg) of stores; specially modified aircraft could carry one 4000 lb (1814 kg) bomb

submarine off the coast of California, only a short time after the Japanese attack on Pearl Harbor.

The original contract for 184 aircraft was completed in 1941 with 120 examples of the B-25B, which North American built with the company designation NA-62B, indicating changes such as the addition of power-operated Bendix turrets, each armed with two 0.5 in (12.7 mm) Browning machine guns, in the dorsal position with 400 rounds per gun and in the retractable ventral position with 350 rounds per gun. The bombardier's 0.3 in (7.62 mm) weapon with 600 rounds was retained in the nose position, but the 0.5 in (12.7 mm) gun in the tail position was removed. The B-25B had a length of 52 ft 11 in (16.13 m), empty weight of 20,000 lb (9072 kg), normal take-off weight of 26,208 lb (11,888 kg), maximum take-off weight of 28,460 lb (12,909 kg), maximum level speed of 300 mph (483 km/h) at 15,000 ft (4570 m), typical range of 1350 miles (2172.5 km) with a 3000 lb (1361 kg) bomb load, and service ceiling of 23,500 ft (10,660 m).

DOOLITTLE RAID

It was 16 aircraft of this type that undertook the celebrated 'Doolittle raid' in April 1942, when they took off from the aircraft carrier USS *Hornet* and attacked

Tokyo before the survivors attempted to fly on to airfields in China.

The B-25C was the first variant to be named Mitchell officially, and was also the initial model to be delivered in large numbers, some 1619 aircraft eventually being built for service from January 1942. The type was indistinguishable from the B-25B in its external features and gun armament, but had a 24 rather than 12-volt electrical system, autopilot, powerplant of two R-2600-13 radial engines each rated at 1700 hp (1267.5 kW) for take-off and 1400 hp (1044 kW) at 13000 ft (3960 m) and driving a three-blade Hamilton Standard metal constant-speed propeller, additional tankage, from the 384th aeroplane onward, for a standard internal capacity of 811 Imp gal (3687 litres) that could be supplemented by 487.1 Imp gal (2214.5 litres) in a droppable weapons bay tank, and a revised weapons bay that could now carry a variety of bomb loads. From the 606th aeroplane onward, the standard switched to the B-25C-1 of which 258 were delivered with provision for external racks that allowed the carriage of a 2000 lb (907 kg) torpedo under the fuselage instead of the internally carried bombs (although the weapons bay could still carry the jettisonable auxiliary fuel tank) or eight 250 lb (113 kg) bombs under the wings in addition to the internally carried bombs, thereby increasing the maximum possible disposable load from 3200 lb (1452 kg) to 5200 lb (2359 kg) on short-range missions. Another change was the replacement of the bombardier's 0.3 in (7.62 mm) Browning machine gun with a 0.5 in (12.7 mm) Browning trainable forward-firing machine gun with 300 rounds, and in the 162 examples of the B-25C-5 that followed between October and December 1942 the pilot was provided with a 0.5 in (12.7 mm) Browning fixed forward-firing machine gun with 300 rounds on the starboard side of the nose. Later blocks ordered in January 1942 were the result of the Lend-Lease Act, although the aircraft did not all go to their intended operators, and comprised 150 examples of the B-25C-10 for the UK, with an improved compass and better winterisation equipment, and 150 examples of the B-25C-15 for China that appeared in January 1943 with individual flame-damped exhausts. In February 1943, the USAAF started to receive 200 examples of the B-25C-20, a variant basically similar to the B-25C-15 but ordered by the service for its own use. The final variant of the B-25C series, delivered up to May 1943 and totalling 100 aircraft, was the B-25C-25 that differed from the C-20 in having a 191.5 Imp gal (870.6 litre) self-sealing fuel tank in the weapons bay, and provision for a 270.6 Imp gal (1230.25 litre) auxiliary tank carried in the weapons bay.

The B-25C had an empty weight of 20,300 lb (9208 kg), normal take-off

BELOW: The Martin B-26 Marauder had a poor early career, in which many aircraft and crews were lost in landing accidents. However it matured into a classic attack bomber.

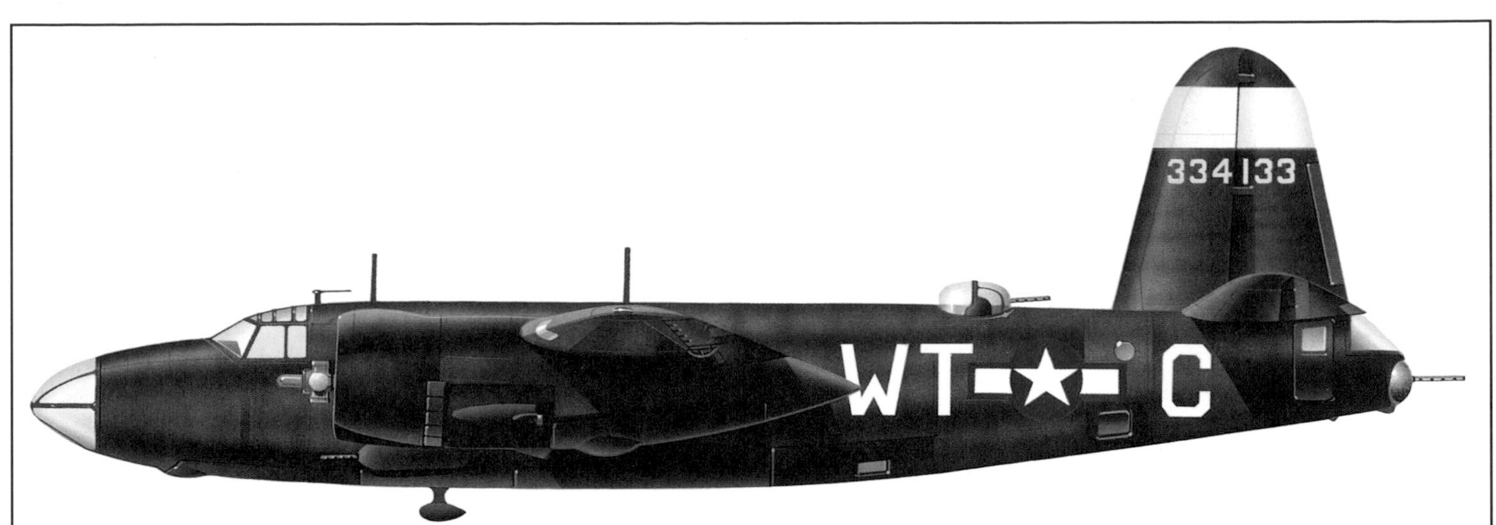

Martin B-26G Marauder

Type: seven-seat medium bomber
Country of origin: USA
Powerplant: two 1920-hp (1431.5-kW) Pratt & Whitney R-2800-43 radial piston engines
Performance: maximum level speed 283 mph (455 km/h); service ceiling 19,800 ft (6035 m); typical range 675 miles (1086 km)
Weights: empty 25,300 lb (11,476 kg); max take-off 38,200 lb (17,328 kg)
Dimensions: wing span 71 ft 0 in (21.64 m); length 56 ft 1 in (17.09 m); height 20 ft 4 in (6.20 m)
Armament: four 0.5 in (12.7 mm) Browning M2 fixed forward-firing machine guns, seven 0.5 in (12.7 mm) Browning M2 trainable machine guns, plus up to 4000 lb (1814 kg) of ordnance

weight of 33,500 lb (15,196 kg), maximum take-off weight of 41,800 lb (18,960 kg), maximum level speed of 284 mph (457 km/h) at 15,000 ft (4570 m) declining to 264 mph (425 km/h) at sea level, cruising speed of 233 mph (375 km/h) at optimum altitude, maximum range of 2500 miles (4023 km) with the weapons bay tank, typical range of 1525 miles (2454 km) with a 3200 lb (1452 kg) bomb load, maximum rate of climb at sea level of 1375 ft (419 m) per minute, climb to 15000 ft (4570 m) in 16 minutes 30 seconds, and service ceiling of 21,200 ft (6460 m). In service, a number of the aircraft were revised with four 0.5 in (12.7 mm) Browning fixed forward-firing machine guns on the sides of the forward fuselage for increased firepower in the attack role.

B-25 SUBCONTRACTORS

Up to the B-25C variant, all the aircraft of the B-25 series were built by North American's main facility at Inglewood in California. By December 1940, however, the US Government had decided that the increasing scope of World War II and the growing level of threat faced by the USA demanded additional production facilities, and that these should be established in the otherwise under-industrialised states of the Mid-West. North American was entrusted with the management of the bomber production plant established in Kansas City, and this facility drew an increasingly large proportion of its components from facilities operated by the Fisher Body Division of the General Motors Corporation. An initial order for 1200 B-25D bombers, identical in all respects to the early-production B-25C, was placed with this facility in June 1941. Inglewood provided knock-down kits for the first six aircraft and then all the detail parts for the following 94 as a means of kick-starting Kansas City production, and the first aircraft was delivered in February 1942. From the 101st aeroplane onward, parts from the Fisher Body Division were used: outer wing panels and fuselage side panels from this source being added to assemblies produced in Kansas City.

The first 200 B-25D aircraft were basically similar to the B-25C with the exception of provision for 104.1 Imp gal (473.2 litres) of auxiliary fuel in a waist tank for a maximum range of 2650 miles (4265 km), but from November 1942 there followed 100 examples of the B-25D-1 with external weapons racks, a scanning blister above the fuselage, outboard fuel tanks, and carburettor dust filters as fitted on the B-25C-1. In December 1942 production switched to 225 examples of the B-25D-5, which was basically similar to the B-25C-5 in features such as it two 0.5 in (12.7 mm) machine guns in the nose. Next came 180 examples of the B-25D-10 with B-25C-10 features such as improved winterisation and a better compass. The 180 aircraft of the B-25D-15 subvariant were basically similar to the B-25C-15 with flame-damper exhausts, and production of the initial order from Kansas City ended in June 1943, with the delivery of the last of 340 B-25D-20 bombers essentially similar to the B-25C-20 in their improved windscreens and improved weapons bay tanks. Further orders had already been placed to raise the Kansas City production total for the B-25D to an eventual 2290 aircraft up to March 1944 by the addition of 750 machines, in the form of 500 B-25D-30 and 250 B-25D-35 aircraft. The former was basically similar to the B-25D-25, and the latter had improved winterisation and defensive armament introduced in the B-25H and B-25J models from Inglewood.

Many of the B-25C and B-25D aircraft were operated in the Southwest Pacific Area by units of the US 5th Army Air Force, most notably the 3rd, 22nd and 345th Bombardement Groups. The experience of these units was that while the airframe/powerplant combination of the B-25 was well suited to this theatre, where there was frequent demand for attacks on shipping and small targets dispersed in jungle, the armament was not ideal. By September 1943, therefore, some 175 examples of the B-25C and B-25D had been modified by the depot at Townsville in Australia for the low-level strafing role with a crew of three, the ventral turret removed, the bombardier position replaced by two pairs of 0.5 in (12.7 mm) Browning machine guns and supplemented by two additional pairs of Brownings on the sides of the forward fuselage for a fixed forward-firing armament of eight heavy machine guns, and the weapons bay adapted for the carriage of 60 small fragmentation bombs and six 100 lb (45 kg) demolition bombs.

The B-25C and B-25D were also flown by the 7th and 341st Bombardment Groups of the 10th Air Force in the China-Burma-India theatre, the 1st Bombardment Group of the Chinese-American Composite Wing of the US 14th Army Air Force in China, the 28th Bombardment Group of the 11th Army Air Force in the Aleutian Islands, the 41st and 42nd Bombardment Groups of the 13th Army Air Force in the Central Pacific, and the 12th, 310th, 321st and 340th Bombardment Groups of the 12th Army Air Force in North Africa and Italy.

THE B-25G VARIANT

With 405 aircraft built, including five B-25C conversions, the B-25G was a dedicated anti-ship model evolved for use in the Pacific theatre with a four-man crew and a 75 mm (2.95 in) M4 gun installed in the nose, where it was complemented by two 0.5 in (12.7 mm) Browning fixed forward-firing machine guns with 400 rounds per gun, and by the four 'package' guns on the sides of the forward fuselage. The last 221 aircraft omitted the ventral turret, which was deemed superfluous for the low-level anti-ship role. The type was not notably successful because of the weight of the 75 mm (2.95 in) gun installation in the lower port side of the forward fuselage, and the slow rate at which the 20 lb (9.1 kg) shells, carried in a 21-round tray, could be loaded by hand. The B-25G had the same powerplant, dimensions and weights as the B-25C, but differed in details such as its maximum level speed of 281 mph (452 km/h) at 15,000 ft (4570 m) declining to 268 mph (431 km/h) at sea level, maximum range of 2200 miles (3540.5 km) with auxiliary fuel, typical range of 1525 miles (2454 km) with a 3000 lb (1361 kg) bomb load, and service ceiling of 24,300 ft (7405 m).

The B-25H was a development of the B-25G, with a five-man crew, the lighter 75 mm (2.95 in) T13E1 gun, eight 0.5 in (12.7 mm) Browning fixed forward-firing machine guns (four in the nose and four on the fuselage sides), six 0.5 in (12.7 mm) Browning trainable machine guns (two weapons each in the dorsal and tail positions and single weapons in the two beam positions), provision for 3000 lb (1361 kg) of bombs in the weapons bay, and provision for eight 5 in (127 mm) rocket under the wings. This NA-92 variant was a truly formidable attack warplane, and production totalled 1000 aircraft. The most extensively produced variant, with deliveries totalling 4318 aircraft, the B-25J was a six-crew development of the B-25H with a glazed nose carrying one trainable and two fixed forward-firing 0.5 in (12.7 mm) Browning machine guns. The dorsal turret was moved farther forward to just to the rear of the flightdeck, and the first 150 were completed with provision for a 2000 lb (907 kg) bomb or torpedo. Many of the aircraft were later adapted with a 'solid' nose accommodating a fixed forward-firing battery of eight 0.5 in (12.7 mm) Browning machine guns.

SOVIET MOSQUITO

Without doubt one of the finest tactical warplanes of the 'Great Patriotic War', the Pe-2 may be regarded as the Soviet counterpart of the de Havilland Mosquito and Junkers Ju 88, although it differed from its British and German counterparts in being optimised for the purely tactical role. A host of variants were built, totalling 11427 aircraft, for service right into the 1950s. Vladimir Mikhailovich Petlyakov was one of the ablest assistants available to Andrei Tupolev at the TsAGI from 1921, and played a major part in the creation of many Tupolev aircraft. Tupolev was a firm believer in using metal structures, and Petlyakov became an expert in light alloy structures after learning the basics with Junkers, the world leader in light alloy structures for aircraft during the 1920s. Up to 1935 Petlyakov was largely responsible for the light alloy wings of aircraft such as the TB-1 and TB-3, and in Tupolev's absence (in the USA learning about American design concepts) was wholly responsible for the development of the TB-4 and ANT-20. In 1936 Petlyakov was appointed manager of the ZOK, which was the factory for special construction attached to the TsAGI, and in this capacity controlled the design of the ANT-42 that was later renamed as the Petlyakov Pe-8. In 1937 Petlyakov was arrested (possibly in relation to Tupolev's similar arrest) for allegedly selling the design of the VI-100 fighter to the Germans for transformation into the Messerschmitt Bf 110 heavy fighter. Petlyakov was imprisoned at a special unit and given the assignment of designing a high-altitude fighter under the auspices of the KB-100 design brigade with A. M. Izakson as his assistant. Such was the success of the design, which finally appeared as the VI-100 and formed the basis of the Pe-2, that Petlyakov was released and installed as head of his own design bureau in July 1940. He was killed in January 1942 when the second Pe-2 off the production line, which he was using as the bureau's liaison aeroplane, caught fire in the air and crashed.

The origins of the Pe-2 can be found in the VI-100 (Vysotnyi Istrebitel-100, or high-altitude fighter no. 100) prototype that first flew in 1930 or 1940, as a

cantilever low-wing monoplane of basically all-metal construction with the exception of its fabric-covered control surfaces. The VI-100 was of conventional layout but extremely advanced design, with turbocharged engines, radiators installed in wing ducts with four upper-surface exits rather than in exterior baths, no hydraulics but a powerful 28-volt electrical system with some 50 actuators controlling most of the moving parts, a pressurised cockpit with tandem two-seat accommodation for the pilot and radio operator/gunner, a dihedralled tailplane carrying endplate vertical surfaces and fully retractable tailwheel landing gear including main units that retracted rearward into the underside of the nacelles for the two wing-mounted Klimov M-105 (later VK-105) Vee piston engines each rated at 1050 hp (783 kW) for take-off. The VI-100 revealed good performance and handling, but was difficult and expensive to make. In May 1940 it was decided that further development would be concentrated on a PB-100 (Pikiruyushchii Bombardirov-shchik-100, or dive-bomber no. 100) with an unpressurised cabin, provision for a prone navigator/bombardier below and ahead of the pilot in the nose, and the powerplant revised from the use of two TK-3 to two TK-2 turbochargers.

The PB-100 prototype was produced as a conversion of the second VI-100 prototype, and made its maiden flight in June 1940. Later in the same month the decision was taken for the PB-100 to be placed in immediate production with minor changes as the Pe-2, and in the following month Petlyakov and his design team were released from detention. The Pe-2 used basically the same airframe as the PB-100 with revised accommodation, M-105R Vee piston engines without turbochargers and installed in different nacelles, a hydraulic actuation system for the main landing gear units, enlarged vertical tail surfaces, and improvements to the protection for the crew and fuel tankage. The opportunity was also taken to revise the airframe structure to help implement mass production. In its initial form with the powerplant of two M-105RA engines, the Pe-2 had a span of 56 ft 3.67 in (17.16 m) with an area of 435.95 sq ft (40.50 m^2), length of 41 ft 6.5 in

BELOW: Partnering the B-26 in the attack bomber role, the North American B-25 Mitchell was fast and well armed for both offensive and defensive needs.

(12.66 m), height of 13 ft 1.5 in (4.00 m), empty weight of 12943 lb (5870 kg), normal take-off weight of 16934 lb (7680 kg), maximum take-off weight of 18728 lb (8495 kg), maximum level speed of 335.5 mph (540 km/h) at 16405 ft (5000 m), cruising speed of 232 kt (267 mph; 430 km/h) at 16405 ft (5000 m), range of 932 miles (1500 km), climb to 16405 ft (5000 m) in 7 minutes, and service ceiling of 28870 ft (8800 m).

MAIDEN FLIGHT

The first drawings of the Pe-2 were released to the factory in July 1940, and the first aeroplane off the production line made its maiden flight in November 1940. The Pe-2 entered service in April 1941, and by the time of the German invasion in June 1941, some 458 aircraft had been delivered and 290 of these were operational. As the Germans advanced into the USSR, the Pe-2 production line was evacuated to Kazan in October 1941 and then merged with another factory for greater productive capability. The success of this relocation and expansion is indicated by the fact that 1405 Pe-2s were built in the second half of 1941, within the context of a steadily growing programme that witnessed the delivery of 11,427 aircraft before production ended in the first quarter of 1945.

The Pe-2FT, the original version of the Pe-2, remained in production up to the spring of 1942, and was then replaced by the Frontovoye Trebovaniye (front-line request) variant which, as its name suggests, was the result of suggestions and requests passed back to the design bureau from front-line units. The changes in this model were the replacement of the original type of dorsal gun position by an MV-3 turret built cleverly into the rear part of the cockpit enclosure and carrying one 0.3 in (7.62 mm) ShKAS trainable rearward-firing machine gun, a second 0.3 in (7.62 mm) ShKAS machine gun installed as a lateral-firing weapon in either the port or starboard side window in the radio operator/gunner's compartment, the removal of the underwing dive brakes, and the amount of glazing reduced. From February 1943 and as demands for the Yakovlev fighters permitted, the Pe-2FT was completed with the uprated powerplant of two Klimov VK-105PF Vee piston engines each rated at 1260 hp (939.5 kW) for take-off. Other improvements added at this time were a number of aerodynamic refinements (a reduction of the gaps between fixed and moving surfaces, a revision of the nacelle shape, and a tightening of the landing gear doors in the closed position) that combined with the more potent powerplant for an overall improvement in performance despite the higher weight of this variant.

There were many variants of the Pe-2 in its basic attack bomber form. The Pe-2MV was a version of the standard Pe-2 for the attack role with two 20 mm (0.787 in) ShVAK fixed forward-firing cannons and two 0.5 in (12.7 mm) Beresin fixed forward-firing machine guns in the front of a ventral gondola replacing the weapons bay, and a single 0.3 in (7.62 mm) ShKAS trainable rearward-firing machine gun in an MV-3 dorsal turret. The Pe-2FZ was delivered in small numbers during 1943 as a Frontovoye Zadaniye (front-line task) variant of the Pe-2FT, with no nose accommodation and an FZ dorsal turret armed with two 0.5 in (12.7 mm) Beresin trainable rearward-firing machine guns. The Pe-2B was the standard bomber version from 1944 with a number of structural and system improvements as well as a gun armament of three 0.5 in (12.7 mm) Beresin machine guns and one 0.3 in (7.62 mm) ShKAS machine gun. The Pe-2R was the Razvyedchik (reconnaissance) day reconnaissance derivative of the Pe-2 with three or four vertical and oblique cameras installed in the lower fuselage and an AK-1 automatic course-control system for maximum accuracy. The type was powered by two M-105PF Vee piston engines, had an armament of three 0.5 in (12.7 mm) UBS machine guns, and could also carry two 31.9 Imp gal (145 litre) drop tanks on the inboard underwing hardpoints for a maximum range of 1056 miles (1700 km).

THE AVRO LANCASTER

The most successful and celebrated heavy bomber used by the Royal Air Force's Bomber Command for its night offensive in the second half of World War II, the Avro Lancaster was built to the extent of some 7300 aircraft during the course of the war but did not even begin life until that war was already three months old. At that time the Avro company's most important design team, under the supervision of Roy Chadwick, was concerned mostly with the development of the Type 679 Manchester twin-engined bomber that had resulted, like the rival Handley Page H.P.56, from the Air Ministry's P.13/36 requirement for a medium bomber with a powerplant of two Rolls-Royce Vulture X-type engines. The

Petlyakov Pe-2FT

Type: four-seat multi-role bomber
Country of origin: USSR
Powerplant: two Klimov 1260-hp (939.5-kW) VK-105PF Vee piston engines
Performance: maximum level speed 360 mph (580 km/h); service ceiling 28,870 ft (8800 m); typical range 817 miles (1315 km)
Weights: empty 13,119 lb (5950 kg); max take-off 18,783 lb (8520 kg)
Dimensions: wing span 56 ft 1.67 in (17.11 m); length 41 ft 11 in (12.78 m); height 11 ft 2.67 in (3.42 m
Armament: five 0.3 in (7.62 mm) ShKAS and 0.5 in (12.7 mm) Beresin UBS machine guns, plus up to 3527 lb (1600 kg) of ordnance

■ **ABOVE: The Soviet counterpart of the Ju 88 and Mosquito, but optimised for the tactical support role, was the superb Petlyakov Pe-2 twin-engined light bomber.**

whole P.13/36 programme was troubled by the slow and uncertain development of the Vulture engine, which eventually materialised as a powerful but unreliable type, and, as early as 1937, Handley Page had received permission to revise its H.P.56 design with two Vultures to a powerplant of four Rolls-Royce Merlin Vee piston engines, thereby creating the H.P.57 Halifax heavy bomber. The Air Ministry persisted with the twin-Vulture Manchester, however, and plans were laid for the large-scale production of this type by a group of manufacturers that included Avro, Armstrong Whitworth, Fairey and Metropolitan-Vickers. Chadwick and his design team still had severe reservations about the long-term viability of the Vulture powerplant, however, and initiated several studies for versions of the Manchester with a different powerplant. At the end of 1939 Avro was informed by the Air Ministry that it should proceed with the detail design of the Manchester Mk II, that would be a minimum-change development of the Manchester Mk I with a powerplant of two Napier Sabre H-type piston engines or two Bristol Centaurus radial piston engines, but this project was soon overtaken by that for the Manchester Mk III with a powerplant of four Merlin engines. Despite the change from two to four engines, the Manchester Mk III was seen as being a relatively straightforward development that would retain the Manchester Mk I's fuselage, tail unit and flat wing centre section, which was of the constant-chord type and carried the nacelles that supported the retractable main units of the tailwheel landing gear. It would now be adapted for the Merlin engine in place of the original Vulture: to the outer ends of this section would now be added new longer-span outer panels that were to be dihedralled, tapered in thickness and chord, and carry the nacelles for the other pair of Merlins.

Avro accorded the new company designation Type 683 to the revised type, and estimated that it would be able to carry a bomb load of 12,000 lb (5448 kg) over a range of 1000 miles (1609 km) at a speed of 245 mph (394 km/h) after take-off at a maximum weight of 57,000 lb (25,878 kg). This estimate suggested that the Type 683 would provide considerably greater capability than the Manchester, even though it would place an additional burden on Merlin production. The Air Ministry thought that the Type 683 would be slightly less capable than the rival H.P.57, but ordered Avro to place the model in production as soon as it had completed its orders for 300 Manchester bombers. As the new model made extensive use of existing components and assemblies, the completion of detail design work and the construction of the two prototypes moved ahead rapidly, and the first prototype made its maiden flight on 9 January 1941 as what was clearly a derivative of the Manchester Mk I with its original type of short-span tailplane carrying small endplate vertical surfaces supplemented by a centre-line surface, and with a defensive armament of two 0.303 in (7.7 mm) Browning trainable forward-firing machine guns in a power-operated Frazer-Nash F.N.5 nose turret and four 0.303 in (7.7 mm) Browning trainable rearward-firing machine guns in a power-operated Frazer-Nash F.N.4A tail turret.

After initial flight trials, the first prototype was delivered to the Aircraft & Armament Experimental Establishment at Boscombe Down for official trials, and the second prototype was completed for a maiden flight in May 1941 with the tailplane increased in span from 22 ft 0 in (6.71 m) to 33 ft 0 in (10.06 m) and carrying larger endplate vertical surfaces that removed the need for the centre-line fin, and the defensive armament of the first prototype upgraded to the planned production standard: this comprised two 0.303 in (7.7 mm) Browning trainable forward-firing machine guns in a power-operated Frazer-Nash F.N.5 nose turret, four 0.303 in (7.7 mm) Browning trainable rearward-firing machine guns in a power-operated Frazer-Nash F.N.20 tail turret, two 0.303 in (7.7 mm) Browning trainable machine guns in the power-operated Frazer-Nash F.N.50 dorsal turret, and two 0.303 in (7.7 mm) Browning trainable machine guns in the power-operated Frazer-Nash F.N.64 ventral turret. The prototypes had a powerplant of four Merlin XX engines each rated at 1280 hp (954 kW) for take-off, 1460 hp (1089 kW) at 6250 ft (1905 m) and 1435 hp (1070 kW) at 11,000 ft (3355 m), and driving a three-blade de Havilland metal propeller of the constant-speed type. The prototypes trials were so successful that the Air Ministry decided to terminate Manchester production immediately, after the delivery of only 200 aircraft, so that construction of the new Lancaster could begin as soon as possible. The first Lancaster Mk I off the production line flew in October 1941, and on Christmas Eve of 1941 three aircraft were delivered to No 44 Squadron for operational trials, which culminated in the type's first operational sorties in March 1942. Deliveries to operational squadrons were not as rapid as had been hoped, for there emerged the need for the wing tips to be strengthened and for a number of changes to be implemented, including a revision of the upper skinning of the wing, but in general the Lancaster Mk I was very similar to the second prototype. Operational squadrons soon discovered that the ventral turret saw little use and therefore often removed it, and two officially inspired changes were the

■ **ABOVE: An Avro Lancaster seen over the fields of England. The Lancaster was an immediate success for the RAF, and fulfilled the service's requirements for a night bomber until the war's end.**

addition of a carefully shaped fairing round the lower edge of the dorsal turret to improve the airflow round this protruding item and also create a taboo track to prevent the gunner firing into any part of the airframe, most especially the vertical tail surfaces, and, from the fifth aeroplane onward, an increase in internal fuel capacity from 1710 Imp gal (7773.7 litres) in four wing tanks to 2154 Imp gal (9792.1 litres) in enlarged standard tanks and additional tanks installed farther outboard in the wings.

IMMEDIATE SUCCESS

The Lancaster Mk I was an immediate operational success, and that the Lancaster was 'right' in all important respects from the very beginning of its service career is attested by the facts that large-scale production saw the delivery of only three more variants (one major and two minor) and that the Lancaster Mk I remained in production right up to the end of hostilities in World War II. This is not to say, however, that there were not considerable developments during the course of each variant's production run: so far as the Lancaster Mk I was concerned, for example, the weapons bay was soon provided with a strengthened support structure for the carriage of a single 8000 lb (3629 kg) bomb, and then fitted with modified doors to permit the carriage of a single 12,000 lb (5443 kg) bomb. As first delivered with a powerplant of four Merlin XX engines, the Lancaster Mk I had a maximum take-off weight of 61,500 lb (27,921 kg) for a maximum level speed of 287 mph (462 km/h) at 11,500 ft (3505 m) and a range of 1660 miles (2671 km) with a 14,000 lb (6356 kg) bomb load. The production standard later switched to the Merlin 22 engine for a maximum take-off weight of 63,000 lb (28,602 kg), maximum level speed of 270 mph (434 km/h) at 19,000 ft (5790 m) and a range of 1020 miles; 1641 km) with a 14,000 lb (6356 kg) bomb load increasing to 2450 miles (3942 km) with a 5500 lb (2495 kg) bomb load. The production standard later switched again to the Merlin 24 engine rated at 1640 hp (1223 kW) at 2000 ft (610 m) and 1500 hp (1118 kW) at 9500 ft (2895 m) for normal and overload maximum take-off weights of 68,000 and 72,000 lb (30,872 and 32,688 kg) respectively. Further improvements introduced to the Lancaster Mk I included H_2S navigation and bombing radar introduced in August 1943 on aircraft without the bulged weapons bay and distinguishable by the large opaque Perspex fairing over its ventral antenna; and the ability to carry the 22,000 lb (9979 kg) 'Grand Slam' transonic penetration bomb in 33 Merlin 24-engined Lancaster B.Mk I (Special) conversions with the weapons bay doors removed and fairings replacing the nose and dorsal turret which were removed to save weight. Production of the Lancaster Mk I (from late 1942 Lancaster B.Mk I and after the war Lancaster B.Mk 1) was 3434 aircraft.

Toward the end of 1941, production of the Lancaster Mk I was accelerating so rapidly that there were fears that airframe production would soon outstrip Merlin availability, and it was decided to consider a derivative using an engine that was in less demand. The choice fell on the Bristol Hercules radial piston engine in its Hercules VI form, rated at 1725 hp (1286 kW). The Air Ministry ordered two prototypes of this Lancaster Mk II: the second was not completed, and the first made its maiden flight in November 1941 with a slight lengthening of the weapons bay and the F.N.64 ventral turret. Trials revealed that the Lancaster Mk II closely resembled the Lancaster Mk I in weights and in performance, with the sole exception that the service ceiling was only slightly more than 15,000 ft (4570 m). Even so, it was decided to place the model in production, and Armstrong Whitworth delivered 300 examples from September 1942, and some of the later aircraft had the bulged weapons bay introduced on later Lancaster Mk Is with the revised powerplant of four Hercules XVI radial engines rated identically to the original Hercules VI engines. The model was soon redesignated as the Lancaster B.Mk II , but production was not as extensive as originally planned, as Merlin production did in fact match demand.

PACKARD ENGINES

Known at the very beginning of its career as the Lancaster Mk III, then as the Lancaster B.Mk III and in the later stages of its life after World War II as the Lancaster B.Mk 3, this was the direct equivalent of the Lancaster Mk I with a powerplant of four Merlin engines built under licence in the USA by Packard with the local designation V-1650. When used in the Lancaster B.Mk III, these engines were the Merlin 28 or 38 equivalent to the Merlin 22, and the Merlin 224 equivalent to the Merlin 24. The first trial installation of American-built engines was made in a Lancaster Mk I conversion that flew in August 1942, and the first production aircraft became available later in the same year. It was 23 examples of the Lancaster Mk III type that were adapted for delivery of the 'bouncing bomb' designed by Dr. Barnes Wallis for the celebrated attack by No 617 Squadron in May 1943 on the Eder, Enepe, Lister, Mohne and Sorpe dams, thought to control the water levels of the Ruhr river as it passed through the Ruhr industrial region. Another special weapon that could be carried by Lancaster Mk III (and also Lancaster Mk I) bombers with the bulged weapons bay designed for the carriage of the 12,000 lb

(5443 kg) high-capacity blast bomb was the 12,000 lb (5443 kg) 'Tallboy', another weapon designed by Wallis. This was a highly streamlined unit intended to reach supersonic speed before impacting, giving it considerable penetration before detonation. The weapon was used successfully against the battleship KMS *Tirpitz*, deep railway tunnels and similar communications targets, and the concrete roofs of U-boat pens. Production of the Lancaster B.Mk III totalled 3030 aircraft, and these had weights and performance identical with those of their Lancaster Mk I equivalents. Changes effected later in the production run with the general omission of the F.N.64 ventral turret, the frequent replacement of the F.N.50 turret in the dorsal position by the F.N.79 or F.N.150 units, and the general replacement of the F.N.20 turret in the tail position by the F.N.121 or F.N.82, the former with four 0.303 in (7.7 mm) Browning machine guns and the latter with two 0.5 in (12.7 mm) Browning machine guns. The heavier-calibre armament was also used in another turret option, the Rose-Rice Type R No 2 Mk I, that was often combined with another development late in the war, namely the 'Village Inn' Automatic Gun-laying Turret, incorporating a radar sight for automatic laying and firing of the turret's guns. Like all other Lancaster variants, the Lancaster B.Mk III was operated solely in the European theatre during World War II.

Inspired by the Lancaster Mk IV, with a powerplant of four Merlin 85 engines each rated at 1635 hp (1219 kW) and driving a four-blade propeller, the Lancaster B.Mk VI was a development of the Lancaster Mk III with the same powerplant but an otherwise unaltered airframe, except for the removal of the nose and dorsal turrets and the fairing of the apertures thus left. The prototype conversion made its maiden flight in the spring of 1944, and there followed another six aircraft. Only four of the aircraft were used operationally by Nos 7 and 635 Squadrons in the electronic warfare role with radar jamming and chaff equipment, and even these were withdrawn in November 1944. The Lancaster B.Mk VII, with 180 examples built, saw service only after the end of World War II mostly in the Far East, and was a development of the Lancaster Mk III with a Martin dorsal turret. This power-operated unit was fitted with two 0.5 in (12.7 mm) Browning trainable machine guns and was installed further forward on the fuselage than the Frazer-Nash turret. The Lancaster B.Mk X designation was accorded to 430 examples of the Lancaster B.Mk III built in Canada by Victory Aircraft and identical in all important respects to the Lancaster B.Mk III.

ABOVE: Supported on arms with a drive to rotate it backward, this was the 'dam buster' bomb carried by Lancaster B.Mk I (Special) aircraft on No. 617 Squadron.

THE HEINKEL HE 177

The Heinkel He 177 Greif (griffin) resulted from the German air ministry's realisation in the middle of 1937 that its heavy bomber programme had lost impetus, with the death in 1936 of Generalleutnant Walther Wever, the Luftwaffe's chief-of-staff and firm believer in strategic heavy bombing. In June 1937, therefore, Heinkel was ordered to proceed without delay on the development of its Projekt 1041 design, originally evolved to meet the 1936 'Bomber A' requirement for a type able to deliver a bomb load of at least 2205 lb (1000 kg) over a range of 4163 miles (6700 km) at a maximum level speed of at least 335.5 mph (540 km/h). The task of developing an improved version of the P.1041 design was entrusted to a team supervised by Dipl.-Ing. Heinrich Hertel with Dipl.-Ing. Siegfried Günter as his prime deputy. Considerable delays, both technical and political, then intervened to slow the programme, and the resulting He 177 V1 prototype made its first flight only in November 1939 as a large shoulder/mid-wing all-metal monoplane. The design was very clean, and this was helped by the unusual powerplant, which appeared to be of the two-engined type but was in fact of the four-engined variety. Each of the two large four-blade propellers was driven by two Daimler-Benz DB 601 inverted-Vee piston engines close-coupled to create a single DB 606 engine.

The aeroplane had a number of advanced features, and eight prototypes were used in the development programme. Three of the prototypes were lost in fatal crashes, resulting mainly from engine fires and a structural weakness in the wing, neither of which was ever fully cured, and there followed 35 He 177A-0 pre-production aircraft before the first of 130 Arado-built He 177A-1 production aircraft entered service from July 1942. The He 177A-1 was produced in four variants as the He 177A-1/R1 basic bomber, the He 177A-1/R2 bomber with a bombing position replacing the two 0.312 in (7.92 mm) MG 81 machine guns in the rear of the ventral gondola, the He 177A-1/R3 bomber with a remotely controlled power-operated barbette under the rear fuselage with a single 0.51 in (13 mm) MG 131 trainable machine gun, and the He 177A-1/R4 with one 0.51 in (13 mm) MG 131 trainable rearward-firing machine gun in the rear of the ventral gondola and one

0.51 in (13 mm) MG 131 trainable machine gun in a manned dorsal turret.

Built to the extent of 170 aircraft by Heinkel and Arado, the He 177A-3 differed from the He 177A-1 mainly in having the engines moved slightly farther forward, the fuselage lengthened by 5 ft 3 in (1.60 m) behind the wing, and a manned dorsal turret added on the rear fuselage with an armament of two 0.51 in (13 mm) MG 131 trainable machine guns. It was planned that this model should be powered by the Daimler-Benz DB 610 engine, which comprised a pair of DB 605 inverted-Vee piston engines close-coupled to provide 2950 hp (2199.5 kW) for take-off and 3100 hp (2311 kW) at 6560 ft (2000 m), but this engine suffered continued development problems and the He 177A-3 was powered like its predecessor with the DB 606 engine. Like the He 177A-1, the He 177A-3 was produced in a number of subvariants: as the He 177A-3/R1 basic bomber; the He 177A-3/R2 bomber with an improved electrical system, a modified gun position at the front of the ventral gondola with a 20 mm (0.787 in) MG 151/20 cannon in place of the slower-firing 20 mm (0.787 in) MG FF cannon originally used, and a redesigned tail position with seated rather than prone accommodation for a gunner who now operated a 20 mm (0.787 in) MG 151/20 cannon in place of the original 0.51 in (13 mm) MG 131 machine gun; the He 177A-3/R3 launch platform for the Henschel Hs 193 air-to-surface missile, of which three were carried under the wings and fuselage; the He 177A-3/R4 improved version of the He 177A-3/R3 with the ventral gondola lengthened by 3 ft 11 in (1.19 m) to provide more space for the missile controller and his FuG 203b Kehl III command transmitter; the He 177A-3/R5 heavy attack model, of which just five were made with a powerplant of two DB 610 engines and the gondola revised for the accommodation of a 75 mm (2.95 in) BK 7,5 anti-tank gun and its hand-loaded ammunition; and the He 177A-3/R7 torpedo bomber of which a mere three were completed with provision for two Italian L5 torpedoes under the fuselage or wings. The He 177A-4 was a planned high-altitude model that was later redesignated as the He 274 and completed after World War II in France as the AAS.01A.

The He 177A-5 was the DB 610-engined model, optimised for the carriage of external loads such as the LT 50 torpedo, Hs 293 air-to-surface missile and FX-1400 Fritz X guided bomb, and thus featured a strengthened wing structure, shortened landing gear legs and the removal of the Fowler flaps along the inboard section of the wings in line with the weapon hardpoints. The basic model had the same armament as the He 177A-3/R2 and was thus designated as the He 177A-5/R2, and while this retained the original type of three-section ventral weapons bay, the doors of the forward section were locked in the closed position and fitted with external hardpoints. Subvariants of this model included the He 177A-5/R5 of which just one was completed with an additional remotely controlled power-operated barbette under the fuselage to the rear of the weapons bay with an armament of one 0.51 in (13 mm) MG 131 trainable machine gun, the He 177A-5/R6 derivative of the He 177A-5/R5 with the two forward parts of the weapons bay closed, the He 177A-5/R7 with a pressurised cabin, and the He 177A-5/R8 of which a single example was completed with remotely controlled chin and tail barbettes. Production of the He 177A-5 series was undertaken only in 1944, and amounted to 565 aircraft. Variants that reached the prototype or development stages but were not used operationally included the He 177A-6/R1 of which six were built with heavier armament and armour protection for the crew and fuel tankage, the He 177A-6/R2 of which one was completed with a new forward fuselage and heavier armament, and the He 177A-7 of which six were produced as He 177A-5 conversions with a wing spanning 118 ft 1.5 in (36.00 m) and a powerplant of two DB 610 engines in place of the planned powerplant of two Daimler-Benz DB 613 engines each rated at 3600 hp (2684 kW).

Enormous effort was expended on the development and production of the He 177, but the type never achieved the reliability required on an effective operational warplane, and although it saw considerable if somewhat sporadic action, the Greif never achieved anything of significance. However, it is worth noting that at the end of the war, one example was under conversion as the delivery platform for the as-yet-unbuilt German atomic weapon.

THE HELEN

The Nakajima Ki-49 Donryu (storm dragon) was known to the Allies by the

Heinkel He 177A-1/R1 Greif

Type: six-seat heavy bomber
Country of origin: Germany
Powerplant: two 2700-hp (2013-kW) Daimler-Benz DB 606 24-cylinder piston engines
Performance: max level speed 317 mph (510 km/h); service ceiling 22,965 ft (7000 m); max range 3480 miles (5600 km)
Weights; empty 39,771 lb (18,040 kg); max take-off 66,139 lb (30,000 kg)
Dimensions: wing span 103 ft 1.75 in (31.44 m); length 66 ft 11 in (20.40 m); height 20 ft 11.75 in (6.39 m)
Armament: three 0.312 in (7.92 mm) MG 81 and two 0.51 in (13 mm) MG 131 machine guns, one 20 mm MG FF cannon, plus up to 13,228 lb (6000 kg) of stores

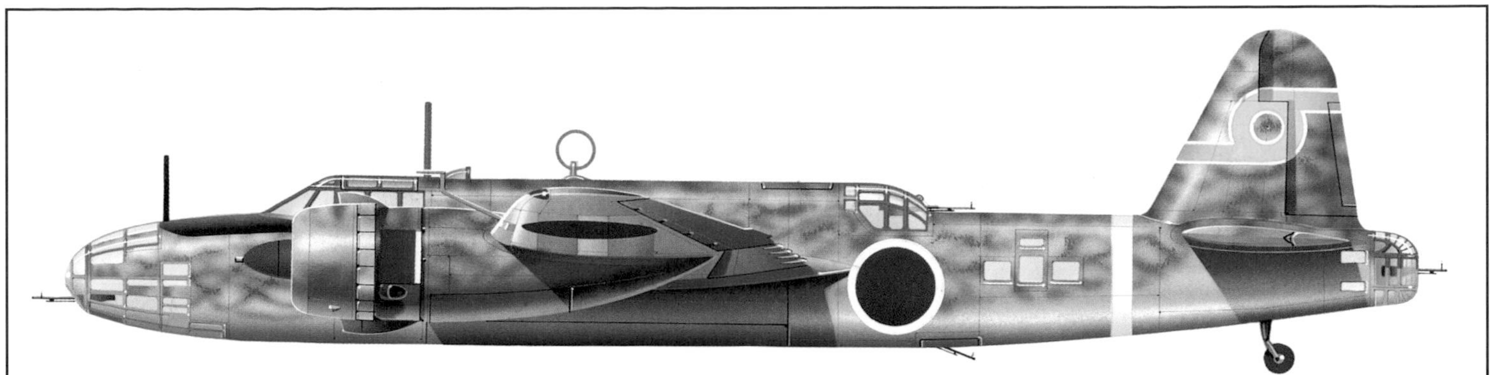

Nakajima Ki-49-IIb

Type: seven-seat heavy bomber
Country of origin: Japan
Powerplant: two 1500-hp (1118-kW) Nakajima Ha-109 (Army Type 2) radial piston engines
Performance: max level speed 306 mph (492 km/h) at 16,405 ft (5000 m); service ceiling 30,510 ft (9300 m); max range 1833 miles (2950 km)
Weights; empty 14,396 lb (6530 kg); max take-off 25,133 lb (11,400 kg)
Dimensions: wing span 67 ft 0.125 in (20.42 m); length 54 ft 1.635 in (16.50 m); height 13 ft 1.25 in (4.25 m)
Armament: one 20 mm (0.787 in) Ho-1 cannon, four 0.5 in (12.7 mm) Ho-103 (Type 1) and two 0.303 in (7.7 mm) Type 89 machine guns, up to 2205 lb (1000 kg) of stores

reporting name 'Helen', and although planned as a replacement for the Mitsubishi Ki-21 proved so unsatisfactory that it supplemented rather than replaced the older type. Designed by a team under the supervision of engineers named Nishimura, Itokawa and Koyama, the Ki-49 resulted from a 1938 requirement and emerged as a cantilever monoplane of clean line and all-metal construction with an oval-section fuselage, a plain tail unit, a mid-set dihedralled wing that was tapered in thickness and chord, and carried the standard trailing-edge arrangement of outboard ailerons and inboard flaps, and tailwheel landing gear that included main units which retracted into the underside of the nacelles for the two wing-mounted engines. The first of three prototype and seven service-trials aircraft made its maiden flight in August 1939 with a powerplant of two Nakajima Ha-5 Kai radial piston engines each rated at 950 hp (708 kW) for take-off and 1080 hp (805 kW) at 13125 ft (4000 m) and driving a three-blade metal propeller of the two-pitch type. In March 1941 the type was ordered into production as the Ki-49-I for service with the designation Army Type 100 Heavy Bomber Model 1 Donryu and a powerplant of two Nakajima Ha-41 (Army Type 100) radial piston engines, each rated at 1250 hp (932 kW) for take-off and 1260 hp (939.5 kW) at 12140 ft (3700 m) and driving a three-blade metal constant-speed propeller. Some 129 examples of this initial model were delivered between August 1941 and August 1942 with a defensive armament that included one 20 mm (0.787 in) Ho-1 trainable cannon in the dorsal position and single 0.303 in (7.7 mm) Type 89 machine guns in the nose, ventral, tail and beam positions.

Delivered to the extent of 617 aircraft by Nakajima between September 1942 and December 1944, and 50 aircraft by Tachikawa between January 1943 and January 1944, the Ki-49-II introduced an uprated powerplant in the hope of overcoming the Ki-49-I's deficiencies in speed and payload/range performance. The Ki-49-IIa (Army Type 100 Heavy Bomber Model 2A Donryu) had the same armament as the Ki-49-I, but the Ki-49-IIb (Army Type 100 Heavy Bomber Model 2B Donryu) replaced the single 0.303 in (7.7 mm) machine guns in the nose, ventral and tail positions with single 0.5 in (12.7 mm) Ho-103 (Type 1) machine guns.

The Ki-49-III, of which only six prototypes had been completed before the termination of the Ki-49 programme in December 1944, was a further attempt to improve capability by the adoption of a considerably higher-rated powerplant in the form of two Nakajima Ha-117 radial piston engines each rated at 2420 hp (1805 kW) for take-off, and in the closing stages of the war a number of Ki-49 bombers were expended in kamikaze attacks with the crew reduced to two and a bombload of 3527 lb (1600 kg).

ATOMIC BOMBER

The Boeing B-29 Superfortress is generally remembered as the only warplane that has yet dropped nuclear weapons in anger, the two instances happening on 6 and 9 August 1945 when the Japanese cities of Hiroshima and Nagasaki were destroyed. The enormous impact of these single events finally persuaded the Japanese authorities to agree to an unconditional surrender rather than face the threat of further bombings and/or an American invasion of the Japanese home islands. Yet by the time of Hiroshima and Nagasaki, the B-29 had effectively neutralised Japan's war-making potential by burning the heart out of her cities, destroying her communications network, crippling her industries, and mining her coastal waters. By any criterion, therefore, the B-29 must be judged one of the most decisive weapons of World War II despite the fact that it only made its first combat sortie in June 1944.

The origins of this potent bomber can be found in 1938, when Major General Oscar Westover, commanding the US Army Air Corps, decided that a new bomber would be needed to supplant the Boeing Model 299 (B-17 Flying Fortress) that was still being evolved through a number of penny-packet procurement orders as a result of Congressional parsimony. Westover was killed in an air crash shortly after setting in motion the process that led eventually to the design of the Boeing Model 345. Reflecting Congressional reservations, the Department of War reacted negatively to Westover's creation of an official requirement for a 'super bomber', but the project was kept alive by Brigadier General H. H. 'Hap' Arnold, Westover's successor, and by Major General Oliver Echols of the procurement executive, who were largely responsible for the eventual

Boeing B-29 Superfortress

Type: long-range strategic bomber
Country of origin: USA
Powerplant: four 2200-hp (1640-kW) Wright R-3350-23 radial piston engines
Performance: maximum level speed 358 mph (576 km/h); service ceiling 31,850 ft (9710 m); max range 5830 miles (9382 km)
Weights: empty 70,140 lb (31,816 kg); max take-off 124,000 lb (56,246 kg)
Dimensions: wing span 141 ft 2.75 in (43.05 m); length 99 ft 0 in (30.18 m); height 29 ft 7 in (9.02 m)
Armament: 10 0.5 in (12.7 mm) Browning M2 machine guns, plus up to 20,000 lb (9072 kg) ordnance

'Hemisphere Defense Weapon' concept and associated requirement issued in February 1940. Boeing responded with its Model 345, whose estimated performance met all the USAAC's requirements except in speed, which was estimated at 382 mph (615 km/h). Boeing submitted the Model 345 design to the USAAC in May 1940, when Consolidated, Douglas and Lockheed also made submissions. The Douglas and Lockheed designs were soon eliminated from the running, and in the final competition between Boeing and Consolidated the decision went to the former's Model 345.

THE XB-29 PROTOTYPES

In June 1940, Boeing received a small initial contract for further design work and the wind tunnel testing of models, and during September of the same year, the USAAC ordered three XB-29 prototypes (one for static tests and two for flight trials) before revising its order in December to demand the construction of three flying prototypes. Boeing started work on the mock-up of the XB-29 in May 1941, and later in the same month, the USAAC announced its intention of ordering 250 B-29 bombers to be built in new government-funded facilities at Boeing's plant in Wichita, Kansas. The contract for these 250 aircraft was signed in September 1941, by which time the USAAC had become the US Army Air Forces, and the order was increased to 500 aircraft in January 1942, the month after the attack on Pearl Harbor had drawn the USA into World War II. Just one month later, the new bomber programme had acquired so high a priority that the US authorities decided that additional production facilities would be created at government-owned plants to be run by Bell at Marietta in Georgia, North American at Kansas City in Kansas, and the Fisher Body Division of the General Motors Corporation at Cleveland in Ohio. In the event the last two did not produce the B-29: the USAAF traded the Kansas City facility to the US Navy in exchange for the latter's Boeing-run facility at Renton in Washington, and Martin at Omaha in Nebraska replaced the Fisher Body Division so that the latter could concentrate of the production of B-29 assemblies including the nacelles.

The aeroplane that emerged from this effort was by any standards a truly prodigious achievement that even so was not without its critics. Adverse comment was centred primarily on the bomber's high wing loading, which resulted from the USAAC's initial demands for additional fuel, bomb load, defensive armament and protection. This made the Model 345 the world's heaviest aeroplane at the time of its conception and development, and there followed many discussions and modifications as the company pressed ahead with construction of the XB-29 prototypes to an exceptionally sleek design based on an all-metal structure employing thick skins that were bolted rather than riveted together to provide the right combination of low drag and high strength. Other features of the advanced design were highly turbocharged engines for good performance at altitude, and defensive armament based on the use of remotely controlled barbettes. The first XB-29 made its maiden flight on 21 September 1942 without its armament but with a powerplant of four R-3350-13 radial engines each driving a three-blade propeller as the planned four-blade units were not yet ready. From April 1943 there followed 14 YB-29 service test aircraft with full defensive armament and a powerplant of four R-3350-21 radial engines each still driving a three-blade propeller. Right from the beginning of the flight test programme it was clear that the Superfortress, as the type had by now been named, had prodigious performance and could be an important weapon. The problem was the fact that the type was beset by a host of technical problems, many of them stemming from the fact that the B-29 had been rushed into production before all its problems had been diagnosed and cured.

PACIFIC DEPLOYMENT

Given the B-29's great range with a useful warload, the USAAF decided that the type should be deployed not in Europe against the Germans, who were already being pounded by the service's B-17 Flying Fortress and Consolidated B-24 Liberator bombers, but rather in Asia against the Japanese, who were all but immune to American air attack. The first unit to operate the Superfortress was the 58th Very Heavy Bombardment Wing, which had been activated in June 1943 before the delivery of its first YB-29 aircraft, and the arrival of these aircraft during July allowed the unit to familiarise itself with the new bomber. The first B-29s were delivered by Boeing in the autumn of 1943, and aircraft from the Bell and Martin production lines started to reach operational units in 1944; B-29 deliveries amounted to 2181 aircraft in the form of 1620 from Boeing, 357 from Bell and 204 from Martin. The 40th, 444th, 462nd and 468th Very Heavy Bombardment Groups of the 58th Very Heavy Bombardment Wing reached India in the spring of 1944, and carried out their first operational mission in June of that year via staging airfields in China to attack Bangkok. The raids were soon extended in scope and range, including the Japanese home islands from the second mission, but it was soon clear that the simple forward bases of the US 20th Army Air Force's XX Bomber Command in China were too distant from Japan and from their rear bases in India for the B-29 bombers to fight an effective campaign: much of the command's B-29 strength was required to ferry fuel, munitions and supplies to China, leaving only a very modest number of aircraft to wage the war against Japan, and then only with indifferent results. This was one of the primary reasons for the US campaign to capture the Marianas Islands, for on Saipan, Tinian and Guam US engineers soon created five air bases each large enough to accommodate a complete 180-bomber wing of XXI Bomber Command. The first raid against Tokyo was flown from the Marianas in November 1944.

The 1,119 examples of the B-29A were delivered from the Boeing-run facility at Renton, and were completed to a standard that differed from that of the B-29 in its powerplant of four R-3350-57 or -59 radial piston engines, its incorporation of the four-gun forward dorsal barbette in place of the original two-gun unit, and its adoption a new wing structure that increased span to 142 ft 2.75 in (43.35 m). Other details of the B-29A included a length of 99 ft 0 in (30.175 m), height of 29 ft 7 in (9.02 m), empty weight of 71,360 lb (32,369 kg), maximum take-off weight of 141,100 lb (64,003 kg), maximum level speed of 358 mph (575 km/h) at 25,000 ft (7620 m), cruising speed of 230 mph (370 km/h) at optimum altitude, typical range of 4100 miles (6598 km), climb to 20,000 ft (6095 m) in 38 minutes 0 seconds, and service ceiling of 31,850 ft (9710 m).

Production of the B-29 series was completed by the B-29B variant, of which 311 were delivered up to May 1946 by Bell with defensive armament limited to a tail position with three guns (laid and fired automatically with the aid of the APG-15B radar system) and two 0.5 in (12.7 mm) Browning trainable lateral-firing machine guns on special mountings in the rear-fuselage gunners' compartment. The lighter weight and lower drag of this model boosted maximum level speed by some 8.75 kt (10 mph; 16 km/h) and allowed a 3000 lb (1361 kg) increase in the bomb load. The other details of the B-29B included a span of 141 ft 2.75 in ((43.05 m) with an area of 1736.00 sq ft (161.27 m2), length of 99 ft 0 in (30.175 m), height of 29 ft 7 in (9.02 m), empty weight of 69000 lb (31298 kg), maximum take-off weight of 137500 lb (62370 kg), maximum level speed of 364 mph (586 km/h) at 25,000 ft (7620 m), cruising speed of 228 mph (367 km/h) at optimum altitude, typical range of 4200 miles (6759 km), climb to 20,000 ft (6095 m) in 38 minutes 0 seconds, and service ceiling of 32,000 ft (9755 m). Production of an additional 5092 bombers of the B-29 series was terminated with the end of World War II, and the last of 3627 aircraft (including prototypes and service test machines) was delivered in June 1946.

FIRST OPERATIONAL JET

The Arado Ar 234 Blitz (lightning) was the only turbojet-powered bomber to achieve operational status in World War II , and as such was an important milestone in the development of military aviation. The origins of the type can be traced to a 1940 requirement issued by the German air ministry for a turbojet-powered fast reconnaissance aeroplane. Early in 1941 the Arado design team led by Professor Walter Blume and Dipl.-Ing. Hans Rebeski started work on its definitive E.370 project, based on earlier work by Emil Eckstein before his January 1941 departure to Henschel, for a cantilever monoplane that would offer high performance through the use of the greatest possible aerodynamic cleanliness to offset the indifferent power output of the axial-flow turbojets then in prospect. Sufficient power and reliability could be provided only by a two or four-engined powerplant, which dictated a wing-mounted engine installation, and the

BELOW: The name 'Enola Gay' identifies this Boeing B-29 Superfortress long-range heavy bomber as the machine that dropped the first A-bomb on Hiroshima.

ABOVE: Marking the way forward for the bomber, this is a captured German Arado Ar 234B Blitz reconnaissance bomber, delivered late in World War II with a powerplant of two turbojets.

anticipated need to undertake extensive maintenance and/or frequent engine changes demanded the adoption of nacelles attached under the wings' lower surfaces for ease of access. The underslung location of the nacelles in turn dictated the adoption of a high-wing configuration, and drag considerations then demanded a fuselage of the smallest possible cross section. This last precluded the use of landing gear units retracting into the fuselage, and the original solution used by the design team was the combination of a tricycle take-off dolly that was jettisoned as soon as the aeroplane had lifted off the runway, and extendible skids for landing. All these factors dictated the initial layout of the aeroplane that the German air ministry ordered as the Ar 234: a high-set and unswept wing tapered in thickness and chord and carrying on its trailing edges outboard Frise-type ailerons and inboard flaps; a conventional tail unit that was also unswept; an oval-section fuselage carrying the pilot in an almost completely glazed nose section; two fuel tanks in the sections fore and aft of the wing; and skid landing gear comprising a large central unit under the fuselage with smaller units under the nacelles for the two wing-mounted engines.

Development and production of the chosen Junkers Jumo 109-004 turbojets took longer than that of the airframe, and Arado received the first set of Jumo 109-004A-0 pre-production engines only in February 1943. These engines were not cleared for flight, so the Ar 234 V1 prototype was initially restricted to taxiing trials and made its first flight only in June 1943 after the delivery of the first flight-cleared engines, which were Jumo 109-004A units each rated at 1852 lb st (8.24 kN) dry. The test and development programme involved no fewer than 18 prototypes in which many different features were evaluated.

The first five of these were intended to pave the way for the planned Ar 234A production model using the take-off dolly/landing skid combination, and these included the Ar 234 V2 that was basically similar to the Ar 234 V1 and first flew in July 1943, the Ar 234 V3 that first flew in August 1943 with a pressurised cockpit carrying an ejector seat and with provision for RATO units, the Ar 234 V4 that was an improved version of the Ar 234 V3 and first flew in September 1943, and the Ar 234 V5 that first flew in December 1943 with an unpressurised cockpit and a powerplant of two Jumo 109-004B turbojets that had an identical rating to the Jumo 109-004A engines but were each some 198 lb (90 kg) lighter. By this time the German air ministry had realised the tactical impossibility of the Ar 234A series' landing arrangement, which left the aeroplane immobile on the airfield until it could be lifted by three jacks so that the take-off dolly could be moved under it, and had cancelled further work on the Ar 234A in favour of the Ar 234B series with conventional landing gear based on a retractable tricycle arrangement. Arado managed this by increasing the cross section of the fuselage very slightly and using the volume of the central fuselage box girder structure to create wells for the retraction of the narrow-track main units, which were complemented by a nosewheel unit that retracted into the underside of the forward fuselage below the cockpit; some central fuselage fuel capacity had to be sacrificed to provide volume for the mainwheel wells, and this loss was offset by an enlargement forward and rearward of the two self-sealing fuel tanks.

FIRST AR 234B

The first prototype of the Ar 234B series was the Ar 234 V9 that made its maiden flight in March 1944 with a pressurised cockpit and ejector seat, and a powerplant of two Jumo 109-004B-1 turbojets each rated at 1962 lb st (8.73 kN) dry, and this was followed by the Ar 234 V10, which lacked cockpit pressurisation and was fitted, later in its development programme, for the bomber role with attachments under the engine nacelles for two 1102 or 551 lb (500 or 250 kg) SC-500 or SC-250 bombs aimed by means of a periscopic sight that permitted glide and shallow dive-bombing attacks. These attachments could also each carry a drop tank, and provision was made for RATO units. There followed the Ar 234 V11 that was similar to the Ar 234 V9, and then came the first of 20 Ar 234B-0 pre-production aircraft that made its first flight in June 1944. This event took place two days after the Allied landing in northwest France, and by this time the Ar 234 programme was enjoying very high priority as the tide of the war turned increasingly against the Germans. This priority was emphasised by the use of the Ar 234 V5 and Ar 234 V7 prototypes, despite their reliance on the original type of dolly/skid take-off/landing gear, for operational evaluation during July 1944,

Mitsubishi Ki-67-I Hiryu

Type: eight-seat heavy bomber
Country of origin: Japan
Powerplant: two 1900-hp (1417-kW) Mitsubishi Ha-104 (Army Type 4) radial piston engines
Performance: maximum level speed 334 mph (537 km/h); service ceiling 31,070 ft (9470 m); max range 2361 miles (3800 km)
Weights: empty 19,068 lb (8649 kg); max take-off 30,347 lb (13,765 kg)
Dimensions: wing span 73 ft 9.75 in (22.50 m); length 61 ft 4.25 in (18.70 m); height 25 ft 3 in (7.70 m)
Armament: one 20 mm (0.787 in) Ho-5 cannon, five 0.5 in (12.7 mm) Type 1 machine guns , plus up to 2359 kg (1070 kg) of ordnance

and in the course of their sorties the two aircraft easily evaded interception by Allied fighters.

The Ar 234B-0 aircraft were also used operationally pending the arrival of the first production models, which were the Ar 234B-1 Blitz optimised for the reconnaissance role with provision for drop tanks, and the Ar 234B-2 Blitz with a dual-role reconnaissance and bombing/ pathfinding capability. Production of these two variants totalled 210 aircraft, and they entered service in September 1944 with the Sonderkommando Götz, a specialised strategic reconnaissance unit, and then in November of the same year with two other reconnaissance units, Sonderkommando Hecht and Sonderkommando Sperling. In the same month the Ar 234B-2 entered service with Kampfgeschwader 76, the first bomber group to receive the type. Thereafter the Ar 234 was used with such regularity as the worsening fuel supply situation permitted, and proved an effective type that could generally achieve its assigned mission without interference from Allied fighters. The primary variants of the Ar 234B-2 were the Ar 234B-2b reconnaissance model with an outfit of two Rb 50/30 or Rb 75/30 cameras or one Rb 75/30 or Rb 20/30 camera, and the Ar 234B-2/1 pathfinder model with the Lofte 7K bomb sight. The two subvariants could also be fitted with the Patin PDS three-axis autopilot and/or drop tanks, indicated by the suffix 'p' and/or 'r' in the aircraft's designation.

A variant that did not reach full operational service was the Ar 234C with the revised powerplant of four BMW 109-003A-1 Sturm turbojets each rated at 1764 lb st (7.845 kN) dry. This uprated powerplant resulted from the realisation that the airframe could employ considerably more power not so much for higher performance, which was limited by the onset of transonic compressibility problems with the straight flying surfaces, but for the carriage of a greater warload or alternatively for more fuel. Two Ar 234A series' prototypes were completed with the revised powerplant, the Ar 234 V8 first flying in February 1944 with the engines in four separate nacelles and the Ar 234 V6 following in April 1944 with the engines in two twin-engine nacelles. The latter arrangement proved more efficient, and was adopted for the true Ar 234C series prototypes with retractable tricycle landing gear. The first of these were the Ar 234 V13 and Ar 234 V15, which began life as Ar 234B series prototypes but were then adapted with the four-engined powerplant as the precursor of the Ar 234 V19, the first machine built as an Ar 234C series prototype with a doubled glazed pressurised cockpit in place of the original type of pressurised cockpit with single-glazed panels sealed by synthetic rubber. Only 14 production aircraft were built, these being small numbers of the Ar 234C-1 Blitz equivalent of the Ar 234B-1 and of the Ar 234C-3 Blitz multi-role version with two 20 mm (0.787 in) MG 151/20 fixed forward-firing cannon.

THE MITSUBISHI KI-67 HIRYU

Known to the Allies by the reporting name 'Peggy' , the Mitsubishi Ki-67 Hiryu (flying dragon) was without doubt the finest bomber to see service with the Imperial Japanese army or Imperial Japanese navy air forces in the Pacific War of World War II, for it combined high performance with good defensive firepower, adequate offensive weapon load, and a structure that was sturdy and provided good protection for the crew and fuel supply.

The type resulted from a 1940 requirement issued by the Imperial Japanese army air force for a heavy bomber optimised for the tactical role, and the first of 17 prototype and service trials aircraft made its maiden flight in December 1942. The capabilities demonstrated by this aircraft were so extensive that the Imperial Japanese army air force wasted considerable time in planning a family of related types. The air force later decided to concentrate on just a single model, which was ordered into production during December 1943 as the Ki-67-I for service with the designation Army Type 4 Heavy Bomber Model 1 Hiryu .

The first 159 aircraft were completed as pure bombers, but later aircraft had shackles for alternative use in the torpedo bomber role, a capacity in which air-to-surface search radar was often added. The Ki-67-I was a formidable opponent, and without doubt one of Japan's best warplanes of the last year of the Pacific War. A number of the aircraft were later converted by the Japanese to the Ki-67-I Kai standard as three-seat kamikaze aircraft, with a long rod extending from the nose to trigger the detonation of two 1764 lb (800 kg) bombs or 6393 lb (2900 kg) of explosive.

CHAPTER 4
THE BOMBER AFTER WORLD WAR II

The Cold War inspired bigger and faster aircraft, capable of the long ranges needed to reach their targets. However, as air defence systems improved, bombers were forced to fly lower, and try to evade detection.

In 1943 the Royal Air Force's Bomber Command was still heavily involved in the nocturnal strategic bombing campaign against Germany. However, RAF planners were already considering the needs of the strategic air campaign against Japan that would become Bomber Command's primary responsibility as soon as Germany had been defeated. The RAF appreciated that its existing types lacked the range and defensive armament for effective use against Japan. It therefore issued a requirement for a Lancaster replacement, and demanded a powerplant of four Rolls-Royce Merlin engines with two-speed superchargers to provide a cruising altitude of 35,000 ft (10,670 m).

The Avro design team had already begun to consider such a bomber on the aerodynamic and structural basis of the Lancaster, and the design for the improved bomber began to take shape with the company designation Type 694. This was based on a longer-span wing of higher aspect ratio, a longer fuselage, a new nose, a modified weapons bay, and beefed-up landing gear to cater for the new type's increased weights. The RAF was impressed with the new type and planned to procure it in two variants as the Lancaster B.Mk IV with a powerplant of four Merlin 85 engines each rated at 1680 hp (1253 kW), and as the Lancaster B.Mk V with a powerplant of four Merlin 68 engines, each rated at 1750 hp (1305 kW). Belatedly, the RAF recognised the nature of the wholesale changes required and decided that the Merlin 85-engined model would be the Lincoln B.Mk 1.

The first of three prototypes made its maiden flight on 9 June 1944. Plans were laid for the production of 2254 aircraft and the first Lincoln B.Mk 1 came off the production line in February 1945. The type entered service in September 1945, the month in which the Japanese signed their surrender, and, with the loss of the new bomber's operating theatre, the RAF curtailed production of this initial model to just 72 aircraft, which remained in service only to 1946 before being relegated to second-line duties and then retirement in February 1949.

LEFT: An American B-1B Lancer flies at low level over an airbase. Unlike its predecessor, the B-52, the B-1B was designed from the outset to penetrate the Soviet air defences at low level.

THE LINCOLN B.MK 2

The definitive model was the Lincoln B.Mk 2, with American-built engines and defensive armament significantly enhanced by the installation of two 20 mm (0.787 in) cannon in the dorsal turret. Production for the RAF totalled 477 aircraft, but 12 of these were diverted during 1947 to Argentina, which also received 18 new-build aircraft. All the aircraft had been delivered by April 1951, and by June 1948 the earlier aircraft had been tropicalised in recognition of the fact that their range suited them to overseas deployments in theatres such as the Far East. By 1947 the Lincoln B.Mk 2 aircraft had been equipped to two standards: those designated Lincoln B.Mk 2/IIIG had H_2S Mk IIIG radar as well as 'Gee Mk II' and 'Rebecca Mk II' navigation systems, while those designated Lincoln B.Mk 2/IVA had H_2S Mk IVA radar as well as 'Gee-H Mk

■ **ABOVE: The first British bomber to enter service after World War II was the Avro Lincoln, a much improved type derived from the Lancaster with greater power and armament.**

II' and 'Rebecca Mk II' or 'Rebecca Mk IV' navigation systems. The last aircraft had been retired from first-line service by 1955, when the Vickers Valiant turbojet-powered bomber became the RAF's premier bomber, and the type made its final flight in March 1963.

The Lincoln B.Mk 30 was the version of the Lincoln built in Australia by the Beaufort Division of the Australian Department of Aircraft Production. The first five aircraft were assembled from British-supplied components, the initial machine flying in March 1946. Australia had planned to build 85 aircraft, but this total was trimmed to 73. The last of these to be built were the Lincoln MR.Mk 31s – 19 aircraft, which were completed to a maritime reconnaissance standard with the nose lengthened by 6 ft 6 in (1.98 m) to provide accommodation for radar and its two operators. The survivors were all retired in 1961.

THE BOEING B-50

The finest strategic bomber of World War II was the Boeing Model 345 that served with the US Army Air Forces as the B-29 Superfortress. It was appreciated, however, that significantly better performance could be provided by an uprated powerplant, and in 1944 Pratt & Whitney was allocated a B-29A for conversion to XB-44 standard with a powerplant of four Pratt & Whitney R-4360 Wasp Major radial piston engines in different nacelles that raised each engine and its four-blade Curtiss Electric constant-speed propeller above the wing and thereby allowed the incorporation below it of an air inlet for cooling and turbocharger air. The conversion proved successful, and in July 1945 the USAAF ordered 200 production examples with the designation B-29D. Japan's surrender resulted in the trimming of the order to just 60 aircraft that in December 1945 received the revised designation B-50.

The B-50 was in fact a machine that differed considerably from the B-29 even though it retained the overall appearance and size of the original Superfortress model. Features in which the B-50 differed were its much revised powerplant offering 59 per cent greater power, structure revised in 75ST aluminium alloy from the original 23ST alloy resulting in greater strength at lighter weight (e.g. a wing that was 16 per cent stronger but more than 600 lb/ 272 kg lighter), larger flaps and taller vertical tail surface of which the top part could be folded down to allow use of existing hangars, hydraulically boosted rudder and nosewheel unit steering, a faster landing gear retraction system, and electrically de-iced flightdeck windows. Other improvements included thermal de-icing of the wing and tail unit using three combustion heaters (one in each outboard engine nacelle for the wing and one in the base of the vertical tail surface for the empennage) and reversible-pitch propellers for a shorter landing run.

This Model 345-2-1 version of the Superfortress was one of the first aircraft to be built after the newly-created US Air Force's decision that the first production model of any type should be indicated by the letter A suffixed to the numerical part of the designation, and the initial B-50 was therefore a production standard B-50A that first flew on 25 June 1947. Another 78 aircraft followed, 11 of them completed to a somewhat different standard as TB-50A Superfortress crew trainers for the Consolidated (later Convair) B-36. Some 57 of the bombers were later revised with provision for inflight refuelling using the British-developed hose-and-drogue system, carried by B-29 bombers converted to KB-29P tankers, and the B-50A became the first new bomber to be delivered to the Strategic Air Command.

The B-50B was a structurally strengthened version of the B-50A for greater payload and range, and the type was later modified for inflight-refuelling capability. Production totalled 45 aircraft, and all but one of the aircraft were subsequently adapted to the long-range strategic reconnaissance role with the designation RB-50B Superfortress with two 582.9 Imp gal (2649.8 litre) fixed underwing tanks for additional range, improved radar, nine cameras in four stations, and the rear section of the weapons bay revised for the accommodation of a pressurised capsule carrying additional crew members and specialised optical and electronic reconnaissance equipment, as well as photo-flash bombs to provide a nocturnal photography capability. Some 43 of these conversions were further adapted in 1951 to other configurations: the RB-50E Superfortress designation was applied to 14 aircraft adapted for special reconnaissance missions, the RB-50F Superfortress designation was applied to another 14 aircraft adapted with the SHORAN (SHOrt-Range Air Navigation) system for special missions, and the RB-50G Superfortress designation was applied to a final 15 aircraft similar to the RB-50F except for their additional radar equipment (identifiable by five small radomes), a nose section derived from that of the B-50D, a 16-man crew, and strengthened defensive armament.

Developed as the Model 345-9-6 and first flown in May 1949, the B-50D replaced the earlier models' seven-piece glazed nose assembly with a single-piece Plexiglas transparency, incorporating an optically flat bombardier's panel. Other changes were a single-point refuelling system, provision for the two underwing tanks or two 4000 lb (1814 kg) bombs carried on hardpoints under the outer wing panels, revised inflight-refuelling capability from the 16th machine onward, with a receptacle for the Boeing Flying Boom system, and a revised forward dorsal turret. The type appeared at a time when the 'Cold War' between the USA and USSR was intensifying, and the production total and rate were stepped up for the rapid delivery of 222 B-50D bombers for SAC.

USAAF'S NEW JET BOMBER

The US Army Air Force was convinced that the new turbojet engines, under serious development since the mid-1940s, would eventually make possible a new generation of advanced bombers. However, the USAAF also believed that the way forward lay with the combination of existing bomber concepts with turbojet propulsion as an improved-performance, low-risk interim plan. In 1944 came a requirement for a tactical light bomber carrying a bomb load comparable with that of current heavy bombers. North American evolved its NA-130 design to satisfy this requirement, and in 1945 secured an order for three XB-45 prototypes. The NA-130 accommodated the pilot and co-pilot in tandem under a fighter-type canopy (with the bombardier in the nose and the gunner in the tail), and was powered by four slim axial-flow turbojets in two underwing nacelles each accommodating two side-by-side engines. The first XB-45 made its maiden flight on 17 March 1947 with a powerplant of four Allison (General Electric) J35-A-4 turbojet engines each rated at 4000 lb st (17.79 kN) dry. The new bomber was ordered into production as the B-45A Tornado and some 96 such NA-147 aircraft were built.

The B-45A entered service in November 1948, with details that included a crew of four (pilot and co-pilot in tandem on North American ejection seats in an enclosed cockpit, bombardier/navigator in a glazed nose position, and gunner in a tail position) and a maximum bomb load of 20,000 lb (9072 kg). The last B-45A was retired in 1958. The B-45B was planned as an improved B-45A with new radar and fire-control systems, but did not enter production. The first of just 10 improved B-45Cs flew in May 1949, and most surviving B-45A bombers were upgraded to this standard. The RB-45C was a development for the day and night photo-reconnaissance roles without bomber capability. The type first flew in April 1950, and the 33 aircraft were delivered between June 1950 and October 1951.

SOVIET COUNTER

By the middle of 1943, the Soviet leadership had at last decided that strategic bombing was an essential component of any modern air war, and requested the USA on three separate

North American B-45C

Type: four-seat light tactical bomber
Country of origin: USA
Powerplant: four 5200-lb st (23-kN) dryGeneral Electric J47-GE-13 or -15 turbojet engines
Performance: maximum level speed 579 mph (932 km/h); service ceiling 43,200 ft (13,170 m); range 1910 miles (3074 km)
Weights: empty 48,903 lb (22,182 kg); max take-off 112,952 lb (51,235 kg)
Dimensions: wing span 89 ft 0 in (27.13 m) without tip tanks; length 75 ft 4 in (22.96 m); height 25 ft 2 in (7.67 m)
Armament: two 0.5 in (12.7 mm) Browning M7 machine guns, plus up to 22,000 lb (9979 kg) of ordnance

occasions for the supply of Boeing B-29 Superfortress bombers. The USA refused and the USSR decided to press ahead regardless, using any and all information that could be garnered via overt as well as covert means. The Tupolev design bureau was ordered to create a Soviet version of the B-29. The USSR realised that this programme might yield results only in the longer term, and, as a shorter-term expedient, ordered Tupolev to initiate Project 64 for a Soviet near-copy of the B-29 using Soviet liquid-cooled engines. Fate then played into the hands of the Soviets, for three B-29 bombers were forced to land in Siberia during July, August and November 1944 after suffering damage in raids on Japan. The aircraft were immediately seized by the Soviets and dismantled so that more than 105,000 components could be analysed for material specification, manufacturing process, function, size and tolerance before an army of 1000 or more draftsmen produced drawings translated into Soviet equivalents.

Right at the beginning of 1945, the programme to copy the B-29 as the Tu-4 received the highest priority, with work on the Project 64 half-brother continued at a lower priority until 1946, only as an insurance against the failure of the Tu-4. Many minor details of the B-29 were changed to facilitate Soviet production, and major alterations were the adoption of 22 flexible fuel cells in place of integral wing tankage, the omission of the tunnel linking the two pressurised compartments fore and aft of the two weapons bays, and a wholly redesigned defensive armament (with guns of steadily increasing calibre). The first of 20 prototype and development aircraft flew in July 1947, and the programme was severely beset by a host of technical problems with the propellers, engine cooling, turbochargers, defensive armament, and blown Plexiglas glazing. The Tu-4 entered service in 1949, and some 400 aircraft were built up to 1952.

CONVAIR'S GIANT B-36

By the early part of 1941, American planners foresaw that the USA would probably be drawn into World War II, and also that the UK could possibly fall to Germany. This raised the problem of how American air power could be deployed against the European members of the Axis alliance. In April 1941 the US Army Air Corps (soon to become the US Army Air Forces and in 1947 the US Air Force) invited Boeing and Consolidated each to prepare design studies for a bomber able to reach 450 mph (724 km/h) at 25,000 ft (7620 m), cover a range of 12,000 miles (19,312 km) at a cruising speed of 275 mph (443 km/h) with a 4000 lb (1814 kg) bomb load, deliver a 10,000 lb (4536 kg) bomb load to a radius of 3400 miles (5472 km), and reach an altitude of 35,000 ft (10,670 m).

Consolidated had already considered such a type, with an airframe that included a tail unit carrying endplate vertical surfaces and with a powerplant of six radial piston engines installed in the rear of the wing halves as pusher units to improve airflow over the wing, and submitted this Model 35 design in May 1941. The company refined this design during the summer of 1941 as Boeing (together with Douglas and Northrop) pressed ahead with rival concepts. In November 1941 the USAAF contracted with Consolidated for two XB-36 prototypes that were to be delivered in May and November 1944. The definition of the design resulted in considerable growth of size and weight, requiring the use of six huge R-4360 radials buried in the wings where they could be reached for inflight maintenance. The envisaged bomb load was 42,000 lb (19,051 kg) carried in four weapons bays below a tunnel 85 ft (25.91 m) long with a wheeled cart that moved on twin rails to provide a means of transfer between the two pressurised compartments (forward crew and rear gunners' sections). In 1943 it was decided to adopt a single vertical tail surface as this would ease the problems of designing the tail structure, and in parallel with the aerodynamic and engineering development of the design went the evolution of the new type's advanced systems, including the defensive armament of remotely controlled cannon in multiple installations.

The first XB-36 flew on 8 August 1946, with a flush flightdeck canopy and main landing gear units each carrying a single wheel 9 ft 2 in (2.79 m) in diameter. These units exerted so great a ground pressure that there were only three airfields in the continental USA with runways offering concrete of the required 22 in (0.56 m) thickness. The XB-36 was therefore revised with a four-wheel bogie on each main landing gear unit, reducing the required concrete thickness to 13.5 in (0.34 m). The machine was also fitted with the raised flightdeck glazing that was adopted as standard, and took to the air in this revised form during June 1948. The second machine was completed to YB-36 standard and used for structural testing after a first flight on 4 December 1947, and there followed 22 B-36A aircraft that were notionally operational bombers, but in reality unarmed pre-production machines. The type had a powerplant of six R-4360-25 radial engines each rated at 3000 hp (2237 kW), and from June 1948 some 19 of these aircraft were delivered to a bomber group for crew training.

The first operational model of what was dubbed the 'Peacekeeper' was thus the B-36B, of which the first made its maiden flight on 8 August 1948. Some 73

BELOW: The North American XB-45 was the prototype of the B-45 Tornado series of four-jet light bombers that were used most effectively as reconnaissance types.

ABOVE: The Convair B-36 was designed in World War II, but operated through the early days of the 'Cold War', with its six piston engines supplemented by four jet engines.

of these aircraft were delivered to the Strategic Air Command with full armament including a maximum bomb load of 86,000 lb (39,010 kg) respectively. Power was supplied by four R-4360-41 radial engines each rated at 3500 hp (2610 kW) with water injection. Convair next proposed a B-36C version with R-4360-51 Turbo-Compound radials each rated at 4300 hp (3206 kW) and driving tractor propellers, but the service preferred the less risky B-36D with higher speed provided by the addition of four turbojet engines in podded pairs mounted on pylons under the outer wings. The concept was pioneered by a converted B-36B that first flew on 26 March 1949, with four Allison J35-A-19 turbojet engines each rated at 4000 lb st (17.79 kN) dry, but the 24 production B-36D bombers used four General Electric J47-GE-19 turbojet engines each rated at 5200 lb st (23.13 kN) dry. The first B-36D flew in July 1949, and 64 B-36B bombers were thus modified.

The B-36F model, first flown in November 1950, was an improved version of the B-36D bomber with the same quartet of J47-GE-19 booster turbojet engines but a more powerful sextet of R-4360-53 radial engines each rated at 3800 hp (2833 kW) together with improved ECM and more advanced nav/attack radar. Production totalled 34 aircraft. The designation GRB-36F was used for about 13 examples of the RB-36F, the reconnaissance counterpart of the RB-36D with greater fuel capacity, modified in the FICON (FIghter in CONvair or FIghter CONveyor) programme to carry a Republic GRF-84F Thunderstreak reconnaissance and strike fighter semi-recessed in the fuselage.

The B-36 bomber was the B-36H that first flew in April 1952 as a derivative of the RB-36F with a number of system and internal changes including a revised flightdeck. A total of 83 such bombers was delivered between May 1952 and July 1953. The B-36J was the last production version of the B-36 series, and first flew in September 1953 with additional fuel capacity, a higher maximum weight, and strengthened landing gear. Production totalled 33 aircraft delivered between October 1953 and 14 August 1954. The last 14 of these machines were completed to the B-36J(III) lightweight standard with all but the tail guns omitted to raise the service ceiling to allegedly 47,000 ft (14,325 m) but actually 50,000 ft (15,240 m) or slightly more. Replacement of the B-36 in SAC service by the Boeing B-52 Stratofortress began in 1955, and the last B-36 was retired in February 1959.

FIRST SOVIET JET BOMBER

The Ilyushin Il-28, which received the NATO reporting name 'Beagle', was a pioneering turbojet-powered tactical light bomber that is often regarded as the Soviet counterpart to an epoch-making British type, the English Electric Canberra. At the time of the Il-28's genesis, the rival Tupolev design bureau was producing a stream of bomber prototypes, so considerable effort had to be made in an attempt to match Tupolev's more advanced schedule and yet produce a type offering performance superior to that of any rival Tupolev type. The Ilyushin design team opted for an all-metal structure for its bomber, which accommodated a three-man crew in separate positions in the circular-section fuselage. This also carried the twin-wheel

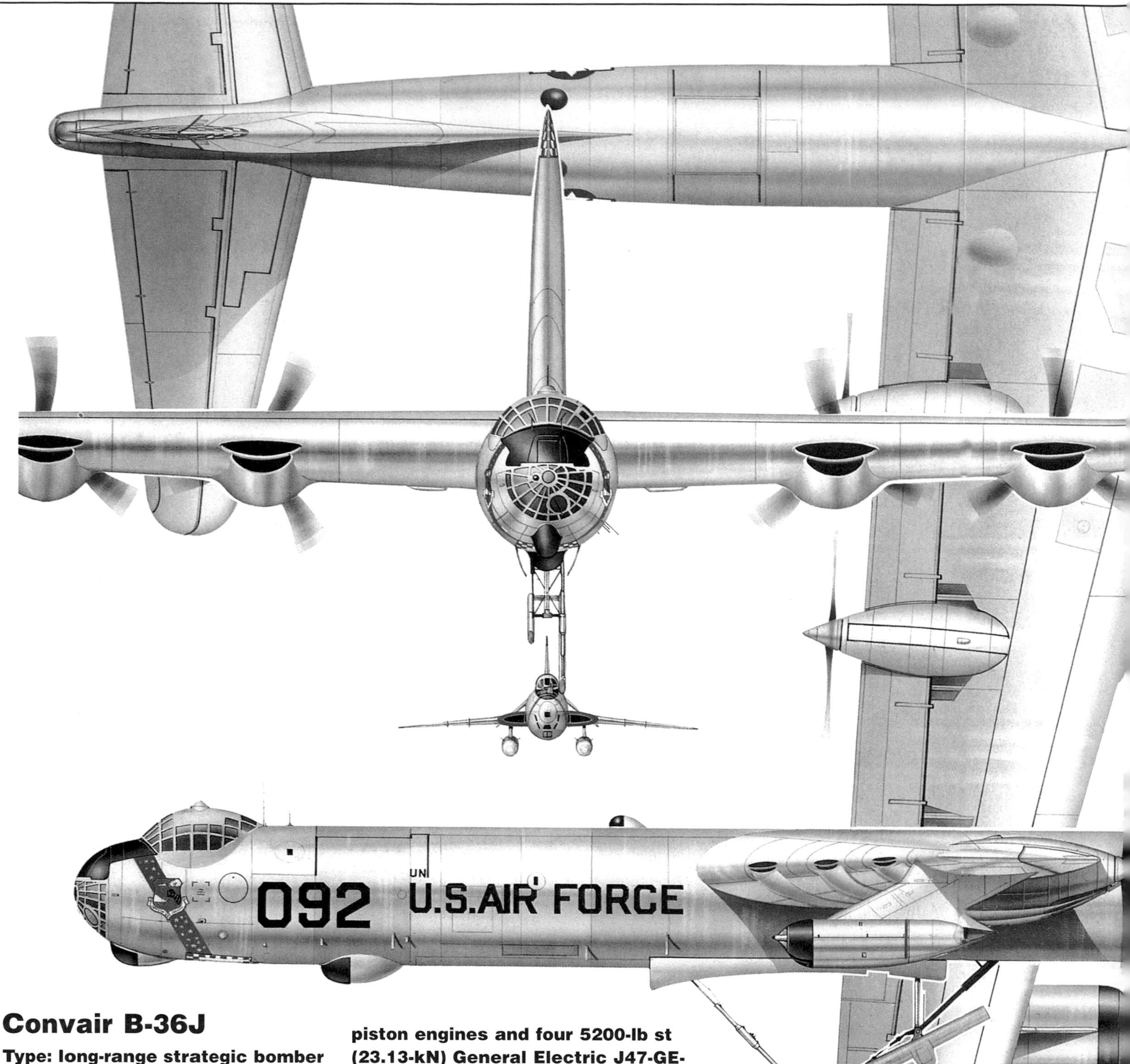

Convair B-36J

Type: long-range strategic bomber and reconnaissance aircraft
Country of origin: USA
Powerplant: six 3800-hp (2834-kW) Pratt & Whitney R-4360-53 radial piston engines and four 5200-lb st (23.13-kN) General Electric J47-GE-19 turbojet engines
Performance: maximum level speed 411 mph (661 km/h); service ceiling 39,900 ft (12,160 m); range

nose unit of the tricycle landing gear, the fuel and the weapons bay, and also supported the tail unit and the high-set wing. The tail unit comprised swept vertical and horizontal surfaces, but the wing was straight and carried two underslung nacelles for the Klimov VK-1A turbojet engines as well as the landing gear's single-wheel main units. The VK-1A turbojet engine was a Soviet development of the RD-45, itself a Soviet copy of the British Rolls-Royce Nene centrifugal-flow turbojet, and was one of the keys to the Il-28's excellent performance in the air.

In October 1948 the Il-28 was evaluated against the Tupolev Tu-78, and emerged as superior on all major counts, and was therefore rushed into production for service from September 1950. Construction is thought to have totalled some 3000 aircraft, of which more than half of them were exported to the USSR's Warsaw Pact allies, China (at least 500 aircraft), and many other countries. The Il-28 was also licensed for production in China as the Harbin H-5 and in small

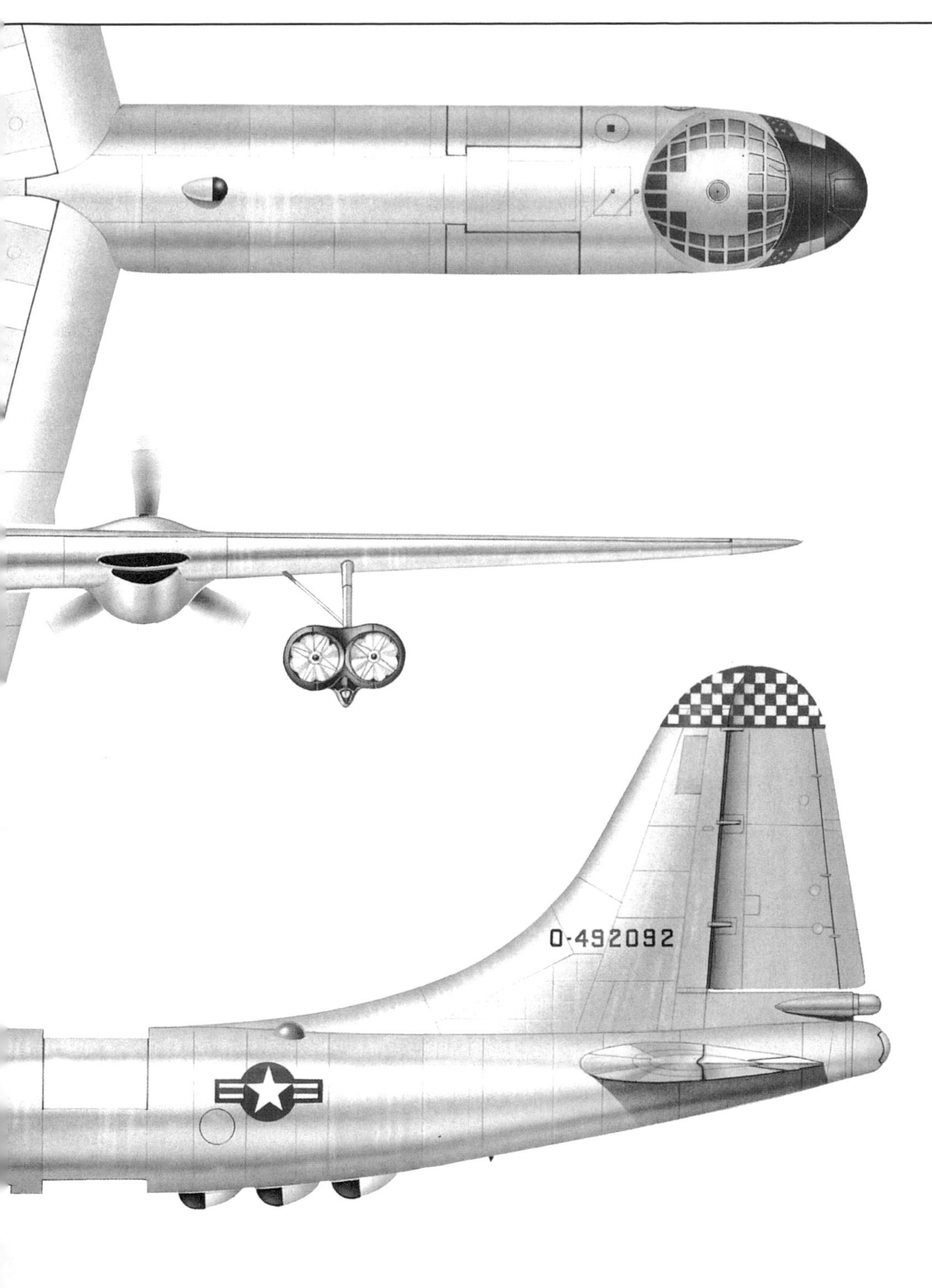

6800 miles (10,944 km)
Weights: empty 171,035 lb (77,580 kg); max take-off 410,000 lb (185,973 kg)
Dimensions: wing span 230 ft 0 in (70.10 m); length 162 ft 1 in (49.40 m); height 46 ft 8 in (14.22 m)
Armament: 16 20 mm (0.787 in) M24A1 cannon, plus up to 86,000 lb (39,009 kg) of ordnance

numbers in Czechoslovakia as the B-228. Subvariants included the Il-28R light bomber model with tip tanks for greater range, and the Il-28T Torpedonosyets (torpedo) variant for the torpedo bombing role with the weapons bay carrying one large or two small torpedoes, or alternatively a few air-dropped mines for the minelayer role.

MOSQUITO REPLACEMENT

In 1944 W.E.W. 'Teddy' Petter, Westland's chief designer, was asked to investigate the possibilities of a turbojet-powered attack warplane to supersede the Hawker Typhoon and Westland Whirlwind. Petter moved almost immediately after this to English Electric, which had large production facilities but up to that time no design capability. Here the designer and his fledgling team were soon hard at work on a type to meet the definitive 1945 requirement, which called for a two-seat bomber to replace the de Havilland Mosquito and, as it turned out, nearly rivalled this classic type in its versatility. The requirement demanded the ability to operate at very high speeds at high altitude to deliver a bomb load of 4000 lb (1814 kg) over a radius of 806 miles (1297 km). The new type was originally planned with only a single Rolls-Royce turbojet engine, rated at 13,000 lb st (57.83 kN) dry, in a circular-section fuselage, but the installation of such an engine was incompatible with the incorporation of an internal weapons bay, and Petter therefore decided to switch to the use of two lower-powered engines in wing-mounted nacelles.

The first prototype flew on 13 May 1949, and this Canberra A.1 impressed all with its quite exceptional agility. The new type had been conceived as a two-seater with radar bombing equipment, and this standard was further evaluated in the three following Canberra B.Mk 1 prototypes. The radar bombing system was not placed into production, however, and the Canberra was revised for a crew of three, all on Martin-Baker Mk 1 ejection seats. This revised arrangement was pioneered on the fifth prototype, which first flew in April 1950 and paved the way for the Canberra B.Mk 2 production type that first flew in October of the same year and entered service in May 1951. British production totalled 413 aircraft for the home and export markets, including two evaluation and pattern aircraft for Australia, whose Government Aircraft Factories then built another 48 aircraft with the designation GAF (English Electric) Canberra B.Mk 20. When replaced by later models, many of the British aircraft were refurbished for export, and specific variants of this series included the Canberra B.Mk 52 for Ethiopia, Canberra B.Mk 62 for Argentina, Canberra B.Mk 72 for Peru and Canberra B.Mk 82 for Venezuela. The next bomber version of the Canberra was to have been the Canberra B.Mk 5 with revised wing leading edges incorporating integral tankage for an additional 900 Imp gal (4091.4 litres) of fuel, an uprated powerplant in the form of two Avon RA.7 Mk 109 turbojet engines each rated at 7500 lb st (33.36 kN) dry, and a 'solid' nose with radar for the blind bombing (later target marking) role. The Canberra

PR.Mk 3 prototype was revised to this standard, but the Canberra B.Mk 5 was then abandoned. The increased fuel capacity and uprated powerplant were clearly advantageous, however, and were therefore applied to the Canberra B.Mk 6, which was the definitive light bomber version and, in essence, the Canberra B.Mk 2 with these enhancements as well as two underwing hardpoints each rated at 1000 lb (454 kg) for an increase in maximum warload to 8000 lb (3629 kg) including, on the underwing hardpoints, two 1000 lb (454 kg) bombs, AS.30 ASMs, or multiple launchers for unguided rockets. Deliveries of the Canberra B.Mk 6 started in June 1954 and totalled 106 aircraft including 94 for the RAF and small batches for Ecuador and France.

First flown in October 1960 and produced by Marshalls and BAC to the extent of 39 conversions, the Canberra B.Mk 15 was a Canberra B.Mk 6 derivative for the Middle East and Far East Air Forces in the nuclear strike and conventional attack roles with improved avionics including Doppler navigation, three cameras and underwing hardpoints. Also produced by Marshalls and BAC as 19 conversions from Canberra B.Mk 6 standard, the Canberra B.Mk 16 was a derivative of the Canberra B.Mk 15 with slightly different avionics.

THE B-47 STRATOJET

By 1944, five US companies were involved in the design of jet-powered bombers, their initial thoughts being centred on conventional (and thus straight-winged) aircraft with turbojets in place of piston engines. Boeing proposed its Model 424 that was in essence a scaled-down Model 345 (B-29 Superfortress), with four turbojets in podded pairs under the wings. The proposal failed to interest the USAAF, and the company revised the concept into the Model 432 with all four engines buried in the fuselage. The new proposal aroused limited interest, and Boeing was contracted for design definition and a mock-up of this XB-47. Many changes were made to this design, inspired largely by the visit by a team of Boeing designers and engineers to inspect captured German factories and research centres in 1945. In the process they discovered the advantages of swept flying surfaces for aircraft of high subsonic performance. After several revisions the new Model 450 emerged with six engines located under the wings as two podded pairs inboard and two podded singletons outboard. This was the definitive design, and was optimised for the carriage of current nuclear weapons, which were both large and heavy, in a large weapon bay. The Model 450 began to mature as a high-altitude type with a crew of three including two pilots in a fighter-type cockpit, all-swept flying surfaces including a cantilever high-set wing of laminar-flow section, and bicycle-type landing gear with tandem twin-wheel units under the fuselage (fore and aft of the weapon bay) and small single-wheel stabiliser units extending from the underside of the twin-engine pods.

The first of two XB-47 (Model 450-3-3) prototypes flew in December 1947 with a powerplant of six General Electric J35-GE-2 turbojet engines each rated at 3750 lb st (16.68 kN) dry, while the second prototype had a powerplant of six General Electric J47-GE-3 turbojet engines each rated at 5000 lb st (22.24 kN) dry. The indifferent power of these engines advocated the use of booster rockets for take-off, and the XB-47 prototypes therefore had provision for 16 solid-propellant RATO units in the fuselage sides aft of the wing. The new bomber clearly possessed exceptional potential and the US Air Force, as the USAAF had now become, ordered 10 B-47A Stratojet (Model 450-10-9) service test aircraft that would assist factory and service personnel in learning about the new type. The first of these aircraft flew on 25 June 1950.

Experience with the B-47A paved the way for the first true production model, the B-47B of which 399 were built with a strengthened structure for operation at higher weights, and provision for underwing tanks for extended range. The first 87 B-47B bombers retained the B-47A's powerplant, but the last 312 had the revised powerplant of six J47-GE-23 turbojet engines each rated at 5800 lb st (25.80 kN) dry. The first B-47B flew on 26 April 1951, and the type entered service in the middle of the same year. Later in the B-47B's career, most surviving aircraft were upgraded to B-47E-II standard with the revised designation B-47B-II Stratojet by the removal of

Ilyushin Il-28 'Beagle'

Type: three-seat light bomber
Country of origin: USSR
Powerplant: two 5952-lb st (26.48-kN) Klimov VK-1A turbojets
Performance: maximum level speed 560 mph (902 km/h); service ceiling 40,350 ft (12,300 m); range 1491 miles (2400 km)
Weights: empty 28,417 lb (11,890 kg); max take-off 46,738 lb (21,200 kg)
Dimensions: wing span 70 ft 4.5 in (21.45 m) without tip tanks; length 57 ft 11 in (17.65 m) for fuselage excluding tail cannon; height 21 ft 11.75 in (6.70 m)
Armament: four 23 mm (0.905 in) Nudel'man-Rikhter NR-23 cannon with 450 rounds per gun in a tail turret, plus up to 6614 lb (3000 kg) of ordnance

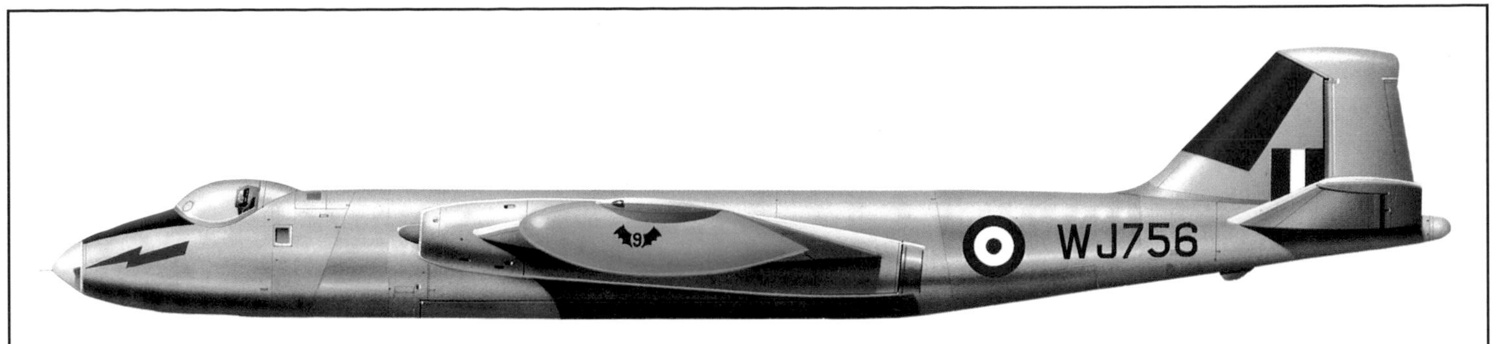

English Electric Canberra B.Mk 2

Type: two-seat light bomber
Country of origin: UK
Powerplant: two 7400-lb st (32.92-kN) Rolls-Royce Avon RA.7 Mk 109 turbojet engines
Performance: maximum level speed 541 mph (871 km/h); service ceiling 48,000 ft (14,630 m); typical range 806 miles (1297 km)
Weights: empty 27,950 lb (12,678 kg); max take-off 54,950 lb (24,925 kg)
Dimensions: wing span 63 ft 11.5 in (19.50 m) without tip tanks and 65 ft 6 in (19.96 m) with tip tanks; length 65 ft 6 in (19.96 m); height 15 ft 8 in (4.77 m)
Armament: up to 6000 lb (2722 kg) of ordnance

inbuilt RATO capability in favour of a strap-on RATO pack capable of carrying 33 rather than 18 units, addition of a brake chute, replacement of the fixed crew seats by ejection seats, installation of a new General Electric radar-directed tail barbette with two 20 mm (0.787 in) cannon, replacement of the original engines by J47-GE-25 turbojet engines each rated at 6000 lb st (26.69 kN) dry and 7200 lb st (32.03 kN) with water injection, and a strengthening of the aircraft's wing structure.

First flown in January 1953, the B-47E was the major production version of the Stratojet family, and was an important milestone in the development of US strategic bombing capability as it introduced a number of major changes such as ejection seats for all three crew members, water-injected engines fed from a reduced internal fuel capacity that could be replenished in the air via an inflight-refuelling receptacle located on the starboard side of the slightly lengthened nose, a jettisonable 19 or 33-unit RATO pack, a tail barbette with two 20 mm (0.787 in) cannon, and a combination of beefed-up landing gear and a strengthened structure for operation at increased weights. Production totalled 1591 aircraft in a programme that lasted to February 1957. The B-47E entered service with SAC in 1953, and at the peak of the Stratojet's importance in 1957 there were 45 B-47 bombers in service with each of SAC's 28 medium bomber wings, 300 used for other roles, and 300 held in reserve: the total was thus 1860.

US LIGHT BOMBER COMPETITION

By 1950 the Korean War forced the USAF into seeking out a light jet bomber design that could be introduced quickly. None of the domestic manufacturers had a suitable design to offer and the USAF finally come to the conclusion that only the British Canberra fitted the bill as a B-26 replacement.

A fly-off competition was held between the various contenders in November 1950, and to the surprise of some Americans the Canberra proved by far the best machine in all-round performance and agility as well as offering the required 'developability'. Martin was very disappointed that its XB-51 had been rejected, but received the consolation prize of an order for 250 licence-built Canberra aircraft. Although the Canberra met the American 'off-the-shelf' criterion, its Americanised version was slow to enter service as the type had been designed to British production tolerances which were too tight for US practice. Thus the airframe had to be re-engineered to meet American hardware, dimension and production standards.

The first American machine, the initial B-57A, flew in July 1953. By comparison with the Canberra B.Mk 2, the B-57A had a two rather than three-man crew under the same type of wide canopy used in the Canberra B.Mk 2, fixed forward-firing gun armament (eight 0.5 in/ 12.7 mm machine guns that were replaced from the 91st B-57B onward by four 20 mm/0.787 in cannon) in the wing leading edges outboard of the engine nacelles, a more advanced bomb-aiming system, a cockpit with American instrumentation and air-conditioning, and a new powerplant in which the two Rolls-Royce Avon turbojet engines of the British bomber were replaced by two examples of another British unit, the Armstrong Siddeley Sapphire turbojet engine built under licence by Buick as the J65-BW-5 and by Wright as the J65-W-5 for earlier and later aircraft respectively. Trials with the first B-57A were highly encouraging so far as performance was concerned, for this machine equalled or outperformed the Canberra B.Mk 2 in all aspects of the flight envelope. The trials were less encouraging so far as operational capability was concerned, for the Canberra had not been designed for the low-altitude nocturnal role and suffered from problems such as flexing of the curved windscreen that distorted the view through the sight and thus made it impossible to harmonise the guns. This problem was solved by replacement of the original windscreen by a flat glass panel, but the B-57A can be considered as a pilot production model of which only eight examples were built.

The B-57B was developed as the definitive night intruder model, and differed from the B-57A in its new forward fuselage and revised weapon capability. The forward fuselage featured a modernised and pressurised cockpit seating the pilot and navigator in tandem on the centre-line under a long clamshell canopy. The revised weapon capability added underwing hardpoints and replaced the original clamshell doors,

which took too long to open and close and also generated a high drag penalty in the open position, with the type of rotary weapons bay door pioneered on the RB-57A. This was carried on fore and aft pivots so that it could be turned by hydraulic power in a maximum of six seconds to expose the bombs, which could vary in size between 1000 and 220 lb (454 and 100 kg) and were carried on a maximum of 21 positions.

The first B-57B flew in June 1954, and production totalled 202 aircraft for first-line service between January 1955 and June 1959, when the second of two operating wings in the continental USA was deactivated. The B-57B was also operated by Pacific Air Force and Air National Guard units, and some of the latter had to relinquish their aircraft for renewed first-line service during the early stages of the Vietnam War, from which the type was finally retired in 1969. In 1959 the Pakistani air force received 21 B-57B and B-57C aircraft modified with the RB-1A 'Georgia Peach' all-weather bombing system with its radar in a modified nose section, and these aircraft were heavily involved in Pakistan's 1965 and 1971 wars with India before being relegated to the target facilities role in the mid-1970s and finally being retired in the middle of the following decade.

The B-57C differed from the B-57B only in having provision for dual controls so that the type could be used for conversion and proficiency training. The variant entered service in 1955, and production totalled 38 aircraft that were later redesignated TB-57C. The B-57E differed from the B-57D only in having provision for dual controls or target-towing equipment (with four banner targets) under the rear fuselage so that the type could be used for conversion and proficiency training or, more generally, the training of fighter pilots in air-to-air gunnery as alternatives to its standard night intruder mission.

It was only at the end of the B-57's development life that the type finally acquired the full night attack capability in which it had originally been considered. This capability was retrofitted in a mere 16 B-57B machines that then received the revised designation B-57G and the name Night Intruder. The B-57G was evolved to detect, acquire, track and destroy targets in total darkness. One crashed before delivery, but 11 of the other 15 were used during the Vietnam War, playing only an undistinguished part as they were underpowered.

THE SOVIET BADGER

For its period a remarkable warplane, the Tupolev Tu-16 was built to the extent of some 2000 aircraft up to 1959, and in mid-1995 it was estimated that some 600 of these aircraft, allocated the reporting name 'Badger' by NATO, still remained in declining service with the air arms of the CIS (350 of them in the bomber and strike roles, and the other 250 in a number of other roles including reconnaissance and inflight refuelling). The factor that made this thoroughly modern bomber possible was the design of the Mikulin AM-3 turbojet engine, a slender axial-flow unit offering high power at a comparatively modest specific fuel consumption. The imminence of this engine opened the way for the Tupolev design bureau to terminate its efforts on smaller turbojet-powered bombers. In the summer of 1950, the bureau was ordered to proceed as rapidly as possible with the construction of three prototypes that were to be evaluated in competition with the smaller Ilyushin Il-46. The weapons bay was sized for the carriage of the USSR's largest conventional bomb, namely the 19,841 lb (9000 kg) FAB-9000 weapon. The fuselage was 'waisted' over its central section in the region where the

ABOVE: The first swept-wing jet bomber to enter large-scale service with the US Air Force, the Boeing B-47 Stratojet is seen here in its definitive B-47E form.

wing was attached, and this did much to ensure the reduction of drag at high subsonic speeds with consequent advantages to speed and range, while the wing itself was altogether more novel as it was not only larger but of swept configuration and based on a new alloy making possible the use of comparatively thick skins for great strength. Another novelty was the nature and arrangement of the main units of the tricycle landing gear. These substantial four-wheel units introduced the bogie to Soviet practice and, being too large for accommodation within the wing, were also designed to retract rearward into large trailing-edge pods that became a trademark of many larger Tupolev aircraft.

The Tu-88 prototype made its maiden flight on 27 April 1952 with a powerplant of two AM-3A turbojet engines, and later evaluation against the Il-46 confirmed that the Tu-88 was an altogether superior warplane. Late in 1952 the Tu-88 was selected as a major service type with the designation Tu-16. Considerable development had to be undertaken as the type was initially overweight and lacked adequate performance, but the Tu-16 entered service in 1954 as a conventional strategic bomber with the FAB-9000 free-fall bomb or larger numbers of smaller weapons, and was later allocated the NATO reporting name 'Badger-A'. Early aircraft were fitted with the powerplant of two Mikulin AM-3 turbojet engines each rated at 19290 lb st (85.81 kN) dry, but later aircraft received the improved powerplant of two AM-3M turbojet engines that increased unrefuelled range to 4474 miles (7200 km) and boosted maximum speed by 62 mph (100 km/h). Subvariants of the basic Tu-16 produced as new-build or converted aircraft were five in number, and all retained the same 'Badger-A' reporting designation in the NATO system of nomenclature for Soviet weapons. The only bomber among these variants was the Tu-16A dedicated nuclear strategic bomber counterpart to the Tu-16 conventional bomber, from which it was externally indistinguishable.

The Tu-16KS-1 'Badger-B' was the Tu-16 variant for the aerial launch of two KS-1 (AS-1 'Kennel') anti-ship missiles carried on underwing hardpoints. Some at least of the surviving aircraft were later rebuilt to 'Badger-G' standard. The Tu-16K-10 'Badger-C' was another anti-ship variant, and was first seen in 1961. The type had provision for one K-10S (AS-2 'Kipper') missile carried semi-recessed under the fuselage. The Tu-16KSR-5 'Badger-C (Modified)' was the variant produced by converting Tu-16K-10 missile-launch warplanes, made redundant by the obsolescence of their K-10S missile, to a more modern standard with the semi-recessed missile position under the fuselage faired over (but otherwise retained internally) and hardpoints added under the wings for a maximum of two but generally just one example of the KSR-5 (AS-6 'Kingfish') anti-ship missile, which had the alternative designation K-26, so that the converted type was also known as the Tu-16K-10-26 or Tu-16KM. The type could also carry an alternative load of bombs or mines. The Tu-16Kh-11-16 'Badger-G' was an advanced anti-ship missile variant produced either as new-build machines and/or as conversions of Tu-16KS-1 aircraft to carry two examples of the more advanced K-11/K-16 (AS-5 'Kelt' anti-ship/stand-off missiles under the wings. First noted in 1977 and otherwise known by the Tu-16K-26 designation, the Tu-16KSR-5 'Badger-G (Modified)' was a variant of the Tu-16Kh-11-16 designed to carry KSR-5 or K-26 (AS-6 'Kingfish') rather than K-11 and K-16 (AS-5 'Kelt') missiles. Some aircraft retained the 'Short Horn' radar of the Tu-16K-11-16 and were perhaps not properly designated Tu-16KSR-5 or Tu-16K-26, for the full standard had the chin radome removed and a much larger radome added just forward of the weapons bay for a new target-acquisition and missile-guidance radar.

BRITAIN'S LACK OF DETERRENT

In the immediate aftermath of World War II, it became clear that Bomber Command in its current form had been rendered obsolete virtually overnight by the existence of nuclear weapons (then only in American hands) delivered by a comparatively small numbers of high-performance bombers. The UK had nothing approaching the capabilities of the B-50, B-36 and B-47, and the situation was worsened in August 1946 when the US Congress passed the McMahon Act prohibiting the export of American nuclear information even to close allies such as the UK, which had been an active participant in the development of the first nuclear weapons. The British Government decided in the spring of 1947 that a strategic nuclear capability was the best means to ensure an effective defence of the realm even though this demanded the vastly expensive process of creating a nuclear weapons industry and evolving at least one type of strategic bomber to carry the resulting weapon.

Drawn up in 1946 and issued early in 1947, the resulting requirement from the ministry demanded a bomber able to carry a 10,000 lb (4536 kg) free-fall nuclear bomb over a range of 3858 miles (6208 km), at a maximum speed of at least 576 mph (927 km/h), and reaching an altitude of at least 50,000 ft (15,240 m) over the target. The aircraft's speed requirement necessitated a swept wing, and submissions for aircraft of this configuration were received from Armstrong Whitworth, Avro, Handley Page, Short Brothers and Vickers, and it was the Avro Type 698 and Handley Page H.P.80 designs that received the initial

BELOW: The Martin B-57 was a night intruder developed from a British type, the English Electric Canberra, and then further developed by the Americans for the reconnaissance task.

contracts that led to the Vulcan and Victor bombers respectively.

The Vickers design for the requirement had been the Type 660, which was a less ambitious concept, and Vickers urged the Air Ministry to order its development as a back-up. The Air Ministry was most attracted by the prospect of early delivery, and in February 1949 ordered two prototypes each with a powerplant of four axial-flow turbojets in the form of Rolls-Royce Avon and Armstrong Siddeley Sapphire units in the Type 660 first and Type 667 second prototypes respectively.

The Type 660 prototype first flew on 18 May 1951 with a powerplant of four Avon RA.3 turbojet engines each rated at 6500 lb st (28.91 kN) dry, and in the following month the new type was officially named Valiant. The Type 667 second prototype, first flew on 11 April 1952. This was to have been powered by Sapphire turbojet engines, but was in fact completed with a powerplant of four Avon RA.7 turbojet engines each rated at 7500 lb st (33.36 kN) dry and aspirated via larger inlets in the deepened leading edges of the wing roots. The day after the Type 667's first flight, Vickers received an order for 25 Valiant B.Mk 1 bombers: the first five were each to have a powerplant of four Avon RA.14 turbojet engines each rated at 9000 lb st (40.03 kN) dry, while the last 20 were each to have a powerplant of four Avon RA.28 turbojet engines each rated at 10500 lb st (46.71 kN) dry and exhausting via longer jetpipes. At much the same time the company received an order for one Type 673 prototype of the planned Valiant B.Mk 2, a somewhat revised type designed as a pathfinder and target marker, and therefore intended for fast low-level flight with a strengthened airframe and revised airframe, Avon RA.14 turbojets and increased fuel capacity. This first flew in September 1953 and the production version was to have been powered by four examples of the Rolls-Royce RB.80 (prototype Conway) turbofan engine, but the Air Ministry decided that the type's role no longer existed and the Valiant B.Mk 2 proceeded no further than the prototype stage. The irony was that in the early 1960s, when the Air Ministry decided that bombers would have to switch to the low-level role for continued survivability, the Valiant B.Mk 1 had to be retired from service after suffering major fatigue problems in this taxing operational environment.

FIRST VALIANT FLIGHT

The first Valiant B.Mk 1 off the production line flew in December 1953, and the 25 aircraft were completed to three different standards as five Type 674 machines with Avon RA.14 turbojets, 15 Type 706 machines with Avon RA.28 turbojets, and five Type 710 machines with Avon RA.28 turbojets and provision in the weapons bay for removable equipment providing a day/night high-altitude photo-reconnaissance capability. The aircraft were all delivered between December 1954 and July 1955, the Type 710 aircraft receiving the service designation Valiant B(PR).Mk 1. The next batch of 24 aircraft, all delivered between August 1955 and March 1956, comprised 16 Type 706 bombers, six Type 710 dual-role bomber and photo-reconnaissance aircraft, and two Type 733 aircraft. These last were accepted into service with the designation Valiant B(PR)K.Mk 1 as bombers with the capability for the weapons bay to be fitted with the photo-reconnaissance package of the Type 710 or alternatively an HDU kit to turn any such machine into an inflight refuelling tanker. The aircraft were also capable of receiving fuel in flight via a nose-mounted probe. The next production batch totalled 17 aircraft delivered between March and July 1956, as 11 examples of the Type 733 and six examples of the Type 758. This last was the fourth subvariant of the basic model, and was a dual-role bomber and inflight refuelling variant that entered service with the designation Valiant B(K).Mk 1. Like its predecessor, it was fitted with an inflight refuelling probe on the nose, and had provision in the weapon bay for an HDU capable of transferring a maximum of 5000 Imp gal (22,730 litres) of fuel to another warplane. Production of the Valiant was completed by 38 (out of an order for 56) examples of the Type 758 delivered by August 1957. Overall totals were therefore 36 Valiant B.Mk 1, 11 Valiant B(PR).Mk 1, 13 Valiant B(PR)K.Mk 1 and 44 Valiant B(K).Mk 1 aircraft. The Valiant entered service in January 1955 and was used for the operational development of the British nuclear and thermonuclear free-fall bombs, which were first air-dropped in October 1956 and May 1957 respectively by Valiant bombers.

Tupolev Tu-16 'Badger-A'

Type: strategic medium bomber
Country of origin: USSR
Powerplant: two 19,158 lb st (85 kN) dry MNPK 'Soyuz' (Mikulin) AM-3A turbojet engines
Performance: maximum level speed 616 mph (992 km/h); service ceiling 40,355 ft (12,300 m); range 3682 miles (5925 km)
Weights: empty 82,012 lb (37,200 kg); max take-off 167,110 lb (75,800 kg)
Dimensions: wing span 108 ft 0.5 in (32.93 m); length 118 ft 11.25 in (36.25 m); height 45 ft 11.25 in (14.00 m);
Armament: seven 23 mm (0.905 in) Nudel'man-Rikhter AM-23 cannon plus up to 19,841 lb (9000 kg) of ordnance

As noted above, the Valiant was switched to the low-level role in 1964. The altogether more taxing nature of this regime was something for which the Valiant had not been designed, and sustained low-level operations resulted in cracking of the wing spars. A programme to re-spar the aircraft was not seriously considered in view of the availability of the superior Victor and Vulcan, and the Valiant was grounded in January 1965.

BOEING'S MIGHTY BUFF

Although the Boeing Model 450 and considerably larger Model 464 bore a strong family resemblance to each other in their production forms as the B-47 Stratojet medium bomber and B-52 Stratofortress heavy bomber, the two types were in fact developed along entirely different lines. The origins of the Model 464 can be found in June 1946, when the US Army Air Forces awarded Boeing a contract to provide a design study for a long-range strategic heavy bomber. Boeing's first thinking was embodied in the Model 462, which had a straight wing carrying six Wright T35 turboprop engines each rated at 5500 hp (4101 kW). This concept lacked the required range, so Boeing revised the basic design with four T35 turboprop engines of an improved version offering 8900 hp (6636 kW). In this form the type was initially acceptable to the USAAF, which ordered two prototypes with a wing swept at 20°, inflight-refuelling capability, and a maximum take-off weight of 350,000 lb (158,760 kg). Even as it pressed ahead with definition of this Model 462, Boeing felt that turbojet power and higher performance were in fact attainable without sacrifice of range, however, and therefore undertook company-funded studies of a more advanced type based on a new turbojet under development by Pratt & Whitney. In October 1948 the US Air Force, as the USAAF had by now become, decided to cancel the turboprop-powered Model 462 as it still lacked the required performance but asked the company to come up with the basic design of a heavy bomber powered by the Pratt & Whitney J57 turbojet.

In just four days, a team of six Boeing designers roughed out the design for a bomber with a powerplant of eight J57 turbojets in podded pairs mounted in pylons below and ahead of the swept wing's leading edges, and this paved the way for more detailed planning for the Model 464, which the USAF ordered initially in the form of one XB-52 (Model 464-67) prototype and one YB-52 service test machine. The design of the Model 464 matured with a number of similarities to that of the Model 450, most notably flying surfaces swept at 35°, tandem main landing gear units (in this instance each comprising two twin-wheel trucks) retracting into the fuselage with

■ABOVE: The Soviet Tupolev Tu-16 'Badger' was powered by only two turbojet engines, but offered high performance, long range and considerable weapon load.

ground stability enhanced by retractable stabilising outrigger units under the outer wings, engines pod-mounted below and ahead of the wing leading edges in a fashion that facilitated design of the high-set wing as a thin structure that drooped (like that of the Model 450) when not supported by aerodynamic lift, and defensive armament limited to tail guns in a manned tail turret that could also be operated automatically by the MD-5 radar fire-control system.

The XB-52 first flew in October 1952 with the two pilots seated in tandem in a fighter-type cockpit with a powerplant of eight YJ57-P-3 turbojet engines each rated at 8700 lb st (38.70 kN). The YB-52 first flew in April 1952, and was externally similar to the XB-52 apart from its flaperons, six rather than three spoilers on each wing half, and tail armament of two 0.5 in (12.7 mm) M3 machine guns. There followed three examples of the B-52A which, despite its full-service designation, was in fact a pre-production model with the pilot and co-pilot seated side-by-side on a conventional flightdeck that required the lengthening of the forward fuselage by almost 4 ft 0 in (1.22 m), four other crew

members including a specialist to man the new ECM system, a powerplant of eight J57-P-1W or -9W turbojet engines each rated at 9000 lb st (40.03 kN) with power-boosting water injection and supplied with fuel from an internal capacity reduced to 29,643.7 Imp gal (134,760.25 litres) but supplemented by two 832.7 Imp gal (3785.4 litre) underwing tanks, inflight-refuelling capability, and the A-3A radar fire-control system for its tail turret.

By this time the B-52 had proved itself so problem-free that the last ten aircraft of the 13-strong B-52A order were completed to B-52B standard and complemented by another 13 such aircraft, which entered service as the first operational Stratofortress model and was used mainly for crew training. The B-52B had the MA-6A radar nav/attack system and the A-3A (later MD-5) radar fire-control system for the tail turret, possessed a maximum take-off weight of 450,000 lb (204,120 kg), and had a powerplant of eight J57-P-19W or -29W turbojet engines each rated at 12,100 lb st (53.82 kN) with water injection. First flown in March 1956 and built to the extent of 35 aircraft for delivery from June 1956, the B-52C was an improved RB-52B with the same dual-role reconnaissance capability and J57-P-29W engines, provision for 4996.1 Imp gal (22,712.4 litres) of fuel in two very large underwing tanks, the tail armament revised to four 0.5 in (12.7 mm) Browning M3 machine guns in a turret controllable by the A-3A or MD-9 radar fire-control system. Evolved in parallel with the B-52C, the B-52D was a pure bomber that first flew in September 1956, and deliveries of an eventual 170 aircraft followed from December of the same year. For service in the Vietnam War the B-52D was modified as a conventional bomber with the standard conventional payload of 20,000 lb (9072 kg) of bombs carried internally revised to 84 500 lb (227 kg) or 42 750 lb (340 kg) free-fall bombs carried internally and supplemented by 24 750 lb (340 kg) free-fall bombs carried externally in the form of 12 bombs on each of the two underwing pylons designed for carriage of two North American AGM-28 Hound Dog missiles on the B-52G but retrofitted on this model.

First flown in October 1957 and built to the extent of 100 aircraft for the pure bomber role, the B-52E was an upgraded B-52D with improved navigation, bombing and electronic systems as well as a revised flightdeck layout to accommodate the more complex displays associated with these enhancements. The B-52F, which was first flown in May 1958, was a further improved bomber externally indistinguishable from the B-52E but powered by J57-P-43W turbojet engines each rated at 13750 lb st (61.16 kN) with water injection from an enlarged capacity. The B-52F entered service in June 1958, and production totalled 89 aircraft.

ABOVE: The first of the trio of British four-engined 'V-bombers' to enter service with the RAF, albeit for a career cut short by structural problems, was the Vickers Valiant.

THE B-52G

The B-52G was first flown in October 1958 for service from February 1959 as the definitive turbojet-powered version of the Stratofortress family and introduced a number of important changes such as integral rather than rubber-bag wing tankage for a total internal fuel capacity of 38,783.3 Imp gal (176,308.8 litres) supplemented by 1165.75 Imp gal (5299.6 litres) in two fixed underwing tanks for significantly improved range, various improvements to the crew's pressurised compartment, a shorter vertical tail surface of broader chord, a tail barbette for the defensive armament of four 0.5 in (12.7 mm) M3 machine-guns remotely controlled by a gunner moved into the main crew compartment or by an ASG-15 radar fire-control system, and provision for McDonnell ADM-20 Quail decoy missiles (four carried internally) and North American AGM-28 Hound Dog stand-off nuclear missiles (two carried externally on large underwing pylons) as an alternative to the other nuclear load of B61 or B83 nuclear free-fall bombs, of which a maximum of 12 but more typically four were carried internally.

Production totalled 193 aircraft, and of the 167 aircraft surviving into the early 1990s, 98 were fitted for the stand-off nuclear role and the other 69 for the force-projection role. The aircraft equipped for the stand-off nuclear role were each equipped for a primary armament of 12 AGM-86B cruise missiles under the wing (six rounds on each of the two underwing hardpoints) with an internal load of eight or AGM-69A SRAM defence-suppression missiles, or alternatively a total of 20 AGM-69A or AGM-86B weapons, or four B83 thermonuclear free-fall bombs. The aircraft could also be fitted on their underwing stores pylons with two Heavy Stores Adaptor Beams allowing the carriage of 45 2000 lb (907 kg) Mk 84 bombs (27 internally and 18 externally), while the use of multiple ejector racks on the underwing stores pylons made it possible to carry 51 1000 lb (454 kg) Mk 83 or 750 lb (340 kg) M117 bombs (27 internally and 24 externally). Some 30 of the aircraft had an alternative sea-control tasking with a primary armament of eight AGM-84 Harpoon anti-ship missiles and/or GBU-15(V) optronically guided glide bombs carried externally, with the powerful AGM-142 'Have Nap' optronically guided ASM possible on the two HSABs. The type could also be used for minelaying with loads such as 12 Mk 52 mines, or eight Mk 55, Mk 56 or Mk 60 mines. As more updated B-52H bombers became available, the B-52G warplanes of the stand-off nuclear type were reassigned to the force-projection role, and in October 1991 the sixth crew member, the gunner, was deleted from the crew as an economy measure. The last aircraft had finally been retired from service by the end of 1994.

THE B-52H

First flown in March 1961 for service from September of the same year at the beginning of a programme that saw the delivery of 102 aircraft up to the end of the B-52 production programme in October 1962, the B-52H was the ultimate development of the B-52 series and was originally schemed as the launch platform for the Douglas AGM-87 Skybolt stand-off nuclear missile. The most obvious external changes were the adoption of a powerplant of eight turbofan engines for about 33 per cent greater range, and a switch to a different defensive armament of one 20 mm (0.787 in) six-barrel cannon. Other changes are much enhanced avionics including provision for terrain-avoidance radar, and the latest electronic countermeasures equipment including the ITT ALQ-172(V)2 radar jammer in place of the B-52G's ALQ-117 or ALQ-172(V)1 system. Some 85 B-52H bombers remained in service by 2000 with a primary armament of 20 Boeing AGM-86B ALCM or Convair AGM-129A ACM cruise missiles (12 externally in four three-round clips and eight internally on the Common Strategic Rotary Launcher).

THE SOVIET BEAR

In 1948 the Soviet air forces demanded a strategic heavy bomber matching the capabilities of the B-36, and the Tupolev design bureau embarked on the design of the Tu-85, which was the ultimate development of the Tu-4's basic concept. The aircraft had two crews for long-endurance missions, greater size, and a considerably higher-rated powerplant

BELOW: Seen in 1967 with AGM-28 Hound Dog stand-off missiles under their wings, these are Boeing B-52 Stratofortress eight-engined heavy bombers of the US Air Force.

supplied with fuel from a virtually doubled internal capacity.

Although it was not in the same class as the B-36, the Tu-85 offered very great advantages over the Tu-4, but was not ordered into production as high expectations were now being entertained for a newer generation of strategic bombers based on swept flying surfaces for high over-target speed and altitude as a result of their turbojet and turboprop propulsion. These were respectively the Myasishchyev M-4 'Bison' and the Tu-95. The latter resulted from a 1950 decision to design and develop a technically less risky bomber that could fill the operational gap that would be left should the M-4 prove unsuccessful. It was based on the extraordinarily powerful NK-12 turboprop engine designed at the Kuznetsov design bureau by a team of German engineers captured in the closing stages of World War II. The design of the Tu-95 was entrusted to Aleksandr Aleksandrovich Arkhangyelskii, whose concept was cleared for prototype construction in 1952. The engine and its contra-rotating propeller unit represented a great technical risk, but in structural terms the Tu-95 was not, for it was derived ultimately from the Tu-4 via the Tu-75, Tu-80 and Tu-85. The fuselage was basically a lengthened version of that designed for the Tu-85 with modifications such as a higher pressurisation differential and thicker skinning, and the tail unit was closely related to that of the Tu-88 prototype of the Tu-16 series. The greatest structural challenge was the wing, but here again Arkhangyelskii was able to draw on the bureau's experience with the Tu-88 in aerodynamic as well as structural matters. As the Tu-95 was designed to cruise at high speed, there was no need for a relief crew and accommodation was fixed at some eight men carried in three pressurised compartments linked by a tunnel. The landing gear was scaled up from that of the Tu-88 and included the same combination of a two-wheel nose unit and main units each carrying a four-wheel bogie that somersaulted through 90º as its whole unit retracted rearward into the underside of the relevant pod extending rearward from the trailing edge of the wing, and the flying surfaces were based on those of the Tu-88. The wing was located in the mid/shoulder-wing position with its leading edges swept at 37º to a point just inside the outer engine nacelles, where the angle decreased to 35º. The swept tail unit comprised single horizontal and vertical surfaces, each carrying the standard type of control surface that was, like those on the wing, hydraulically boosted.

FIRST FLIGHT OF THE TU-95

The Tu-95/1 first of two prototypes flew in September 1955 after a delay occasioned by lack of flight-cleared Kuznetsov 2TV-2F turboprop engines, each rated at 12,000 ehp (8947 ekW) for take-off, and revealed generally satisfactory performance and handling even though there were severe engine/propeller problems that possibly were responsible for the loss of this aeroplane. The Tu-95/2 second prototype, with a powerplant of four Kuznetsov TV-12 turboprop engines each rated at 12,000 ehp (8947 ekW) for take-off, followed the Tu-95/1 into the air in February 1955, and then there came a possible ten aircraft that were used for state trials. With the engine/propeller problems reduced though not eliminated, the new bomber entered service in April 1956 as the Tu-20 that had the bureau designation Tu-95M and soon received the NATO reporting name 'Bear-A'. This differed from the earlier aircraft in having reversible-pitch propeller units instead of a very large brake chute, and had the ability to carry a 44,092 lb (20,000 kg) warload of free-fall nuclear or conventional bombs. The Tu-20 soon lost its official designation and was generally known by just its bureau designation.

The Tu-95 'Bear' was soon developed into important variants optimised for the maritime and strategic reconnaissance roles, and for the missile-launch role that became far more significant than the originally demanded task of level bombing. Production of the basic bomber lasted to 1961 and totalled some 300 aircraft. Many of these were converted to other roles, but others remained operational in their original role, and

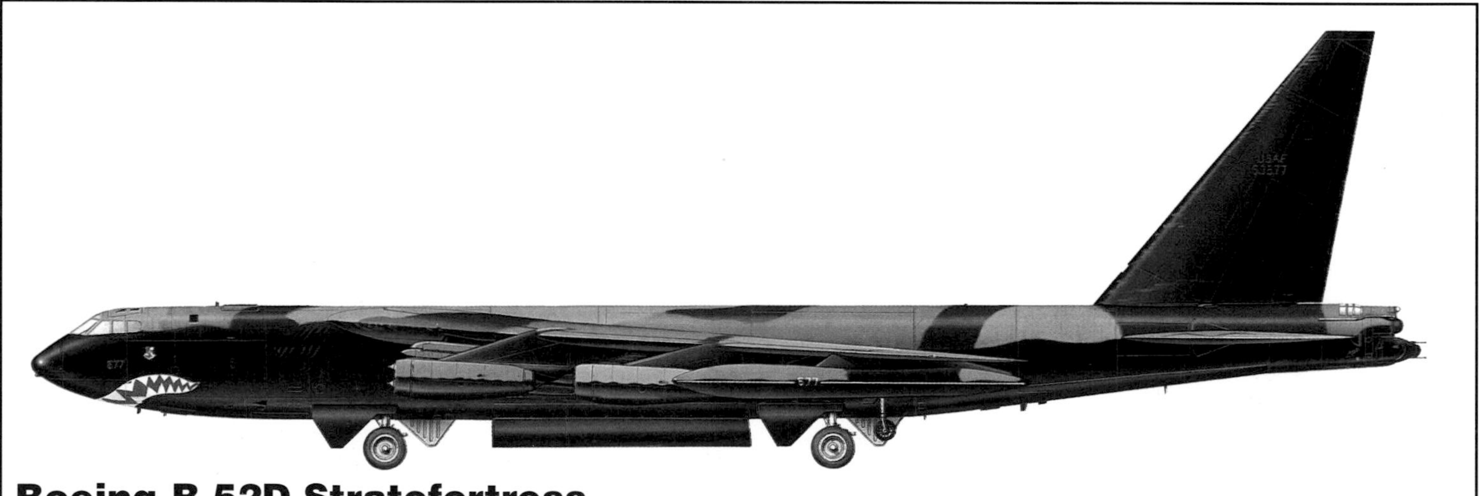

Boeing B-52D Stratofortress

Type: strategic heavy bomber and missile-launch platform
Country of origin: USA
Powerplant: eight 10,000-lb st (44.5-kN) Pratt & Whitney J57-P-19W turbojet engines
Performance: maximum level speed 630 mph (1014 km/h); service ceiling 45,000 ft (13,720 m); range 6200 miles (9978 km)
Weights: maximum take-off 450,000 lb (204,115 kg)
Dimensions: wing span 185 ft 0 in (56.39 m); length 160 ft 10.9 in (49.05 m); height 48 ft 4 in (14.74 m)
Armament: four 12.7 mm (0.5 in) machine guns, plus up to 60,000 lb (27,215 kg) of ordnance

ABOVE: A B-52 takes off during Operation Desert Storm, the United Nations operation against Iraq. It looks certain that the B-52 will remain part of the USAAF's armoury for many years.

some 65 such aircraft were still available to the Long-Range Aviation arm of the CIS air force during the mid-1990s.

Comparatively soon after the Tu-95M's entry into service it became clear that, to survive, it would have to be adapted as the platform for the carriage and launch of a large air-to-surface missile with the stand-off range that would permit launch at a range outside the enemy's main defensive perimeter. In the case of the Tu-95 series, the first missile-armed variant was the Tu-95K-20 'Bear-B' that was first produced by conversion of existing Tu-95M bombers and then manufactured as such. The Tu-95K-20 was first seen in 1961 with provision for one Mikoyan-Gurevich Kh-20 (AS-3 'Kangaroo') ASM to be carried in a position semi-recessed into the revised weapons bays.

From 1962 the type was revised with an inflight-refuelling probe above the nose and the modified designation Tu-95KD, and some aircraft were later adapted for the strategic reconnaissance role with a blister fairing on the starboard side of the rear fuselage for the receiver of an Elint system. As the Kh-20 missile became obsolescent, some of the aircraft were further modified to different standards while a few aircraft were converted to the training role with their inflight-refuelling probes removed.

Further development of the series led to a number of types for roles other than bombing and missile launching. These included the Tu-95KM 'Bear-C' introduced in about 1963 for the dedicated maritime reconnaissance and Elint roles, the Tu-95RTs 'Bear-D' introduced in about 1966 for the maritime multi-sensor reconnaissance and missile-support roles, and the Tu-95MR 'Bear-E' introduced in the later 1960s for the multi-sensor maritime reconnaissance role. The Tu-95K-22 'Bear-G', produced only as conversions from the Tu-95K-20 and Tu-95KM standards, were Elint platforms and missile-launch machines for two Kh-22 Burya (AS-4 'Kitchen') missiles carried on substantial pylons under the inner parts of the wing and used in conjunction with the new 'Down Beat' radar that has its antenna in the nose radome that differs only in small details from that of the earlier aircraft.

The Tu-95MS 'Bear-H' late-production version was, together with the Tu-142 'Bear-F', the reason for the reopening of the production line during 1983. The type has a reduced crew and an airframe based on that of the Tu-142 (and therefore including features such as the slightly longer nose and revised flightdeck, revised landing gear units characterised by bulged doors, wider-chord rudder, and removal of the sighting blisters under the tailplane, as no cannon barbettes are retained) without any significant increase in length over the Tu-95. Although based on a type for the dedicated maritime reconnaissance and anti-submarine roles in Soviet naval air force service, the Tu-95MS was developed as a modernised missile-launch platform for the Soviet air forces' Long-Range Aviation optimised for the carriage and launch of Kh-55 or RKV-500 (AS-15A 'Kent') cruise missiles. The Tu-95MS was produced to the extent of some 80 aircraft for service from 1984, in two subvariants known as the Tu-95MS-6 'Bear-H6' with provision for six missiles carried on a rotary launcher in the weapons bay, which is reduced in length to 24 ft 7.25 in (7.50 m), and as the Tu-95MS-16 'Bear-H16' with provision for 16 missiles carried as six on the rotary launcher, another four as twins on two pylons under the wing roots, and six more as triplets on two pylons between the engine pairs on each wing half. These missiles were to have been supplemented and then replaced by the more advanced

■ **ABOVE: Old Cold War enemies seen together in less stressful times at a British air display in the 1990s. These are a Boeing B-52H Stratofortress (left) and a Tupolev Tu-95MS (right).**

BL-10 (AS-19 'Koala'), a supersonic type under final development in the early 1990s but which was cancelled in 1995. The fuselage has been considerably refined, the ventral barbette being eliminated to leave only the tail turret (now fitted with one 23 mm (0.905 in) Gryazev-Shipunov GSh-23L two-barrel cannon rather than the original two 23 mm (0.905 in) Nudel'man-Suranov NS-23 single-barrel cannon), and external ECM and ESM equipment being replaced by internal units. It was with this variant that production of the Tu-95 family ended in 1992.

THE BISON

In 1949 Stalin, the Soviet dictator, directed the design bureau headed by Vladimir Mikhailovich Myasishchyev to design a jet-powered strategic bomber capable of delivering free-fall nuclear weapons from bases in the northern and eastern USSR to targets in North America. The technical task of developing a bomber able to fly some 9942 miles (16,000 km) with the required warload of 11,023 lb (5000 kg) was daunting in the extreme, and after the rejection of an initial concept for a bomber with a turboprop powerplant thought was then given to a bomber weighing some 551,146 lb (250,000 kg) and possessing a powerplant of no fewer than eight Mikulin AM-3 turbojet engines. The bureau soon scaled down its thinking on the basis that an excellent medium-range strategic bomber with a more realistic powerplant of four AM-3 turbojet engines would be better than no strategic bomber at all, and, as first flown late in 1953, the prototype was more conventionally sized but nonetheless an advanced and technically sophisticated machine with modestly swept flying surfaces including a high-aspect-ratio wing in the shoulder-set position, the four powerful axial-flow turbojets located in nacelles carried on pylons below and ahead of the wing leading edges, and landing gear that comprised two bicycle-type four-wheel main units under the fuselage and two twin-wheel stabilising outriggers extending from the bottoms of the two outer engine nacelles. Despite the fact that it lacked the range to attack North American targets from Soviet bases, the type was ordered into production as the M-4 with the powerplant relocated to the wing roots for reduced drag and the stabilising outrigger units relocated to pods that were now added at the wing tips for this purpose. The first of an eventual 200 or so bombers were completed to the initial M-4 standard that later received the NATO reporting designation 'Bison-A'. The new bomber entered service in 1956 and, despite the fact that it offered considerably greater capability than the Tupolev Tu-16 'Badger' in the medium-range role, was produced in what were by Soviet standards only modest numbers. This probably reflected a measure of official pique that the bomber did not offer a genuinely long-range capability, but also the fact that the M-4 required twice as many engines as the Tu-16 and was therefore more expensive to build, maintain and operate, and the fact that the 'developability' of the M-4 was limited by the size of its weapons bay, which extended between two immovable points, the two main landing gear units.

It was appreciated by the early 1960s that the day of the high-altitude bomber was over, and that superior range and payload capabilities were in any event offered by the Tupolev Tu-95 'Bear'. The M-4 was still a capable type, however, and it was accordingly decided to remanufacture existing aircraft for other roles, all without the fixed nose gun. One of the M-4's most important developments was therefore as an inflight-refuelling tanker, with the erstwhile weapons bay revised to accommodate an HDU with its associated hydraulic drive and tankage for some transfer fuel that was augmented by additional tankage in the front and rear fuselage sections.

THE HANDLEY PAGE VICTOR

The UK started to develop its own nuclear weapons in the period after World War II, and in 1946 the Royal Air Force issued an ambitious requirement for a bomber to carry such a 10000 lb (4536 kg) 'special weapon' or a heavy load of conventional bombs over a great range at high subsonic speed at an altitude of over 50000 ft (15240 m). Among the several companies that responded to this requirement, which was technically feasible in all aspects except the stipulated maximum take-off weight of less than 100000 lb (45360 kg), were the two companies which had supplied the RAF's two most important heavy bomber types of World War II, the Avro Lancaster and the Handley Page Halifax. The design from Handley Page was the H.P.80, which was based on a circular-section fuselage whose forward section was pressurised for crew accommodation and extended in depth to provide the volume for the large radar that was to be the primary nav/attack system. The first of two prototypes flew on 24 December 1952 with a powerplant of four Armstrong Siddeley Sapphire ASSa.7 Mk 200 series turbojets, the second following only on 11 September 1954. Trials revealed the need for a number of modifications such as a reduction of 1 ft 3 in (0.381 m) in the height of the fin and an increase of 3 ft 4 in (1.016 m) in the length of the nose to improve the centre of gravity range, and this paved the way for the Victor B.Mk 1 initial production model that first flew in February 1956 for a service debut in November 1957.

Delays in developing the Victor to service standard meant, however, that the type was seen as increasingly vulnerable to modern fighters and air-defence systems, and in the early 1960s 24 of the aircraft were revised to Victor B.Mk 1A standard with a powerful ECM system located in the extensively altered tail cone. As the early Victors were partially retired from service in favour of the much improved Victor B.Mk 2, it was decided to convert a number of them into reconnaissance aircraft and inflight-refuelling tankers. The reconnaissance standard was designated Victor B(PR).Mk 1, and the first six tanker conversions retained a bombing capability and were redesignated Victor B(K).Mk 1A after they had been retrofitted with two Mk 20B HDUs under the outer wings. These latter aircraft returned to service in May 1965, and in 1968 received the revised designation Victor B.Mk 1A(K2P). These machines were followed by 24 pure tankers with the underwing HDUs supplemented by a Mk 17 HDU in the rear part of the weapon bay, which was permanently sealed and revised to carry two additional fuel tanks. These 24 tankers were 10 Victor K.Mk 1 and 14 Victor K.Mk 1A machines converted from Victor B.Mk 1 and Victor B.Mk 1A standard aircraft respectively.

By 1954, work was well advanced on a version of the Victor bomber with turbofan rather than turbojet power, as this would considerably extend the type's range. The selected engine was the Rolls-Royce Conway in its RCo.11 Mk 103 form rated at 17,250 lb st (76.73 kN) dry, and the first Victor with such a powerplant flew in February 1959 as a Victor B.Mk 2 production-standard machine that was followed by another 33 bombers all fitted at delivery with the ECM system of the Victor B.Mk 1A. The wing roots of the Victor B.Mk 2 had to be extended by 3 ft 0 in (0.91 m) on each side to accommodate the Conway engines, and other changes included larger inlets, a dorsal fin fillet, two retractable scoops on the fuselage sides to feed air to the two turbo-alternators that powered the wholly revised electrical system, a Turbomeca Artouste auxiliary power unit in the starboard wing root to make the type independent of ground services, and provision for the carriage of the Avro 'Blue Steel' stand-off nuclear missile in a semi-recessed installation under the fuselage. The Victor B.Mk 2 entered service in October 1961, and was soon tasked with the low-level penetration role in succession to the Vickers Valiant. The low-level role placed considerable strain on the Victor's airframe, which had been designed for the high-altitude role. However, these strains were alleviated by the type's drooped leading edges and 'Küchemann carrots', which were a pair of large pods that extended rearward from the wing trailing edges to delay the appearance of shock waves at high subsonic speeds. The 'carrots' also provided useful accommodation for chaff dispensers, and were retrofitted on 21 Victor B.Mk 2 aircraft, together with improved ECM and an uprated powerplant to create the Victor B.Mk 2R. Another retrofit programme resulted in the Victor B(PR).Mk 2 (later Victor SR.Mk 2) variant intended for the maritime strategic reconnaissance role. Nine aircraft were adapted for this task with two additional fuel tanks in the erstwhile weapon bay, revised radar, cameras and a large number of photoflash bombs. The only Victor variant to remain in service into the 1990s before its retirement airframe hours expired, was the Victor K.Mk 2 of which 24 were produced in the early 1970s by the conversion of Victor B.Mk 2 bombers to provide a supplement to the Victor K.Mk 1/1A better suited to hot-and-high operations without sacrificing payload.

A NEW AVRO DESIGN

The design from Avro to meet the same requirement that led to the Victor, was the Type 698, which was based on a circular-section fuselage that accommodated, from front to rear, the large bombing radar, pressurised flightdeck, twin-wheel nose unit of the retractable tricycle landing gear, fuel tankage, weapon bay, and bays for avionics and electronic countermeasures. The fuselage supported the large vertical tail surface and the wing's centre section, which was a deep structure that carried two Bristol Aero-Engines BE.10 (later Bristol Siddeley Olympus) turbojets on each side. These were located in the rear part of the centre section with their nozzles projecting slightly to the rear of the trailing edges, and were aspirated via

Tupolev Tu-95MS-16 'Bear-H'

Type: long-range strategic missile launch aircraft
Country of origin: USSR
Powerplant: four 14,800-hp (11,035-ekW) KKBM (Kuznetsov) NK-12MV turboprop engines
Performance; maximum level speed 575 mph (925 km/h); service ceiling 39,370 ft (12,000 m);
Weights: empty 264,455 lb (120,000 kg); maximum take-off 412,257 lb (187,000 kg)
Dimensions: wing span 164 ft 2 in (50.04 m); length 161 ft 2.25 in (49.13 m) including refuelling probe; height 43 ft 7.75 in (13.30 m)
Armament: two 23 mm (0.905 in) Nudel'man-Rikhter NR-23 cannon or two 23 mm (0.905 in) Gryazev-Shipunov GSh-23L cannon, plus up to 16 Kh-55 (AS-15 'Kent') cruise missiles

a large letter-box inlet on each side. Outboard of the centre section were the main panels of the delta wing, each swept at 50º, accommodating one of the main landing gear units (each carrying four small twin-tyred wheels) and five large fuel tanks, and carrying on their trailing edges two-section inboard elevators and two-section outboard ailerons. Two Type 698 prototypes were ordered, but it was also decided to examine a number of the bomber's advanced aerodynamic features in five Type 707 aircraft, which differed between each other but were all about one-third the size of the Type 698. The Type 707 programme was launched almost as an afterthought, and thus ran in parallel with the Type 698 programme rather than before it, but nonetheless contributed considerably to the development of the big delta-winged bomber. The first Type 698 prototype was completed before its engines were ready, and therefore made its first flight on 30 August 1952 with an interim powerplant of four Rolls-Royce Avon RA.3 turbojets each rated at 6500 lb st (28.91 kN) dry, but these were soon replaced by Armstrong Siddeley Sapphire ASSa.6 turbojets each rated at 7500 lb st (33.36 kN) dry and later by Olympus BOl.1/28 turbojets. First flown on 3 September 1953, the second prototype was closer to the planned production standard with its forward fuselage lengthened by 1 ft 4 in (0.406 m) to accommodate the longer nose unit leg that had been installed to provide the wing with a greater angle of incidence at take-off. The type was

powered by four Olympus Mk 100 turbojets each rated at 9750 lb st (43.37 kN) dry, introduced a ventral blister with a visual bomb-aiming panel, and pioneered the production-standard flightdeck with the pilot and co-pilot on the upper deck on Martin-Baker Mk 3K ejection seats, and the navigator, radar operator and systems operator on the lower deck on ordinary seats.

THE AVRO VULCAN

The name Vulcan had by now been selected for the bomber, and the first Vulcan B.Mk 1 to emerge from the production line flew in February 1955 with the Olympus Mk 100 turbojet that was soon replaced by the Olympus BOl.1/2C Mk 101 rated at 11,000 lb st (48.93 kN) dry, the Olympus Mk 102 rated at 12,000 lb st (53.38 kN) dry, and finally the Olympus BOl.12 Mk 104 rated at 13,400 lb st (59.61 kN) dry. Production totalled 45 aircraft that entered service from February 1957. The higher power of the Olympus Mk 104 yielded an overall improvement in performance, especially in speed, but also resulted in mild buffeting of the outer wings. This threatened to erode the type's airframe fatigue life, but was cured by the retrofit on most aircraft of the so-called Phase 2 wing with a kinked and downward-cambered leading edge that increased the chord of the outer wing panels and thus decreased its thickness/chord ratio. By the time the last Vulcan B.Mk 1 had been delivered in April 1959, the Olympus Mk 104 engine and retrofitted inflight-refuelling probe had become standard, and most aircraft were revised with improved ECM capability in an enlarged tail cone that resulted in redesignation to Vulcan B.Mk 1A for aircraft that had a span of 99 ft 0 in (30.18 m) with an area of 3554.00 sq ft (330.17 m2), length of 97 ft 1 in (29.59 m), height of 26 ft 6 in (8,08 m), normal take-off weight of 160,000 lb (72,567 kg), maximum take-off weight of 200,000 lb (90720 kg), maximum level speed 'clean' of 628 mph (1010 km/h) at 40,000 ft (12190 m), cruising speed of 599 mph (964 km/h) at optimum altitude, range of 2994 miles (4818 km), and service ceiling of more than 50,000 ft (15240 m). In addition to the

■LEFT: Despite its turboprop engines, the Tu-95 (here a Tu-95KM 'Bear-C' dedicated maritime reconnaissance platform) offered jet-like performance and very long range.

conventional load of 21 1000 lb (454 kg) HE bombs available as a tactical loading, the free-fall thermonuclear bombs qualified for the Vulcan B.Mk 1 and Vulcan B.Mk 1A were, in order of acceptance for service, the 11,000 lb (4990 kg) 'Blue Danube', the 9000 lb (4082 kg) 'Violet Club', the 6000 lb (2722 kg) US Mk 5 (under US key on the aircraft of the Waddington Wing between 1958 and 1962), the 7000 lb (3175 kg) 'Yellow Sun Mk 1' (between 1962 and 1966) and the 7250 lb (3289 kg) 'Yellow Sun Mk 2' (between 1962 and 1966); the 2000 lb (907 kg) 'Red Beard' free-fall tactical nuclear bomb was also available.

During the second half of the 1950s, the Olympus turbojet was developed so extensively and successfully that a new version of the Vulcan was thought necessary to exploit the additional power that was now available from the Olympus BOl.6 Mk 200 series of engines. The new model was based on the Phase 4 wing, in which span was increased by 12 ft 0 in (3.66 m), the thickness/chord ratio was reduced still further, and larger inlets were provided for greater air flow required by the uprated powerplant. In 1956 and 1957, the second Type 698 prototype was rebuilt to the aerodynamic standard of the planned Vulcan B.Mk 2 and first flew in its revised form on 31 August 1957. Such was the importance attached to the Vulcan B.Mk 2 that 15 aircraft were allocated to the development programme, which involved no fewer than 90 major modifications including the new wing, replacement of the original elevator/aileron combination by four elevons on each side, enlargement of the inlets and jetpipes to cater not only for the Olympus Mk 200 series but also the planned Olympus BOl.21 Mk 300 series, restressing of the airframe to cater for much increased maximum take-off weights with an enlarged internal fuel capacity, the shortening of the nose unit leg and the redesign of the main units, the incorporation of a Rover 2S/150 gas turbine auxiliary power unit, a completely new electrical system, and provision for the Avro 'Blue Steel' stand-off nuclear missile (carried semi-recessed into the weapons bay) as its primary weapon. Some 17 aircraft under construction as Vulcan B.Mk 1A bombers were completed to the new standard, and the first of these flew in August 1958 with Olympus BOl.7 Mk 200 engines each rated at 16,000 lb st (71.17 kN) dry. The aircraft were soon revised with the Olympus Mk 201 rated at 17,000 lb st (75.62 kN) dry, and by 1961 this engine had been upgraded to Olympus Mk 202 standard with a pneumatic engine starting system for faster getaway. The Vulcan B.Mk 2 entered service from July 1960, and production of 89 aircraft was completed in January 1965.

BLUE STEEL CARRIER

The definitive standard, to which most aircraft were revised or delivered, was the Vulcan B.Mk 2A with 'Blue Steel' capability, terrain-following radar for the low-level penetration role that became the Vulcan's primary tasking in 1966, a powerplant of four Olympus Mk 301 turbojets, and an advanced ECM capability including the ARI.18228 RWR. By the time the last Vulcan B.Mk 2 had been delivered, most of the Vulcan B.Mk 1/1A bombers had disappeared from service, and early diminution of the Vulcan B.Mk 2/2A force followed in the late 1960s with the disbanding of two of the eight home-based squadrons, and the reallocation of another two squadrons to Cyprus. In 1973 another squadron was re-tasked with the maritime strategic reconnaissance role with aircraft revised to Vulcan SR.Mk 2A standard with classified electronic, optical and other sensors as well as, it is supposed, additional fuel in the erstwhile weapon bay. In the early 1980s it was decided that the cost of extending the fatigue life of the surviving aircraft was too high to be acceptable, and it was decided to withdraw all Vulcans between June 1981 and June 1982. This process was virtually complete when Argentine forces invaded the Falkland Islands in April 1982, and the last few aircraft were pooled from three squadrons to constitute an ad hoc force that could attack the Falkland Islands from a base on Ascension Island. Another six aircraft were revised to Vulcan K.Mk 2 inflight-refuelling tanker standard with an HDU in the erstwhile ECM bay and extra fuel in the erstwhile weapons bay. These aircraft were the last Vulcan machines to remain in service, and were retired in 1983.

THE AMERICAN HUSTLER

As early as 1946, Convair was digesting the mass of German research data it had received after World War II. With the aid of the German theoretician and delta-wing protagonist Dr. Alexander Lippisch, Convair was able to draw on German thinking in the evolution of a number of fascinating delta-winged warplane concepts. Such a configuration was selected for the company's GEBO IV (GEneralized BOmber no. 4) or Model 4 submission to meet the USAF's requirement for a long-range supersonic reconnaissance and bomber type. The Model 4 was designed to carry the bomb and fuel loads for the outward leg of the mission in a large ventral pod, a finned unit resembling a massive bomb that was jettisoned over the target, leaving the basic warplane to escape at very high speed and return home on its modest internal fuel capacity. The diameter of the external pod was so great that adequate ground clearance could be provided only by the use of very long legs on the tricycle landing gear, which comprised a nose unit with twin wheels and two main units each carrying a eight-wheel bogie. In this form the Model 4 was seen to offer considerable promise, and Convair was contracted to develop this first true weapon system in bomber and reconnaissance forms, although the latter was soon abandoned.

In October 1952, the USAF awarded a contract for two XB-58 prototypes, following in October 1954 with an order for 16 (later reduced to 11 and then supplemented by another 17) YB-58A service test aircraft and 31 ventral pods. Convair continued work on the advanced airframe, using a large proportion of bonded honeycomb sandwich skin panelling to resist the effect of aero-dynamic heating during sustained flight at Mach 2.

The first XB-58 prototype flew in November 1956, with a powerplant of four J79-GE-1 turbojets each rated at 14,300 lb st (63.61 kN) with afterburning, and soon revealed that the new bomber would satisfy the requirement without major modification even though many design decisions had been taken on the basis of informed guesswork rather than empirical data. Named Hustler in 1956, the B-58 was nonetheless an enormously complex and difficult type to prepare for full service, and the development programme involved no fewer than 30 aircraft (the two XB-58 and 28 YB-58A aircraft) with 35 MB-1C ventral pods each configured for one W39 nuclear warhead and 3474 Imp gal (15,792.7 litres) of fuel. The severity of the development programme and the highly advanced nature of the Hustler is indicated by the fact that no fewer than seven of these 30 aircraft were lost. The tactic evolved for delivery of this weapon/fuel pod was an inflight refuelling to top off the tanks and produce a maximum flight weight of 177,120 lb (80,342 kg), low-level ingress at about 691 mph (1112 km/h), a sharp climb to 55,000 ft (16,765 m) and 1321 mph (2126 km/h) or Mach 2.0 before release of the pod in a toss-bomb manoeuvre, and then egress at maximum speed. From 1960 the MB-1C pod was complemented by the TCP (Two-Component Pod), which was 62 ft 0 in (18.90 m) long and comprised a BLU-2/B-2 fuel-carrying lower section that was jettisoned after the fuel had been consumed, and a BLU-2/B-3 upper section carrying the BA53 warhead, cameras, ECM and/or fuel that was delivered over the target.

The YB-58 and YB-58A aircraft were each powered by J79-GE-5 or -5A turbojets, and the latter was used in the first of an eventual 86 B-58A Hustler production bombers, whose later examples had improved J79-GE-5B or -5C engines. The first of the production aircraft was delivered in March 1960, and these 86 aircraft were supplemented by 11 service-test aircraft brought up to full service standard. Other variants of the production standard bombers were the RB-58A Hustler and TB-58A Hustler. The RB-58A was a reconnaissance type produced by the conversion of 17 service test aircraft to carry a multi-sensor (optical and IR linescanning) reconnaissance pod, and the TB-58A was a dual-control conversion trainer produced by the conversion of eight service test aircraft.

The B-58A reached initial operational capability in August 1960, was switched to the shorter-range, low-level role in the mid-1960s (often with two wing-root hardpoints for an additional 7000 lb/3175 kg of disposable stores generally comprising four B41 low-drag nuclear bombs), but was withdrawn from service in January 1970 as a result of its relatively high accident rate and very high maintenance costs.

THE SOVIET BLINDER

The Tu-22 entered service in 1961 as the planned successor to the Tu-16 in the role of high-altitude penetration bomber against increasingly sophisticated Western defences, but, despite a good dash speed of Mach 1.5, its poor radius meant that the type was soon seen as a

Myasishchyev M-4 'Bison-A'

Type: strategic heavy bomber
Country of origin: USSR
Powerplant: four 19,180-lb st (85.32-kN) MNPK 'Soyuz' (Mikulin) AM-3D turbojet engines
Performance: maximum level speed 620 mph (998 km/h); service ceiling 44,950 ft (13,700 m); range 5033 miles (8100 km)
Weights: empty 198,413 lb (90,000 kg); maximum take-off 462,963 lb (210,000 kg)
Dimensions: wing span 165 ft 9.25 in (50.526 m); length 154 ft 10 in (47.20 m); height 46 ft 3 in (14.10 m)
Armament: nine 23 mm (0.905 in) Nudel'man-Rikhter NR-23 cannon , plus up to 19841 lb (9000 kg) of ordnance

ABOVE: Last of the 'V-bombers' to enter (and also to leave) service was the Handley Page Victor with a pod-and-boom fuselage and crescent-shaped flying surfaces.

supplement to the Tu-16 rather than its replacement. The NATO reporting designation initially allocated to the type, of which only some 250 examples were delivered, was 'Beauty' but this was soon altered to 'Blinder' once the Air Standards Coordinating Committee had decided that the original name was too flattering. The initial 'Blinder-A' variant was a reconnaissance bomber with cameras of both the reconnaissance and damage-assessment types in the rear of the main landing gear fairings, and SLAR or IR linescan equipment between the nose radar and the crew compartment. The Tu-22K 'Blinder-B' was the basic missile-carrying variant of the Tu-22 with the weapons bay revised with cutaway doors for the semi-recessed carriage of one Kh-22 Burya (AS-4 'Kitchen') air-to-surface weapon used with the 'Down Beat' radar that replaced the 'Short Horn' type of the Tu-22 bomber. The variant also introduced an inflight-refuelling probe of the semi-retractable type in a fairing above the nose.

The other variants were the Tu-22R 'Blinder-C' dedicated maritime reconnaissance model, the Tu-22UB 'Blinder-D' operational conversion trainer variant, and the Tu-22P 'Blinder-E' EW and Elint subversion of the Tu-22R, which had a modified nose radome and a number of additional dielectric panels for added sensors, but no provision for optical reconnaissance.

FRENCH FORCE DE FRAPPE

The French Government decided in 1954 to create a Force de Frappe (strike force) as the main element of a national nuclear deterrent capability, designed to maintain France in the forefront of the world's powers. A key element of this capability was a manned bomber to deliver the AN-22 weapon, a French-developed free-fall nuclear bomb with a 60 kiloton warhead. At this time Dassault was involved with the design of the Mirage III interceptor with a powerplant of one SNECMA Atar 101G-1 turbojet engine and one SEPR booster rocket, and the Mirage IV heavy fighter with a powerplant of two Atar 9 turbojet engines. The Mirage III finally matured with a powerplant of one Atar 9 turbojet engine and one SEPR rocket as an optional booster for improved high-altitude performance, and serious consideration was also given to procurement of the more capable Mirage IV with a wing area of 312.16 sq ft (29.00 m2) in either of two variants known as the Mirage IVA and Mirage IVB with maximum take-off weights of 14,109 and 16,270 lb (6400 and 7380 kg) respectively. Dassault next offered the French air force the scaled-up Mirage IVC with a powerplant of two Atar 9 turbojet engines, a wing area of 462.86 sq ft (43.00 m2) and a maximum take-off weight of 24,251 lb (11,000 kg), but then replaced this proposal with an identically designated proposal for a fighter with a powerplant of one de Havilland PS.26-3 Gyron afterburning turbojet engine and a wing area of 538.21 sq ft (50.00 m2). By November 1956 the Mirage IVA had been turned into the Mirage IVF with a SEPR rocket booster increasing the estimated service ceiling to 78,740 ft (24,000 m), and the French navy was expressing interest in the Mirage IVM navalised version of the Mirage IVC. Ultimately all of these Mirage IV fighter variants were abandoned, but the company's work was not wasted as the Mirage IVC became the basis for the medium strategic bomber required by the French air force. After a year of work trying to turn the Mirage IVC into such a warplane, Dassault rightly opined that greater size and weight were necessary to provide the warload, speed and range demanded by the French air force. This enlarged type would have been the Mirage IV with a powerplant of two large Pratt & Whitney J75-B turbojet engines, but the French air force then decided that inflight refuelling offered greater capabilities. Some 12 Boeing C-135F tankers were therefore ordered for the support of a force planned at 62 bombers, but even so the need to strike at targets deep in the USSR required that even after refuelling from a tanker in friendly airspace, missions would have to be flown by pairs of aircraft in which one carried the nuclear weapon and the other additional fuel and a 'buddy' refuelling pack.

The bomber finally developed for this role was the Mirage IVA, which first flew in June 1959 as a large warplane with a low/mid-set delta wing, the navigator/ systems operator in a small and virtually unglazed cabin behind the pilot's cockpit, a powerplant of two Atar 9 afterburning turbojet engines located side-by-side in the rear fuselage, and retractable tricycle landing gear. This last was optimised for the Mirage IVA's dispersed-site role, which envisaged RATO-boosted take-off from unprepared strips hardened by spray application of a quick-setting chemical compound. The landing gear comprised a twin-wheel nose unit and two main units, each carrying a four-wheel bogie.

The prototype was followed by three slightly larger pre-production aircraft. The first of these flew in October 1961 with a powerplant of two Atar 9C turbojet engines each rated at 14109 lb st (62.76 kN) with afterburning, and the third of them flew in January 1963 to a standard fully representative of the Mirage IVA production type with Atar 9K-50 turbojet engines, an inflight-refuelling probe on the nose, full operational equipment, and provision for armament. The first of 62 Mirage IVA bombers in total entered service in 1964 as the bomber component of France's nuclear deterrent force, comprising the 91e, 93e and 94e Escadres de Bombardement, each bomber being equipped with Thomson-CSF DRAA 8A surveillance radar, Marconi Doppler navigation, Dassault mission computer, and provision for one AN-22 free-fall nuclear weapon semi-recessed into the lower fuselage on intermediate-range sorties at a maximum weight of 73,799 lb (33,475 kg). Alternative loads were 16 992 lb (450 kg) conventional bombs or four AS.37 Martel ASMs.

During the mid- and late 1980s, with their free-fall bombing capability now obsolete, 19 Mirage IVA bombers were converted to carry the 150/300 kiloton ASMP short-range missile. In this role the Mirage IVP was optimised for low-level penetration with the aid of new Thomson-CSF Arcana radar, upgraded nav/attack and EW equipment including the Thomson-CSF Serval RWR, dual Sagem Uliss INSs, and flare/chaff dispensers on the outboard underwing hardpoints. Twelve aircraft were also converted to the Mirage IVR standard for the high/low-level strategic reconnaissance role with special navaids, revised EW system and specific sensor systems including the CT52 pod designed to fit the underfuselage recess previously used for the free-fall nuclear weapon. At the end of the 20th century, there survived only five Mirage IVP warplanes converted to the reconnaissance role.

THE TU-22M

For some time this aircraft was believed in the West to be designated the Tu-26 in its full production form, with the Tu-22M designation used only for a small number of early prototype and service trials conversions from Tu-22 'Blinder' standard. The warplane now known to be the Tupolev Tu-22M by proper designation is a powerful bombing, missile-launching and reconnaissance warplane that was clearly derived from the Tu-22, which had itself proved disappointing in terms of field performance and cruising range as a result of its high swept wing planform, which had been optimised for supersonic flight. The process of turning the Tu-22 into the Tu-22M involved the replacement of the original fixed-geometry wing with a revised type whose fixed inner sections supported pivoting outer panels to provide improved field performance with the outer wing panels in the 20º minimum-sweep position, better range in the cruising regime with the outer wing panels in the intermediate-sweep position, and high dash performance with the outer wing panels in the 65º maximum-sweep position. The engine installation was modified from a pair of afterburning turbojet engines pod-mounted on each side of the vertical tail surface with aspiration via circular inlets to a pair of afterburning turbofan engines in a conventional lateral installation with aspiration via rectangular-section inlets with variable ramps that doubled as splitter plates.

The revised type featured a number of other improvements and differences, and the first of two Tu-22M-0 (Tu-126) prototypes flew probably in the summer of 1969, at the beginning of a flight test programme that also involved seven pre-production aircraft. The Tu-22M-1 initial production variant was built to the extent of only nine aircraft (perhaps enough to equip just one squadron) and entered service in 1973. As might have been expected, the most notable aerodynamic feature of the type was its wing, which

Avro Vulcan B.Mk 2A

Type: strategic heavy bomber
Country of origin: UK
Powerplant: four 17,000-lb st (75.62-kN) Rolls-Royce (Bristol Siddeley) BOl.6 Olympus Mk 201 turbojet engines
Performance; maximum level speed 645 mph (1038 km/h) at 40,000 ft (12,190 m); service ceiling 55,000 ft (16,765 m); range 4606 miles (7412.5 km)
Weights: maximum take-off about 250,000 lb (113,400 kg)
Dimensions: wing span 111 ft 0 in (33.83 m); length 100 ft 1 in (30.50 m) excluding probe; height 27 ft 2 in (8.29 m)
Armament: up to 21,000 lb (9526 kg) of ordnance

was interesting not only for its variable-geometry capability but also for its complex high-lift and control features. The high-lift devices on each half of the wing comprised four-section flaps (including outer sections often claimed to be ailerons) of the double-slotted type on each trailing edge, and an automatically operated slat along the full span of the leading edge, while the control features on each wing half comprised three-section spoilers on the upper surface for lateral control, and some of these spoilers were also designed for use as air brakes and lift dumpers. The rest of the flying surfaces comprised a 'slab' horizontal surface in two halves, extending outward from points alongside the lower corners of the two engines' afterburner units, and a vertical surface with an inset rudder.

Despite its improvements over the Tu-22, the Tu-22M-1 was still disappointing in range, possibly as a result of the drag imposed by the pods projecting rearward from the wing trailing edge. It was at first thought in the West that these pods were of the typical Tupolev type and therefore accommodated the retracted main units of the tricycle landing gear, but this is now known not to have been the case.

THE BACKFIRE-B

The Tu-22M-2 'Backfire-B' was the first definitive version of the basic design, considerably revised and re-engineered for better performance and offensive capability. The only parts of the Tu-22M-1 retained were the vertical tail, fuselage shell and inner wing structure, the rest of the airframe being new and featuring longer-span wings without the rearward-protruding pods, a powerplant of two KKBM (Kuznetsov) NK-22 turbofan engines each rated at 48,501 lb st (215.74 kN) with afterburning, accommodation for a crew of four in a tandem arrangement of side-by-side upward-firing ejection seats, and a revised arrangement for the tricycle landing gear that comprises a rearward-retracting nose unit with two wheels and two main units each carrying a six-wheel bogie and retracting inward into wells in the lower part of the inner wing panels and fuselage. As first operated, the Tu-22M-2 had a single Kh-22 Burya (AS-4 'Kitchen') ASM semi-recessed into the lower-fuselage weapons bay, but the type was later revised with two underwing missiles of the same type as external weapon racks were added under the inlet ducts to increase the maximum weapons load to 46,296 lb (21,000 kg) including 26,455 lb (12,000 kg) of stores in the weapons bay. The defensive armament comprised two 23 mm (0.905 in) Gryazev-Shipunov GSh-23L rearward-firing two-barrel cannon in a tail barbette controlled by the 'Fan Tail' radar. Production of the Tu-22M-2 totalled 211 aircraft. Until the early 1990s, it is worth noting, the Western consensus was that this and later variants were designated Tu-26 to indicate the changes from the Tu-22M-1 standard, but this assessment was later revealed as false.

Introduced in 1984, the Tu-22M-2 'Backfire-C' is a revised version of the Tu-22M-2 with higher performance provided by the uprated powerplant of two Kuznetsov NK-25 turbofan engines each rated at 55,115 lb st (245.16 kN) with afterburning and aspirated via wedge inlets, possibly a retractable inflight-refuelling probe in place of the earlier models' fixed probe, a revised and upturned nose radome carrying a different nav/attack radar (or possible a nav/attack radar and a terrain-following radar), the offensive armament made more versatile by the introduction of a six-round rotary launcher system and its associated RKV-500B or Kh-15 (AS-16 'Kickback') defence-suppression missile of which a further four can be carried in two pairs under the fixed inner wing panels on the former Kh-22 hardpoints, and the defensive armament revised to just a single 23 mm (0.905 in) GSh-23L two-barrel cannon in a tail barbette of improved aerodynamic shape under a drum-shaped radome of the type introduced part-way through the Tu-22M-2 production run. The Tu-22M is used by the bomber force for strategic operations with free-fall weapons and cruise missiles, and by the naval air force for electronic reconnaissance and anti-shipping attack with ASMs. Production ended in 1993 with the delivery of the 268th aeroplane.

ABOVE: The most popular, and visually the most impressive, of the 'V-bombers' was the Avro Vulcan, a flying wing design later adapted from the high- to low-level penetration role.

THE BIRTH OF THE B-1

Since the commissioning of the US Navy's first nuclear-powered ballistic missile submarine in December 1959, the USA had relied for its primary strategic defence on a 'triad' of delivery systems for nuclear weapons. This triad comprises the submarine-launched ballistic missile submarine, the ground-launched ballistic missile and the manned bomber. The last is generally thought to have the highest vulnerability, but also to provide unrivalled flexibility of operation (including the ability to delivery conventional weapons as alternatives to nuclear bombs) and possibility of recall right up to the moment of weapon release. In the 1950s and first part of the 1960s the US Air Force operated a trio of manned bombers for the strategic role, these comprising the Boeing B-47 Stratojet subsonic medium bomber, Boeing B-25 Stratofortress subsonic heavy bomber, and the Convair B-58 Hustler supersonic medium bomber. All three of these aircraft had been designed for the high-altitude penetration role, but in the early 1960s it became clear that the development of the USSR's defensive

capabilities against such penetration, largely through the introduction of increasingly capable surface-to-air missiles complemented by higher-performance manned interceptors with advanced air-to-air missiles, dictated a switch to low-level penetration under the edge of the Soviets' radar coverage. The current bombers could be switched to this role, albeit at the expense of their airframe lives and performance, but the B-47 and B-58 were approaching the end of their operational lives and in 1962 the USAF started to plan an Advanced Manned Strategic Aircraft. This resulted in the issue during 1965 of a requirement that elicited responses from Boeing, General Dynamics, North American and Rockwell. Of these it was the North American offering that was selected for further development, and it was a combination of anticipated development costs and coincidence of other interests that led to the merger of North American and Rockwell in September 1967 as the North American Rockwell Corporation that became the Rockwell International Corporation in 1973.

In June 1970 the USAF ordered the construction of four B-1A prototypes as a prelude for full-scale development of the new bomber, and the first of these machines made its maiden flight on 23 December 1974. At that time the USAF's Strategic Air Command hoped to order some 250 examples of the new bomber to start the process of replacing its now ageing force of B-52 bombers.

Congressional opposition and a new administration led to the humbling of such plans, however, and in June 1977 President 'Jimmy' Carter announced that testing of the four prototypes would continue only as a form of insurance against the failure of the strategic cruise missile programme that was now seen in the administration and political circles as offering superior capability at lower cost. At the same time, President Carter confirmed that production of the B-1A would be shelved.

REAGAN'S SUPPORT

By 1981 the political climate had changed once more and Ronald Reagan, the new president, was taking a considerably harder line in his attitude to the USSR. An immediate beneficiary of the new concept of a strengthened military capability relying strongly on the USA's greater economic strength and technological superiority over the USSR was SAC, which received information during September 1981 that it would finally receive the much-overdue new bomber in the form of a reduced total of 100 examples of the B-1B derivative based on the external configuration of the fourth B-1A. The second and fourth B-1A prototypes were used from March 1983 to flight-test features of the B-1B, which is based on a blended wing/fuselage design with a low-set wing whose outer panels are of the variable-geometry type with a leading-edge sweep angle that can be varied between a minimum of 15º and a maximum of 67º 30'. The B-1B is powered by four General Electric F101 turbofan engines mounted in side-by-side pairs below and to the rear of the wing's fixed centre section. The nacelles are located close to the centre of gravity for optimum stability in the turbulent air typical of high-speed flight by an aircraft in the low-level flight regime.

ABOVE: Carrying its nuclear payload and the fuel for the outward leg of its mission in a large ventral pod, the Convair B-58A Hustler offered high supersonic performance.

To ensure that the B-1B could take-off more rapidly than the B-52, and in crisis operate from more austere forward airfields, the B-1B is fitted with high-lift devices: the wing therefore incorporates full-span slats on the leading edges in seven segments on each side, and single-slotted flaps on the trailing edges in six segments on each side. There are no ailerons as control in roll is provided by four-segment air brake/spoiler surfaces on each outer wing panel. With the exception of the electrically powered outboard spoilers that are controlled by a fly-by-wire system, all the flying controls are electro-hydraulically powered and also include the moving elements of the tail unit, which comprise a rudder and a tailplane with all-moving 'taileron' halves that operate collectively as elevators and differentially as ailerons; the tail surfaces have a fly-by-wire backup control system. Small movable vane-like surfaces of composite construction and anhedralled at 30º are fitted below and ahead of the flightdeck: these sense lateral and vertical motion in turbulent flight and provide both yaw and pitch damping for the aircraft.

B-1B LIMITATIONS

The absolute performance of the B-1B has been downgraded in comparison with that of the B-1A by changes dictated largely by cost factors, and major airframe improvements introduced at this time included strengthened landing gear, a movable bulkhead in the forward double weapons bay to allow for the carriage of a diverse range of differently sized weapons, provision for weapons bay fuel tanks for increased range, and external hardpoints under the fuselage for additional fuel or weapons. The reduction in the B-1A's capability for a high-level dash speed of some Mach 2.5 to a figure of about Mach 1.25 allowed the replacement of the variable-geometry engine inlets with lighter, cheaper and more reliable fixed-geometry inlets.

The low-altitude, high-speed penetration role against sophisticated air defence systems was to be carried out using electronic jamming equipment, IR countermeasures, radar location and warning systems, and application of 'low-observability' technology. Careful attention to inlet geometry resulted in the flat faces of the four engines' compressors being hidden from radar by S-shaped inlet trunks carrying streamwise baffles, and much use was also made of RAM (Radar Absorbent Materials) on key components. Perhaps the best evidence of success in reducing the electromagnetic signature of the aircraft is provided by the fact that its radar cross-section is at least an order of magnitude smaller than that of a B-52, despite the fact that the B-1B is only a marginally smaller aircraft and is of comparable weight.

The four-man crew of the B-1B comprises the pilot, co-pilot, OSO (Offensive Systems Operator) and DSO (Defensive Systems Operator). The pilot and co-pilot are seated side-by-side in the cockpit with the OSO and DSO in a similar arrangement in a compartment to the rear of the cockpit. All the windows can be fitted with PLZT (zirconium titanate) radiation glare shields. All four members of the crew are located on McDonnell Douglas/Weber ACES II zero/zero ejection seats in an arrangement that replaces the B-1A's capable yet complex and expensive crew escape capsule. The FBW and electro-mechanical flight control systems are operated by the pilot and co-pilot, with common reversionary links in event of failure. The OSO functions mainly as the navigator, and his primary tasks are guidance of the B-1B to its target and the release of the weapons at the optimum moment, while the DSO controls the B-1B's defensive electronics.

The development of the offensive avionics system was entrusted primarily to Boeing, and its primary system is the Westinghouse APQ-164 multi-mode offensive radar derived from the APG-66 of the General Dynamics (now Lockheed Martin) F-16 Fighting Falcon and including a low-observability phased-array antenna for low-altitude terrain-following and accurate navigation. Other navigation systems include a highly accurate Singer-Kearfott INS, Teledyne Ryan APN-218 Doppler, and Honeywell ASN-121 radar altimeter. The Honeywell offensive display sets comprise three MFDs with two for the OSO and one for the DSO: of the former, one shows threats on alphanumeric labels and the other carries tabulated threat information. The DSO is concerned primarily with the demands of countering external threats using the much-troubled Eaton AIL ALQ-161 system that constitutes the core of the B-1B's continuously upgradable defensive capability. The system comprises an ALQ-161A radio frequency surveillance/ECM system, a tail-warning unit, the ASQ-184 defensive management system, and an expendable counter-measures system (chaff and flares). The system can detect, locate and classify signals from hostile emitters transmitting simultaneously via a number of receivers situated around the airframe in order to provide full 360º coverage. The system can also prioritise the threats and automatically initiate the counter-measures via a large number of Northrop jamming transmitters and Raytheon phased-array antennae.

FIRST FLIGHT OF THE B-1B

The first B-1B off the production line made its maiden flight on 18 October 1984, deliveries began to Offutt Air Force Base in Nebraska in July 1985, and SAC reached initial operational capability with the B-1B, later named Lancer, exactly one year later before the completion of a rapid build-up to a force of four bomb wings. With the exception of the ninth machine, which was delivered to Edwards AFB in California for test duties, the first 29 B-1B warplanes were assigned to the 96th BW at Dyess AFB in Texas, and subsequent units were the 28th Wing at Ellsworth AFB in South Dakota, the 319th BW at Grand Forks AFB in North Dakota, and the 384th BW at McConnell AFB in Kansas.

The career of the B-1B has been marked by controversy and frequently interrupted by long grounding orders. There have also been several highly publicised losses. Problems were caused

ABOVE: The Tupolev Tu-22 'Blinder' provided the Soviets with a supersonic nuclear bombing capability, but was notably short on range, and had poor field performance.

by false alarms from the computerised self-diagnostic systems, non-functioning terrain-following radar, and repeated failures of the ALQ-161 system. Engine problems were also a significant factor in the type's grounding, and perhaps some of the losses. One of the more recent periods of enforced inactivity prevented the B-1B from playing any operational role in the 'Desert Storm' operations to drive the Iraqi occupying forces out of Kuwait in the first part of 1991 despite the fact that it was still nominally undertaking SAC's 'alert' nuclear role.

FUTURE PLANS

Future plans for the B-1B fleet include the addition of GPS, a MIL-1760 databus, ECM improvements, and a more advanced weapons capability with conventional as well as nuclear weapons as it is complemented in the penetration role by the Northrop Grumman B-2A Spirit. A six-month operational readiness assessment began in June 1994, and the successful assessment was largely responsible for the partial breaking of Congressional opposition to further funding for improvement of the type. Up to the present, the B-1B's primary task has been of a strategic nature with free-fall nuclear weapons, although the type has been cleared for carriage of cruise missiles. The B-1B had an in-line arrangement of three weapons bays, the adjacent forward pair ahead of the wing carrythrough structure having an overall length of 31 ft 3 in (9.53 m) and the rear unit aft of the wing carrythrough structure having a length of 15 ft 0 in (4.57 m). The bays are covered by hydraulically operated doors, and the weapons they generally carry include B61 and B83 thermonuclear bombs up to a maximum weight of 75,000 lb (34,020 kg). Alternatively the weapons bays can be equipped with three racks or SRAM launchers for up to 24 examples of the AGM-69A Short-Range Attack Missile (later SRAM-A and now out of operational service), 12 2170 lb (984 kg) B28 or 28 750 lb (340 kg) B61 or 2400 lb (1089 kg) B83 free-fall nuclear bombs. The B-1B also has the capacity to carry eight AGM-86B Air-Launched Cruise Missiles (possibly replaceable on a one-to-one basis by the AGM-86C version with a 1000 lb/454 kg unitary HE warhead) or AGM-129A Advanced Cruise Missiles on the Common Strategic Rotary Launcher that can be installed after modification of the forward double bomb bay using the movable bulkhead introduced on the ninth aeroplane, although the ALCM has never been carried in routine operations. The six underfuselage stores stations can lift an additional 12 ALCMs, or additional conventional stores for a maximum total of 134,000 lb (60782 kg). The B-1B is also cleared for the delivery of conventional weapons, the first load to be cleared in the Block B upgrade being up to 84 500 lb (227 kg) Mk 82 bombs or Mk 36 mines carried internally, followed by the 950 lb (431 kg) CBU-87/B Combined Effect Munition cluster bomb that was added in the Block C upgrade together with capability for the CBU-89 (Gator anti-tank and anti-personnel minelets) cluster bomb and the CBU-97 Sensor-Fused Weapon cluster bomb with ten BLU-108 submunitions each carrying four 'Skeet' anti-tank weapons. The Block D upgrade, implemented by the end of 1998, adds improved communications, the Raytheon ALE-50 Towed Decoy System, GPS update of the INS, a MIL 1760 databus for better integration of weapon features, and provision for advanced conventional weapons such as the 1985 lb (900 kg) GBU-31 Joint Direct-Attack Munition, a guided unit available as the GBU-31(V)1 with a fragmentation warhead or the GBU-31(V)3 with a penetration warhead. Future weapon options of the conventional type, now being developed in the Block E upgrade scheduled for implementation by 2002 and based on improved computer architecture and software to permit the carriage of up to three different types of weapon, include varying numbers of more advanced types such as the Texas Instruments JSOW (Joint Stand-Off Weapon), the JASSM (Joint Air-to-Surface Stand-off Missile) and the WCMD (Wind-Corrected Munitions Dispenser) inertially guided tail kit for addition to cluster bombs (CBU-87, CBU-89, CBU-97, CBU-103, CBU-104 and CBU-105) as well as better established weapons such as the AGM-84 Harpoon anti-ship missile and AGM-142 'Have Nap' ASM. In the late 1990s responsibility for the maintenance and further improvement of the B-1B, including the addition of the Raytheon ALE-50 towed missile decoy system, became a Boeing responsibility.

THE TUPOLEV TU-160

The heaviest warplane ever built and dwarfing in size the similarly configured B-1B Lancer, the Tupolev Tu-160 is the largest bomber in the world. There can be little doubt that the design of the Soviet bomber was heavily influenced by that of the B-1A precursor of the Lancer which made its maiden flight on 23 December 1974, but was cancelled by President 'Jimmy' Carter in 1977. Originally known as Product 70, the Tu-160 made its maiden flight on 19 December 1981 at Zhukhovskii, then known in the West as

Tupolev Tu-22M 'Backfire-A'

Type: medium strategic bomber and maritime strike aircraft
Country of origin: USSR
Powerplant: two 35,273-lb st (156.90-kN) RKBM (Koliesov) VD-7M turbojet engines
Performance: maximum level speed 920 mph (1480 km/h) or Mach 1.40 at 39,370 ft (12,000 m);

Ramenskoye. This aeroplane had been spotted by a US reconnaissance satellite some three weeks before its first flight, and received the temporary reporting designation 'Ram-P' before being redesignated as the 'Blackjack'. Photographed as it rested between two Tupolev Tu-144 'Charger' supersonic transport aircraft, the Tu-160 revealed many features in common with the B-1, although comparison with the Tu-144 almost immediately revealed that the Soviet bomber was very much larger than its American counterpart. The B-1A had been designed for the penetration of enemy air defences at high altitude with high performance and a highly sophisticated ECM suite offering a way through these defences without undue losses. When the project was reborn as the cheaper, less complex but more practical B-1B, all thoughts of high-level penetration had been relinquished and the less sophisticated machine was now expected to use a combination of low-level flight (where speed is limited to the transonic region) and reduced radar

service ceiling 60,040 ft (18,300 m); radius 1491 miles (2400 km) without inflight refuelling
Weights: empty about 88,183 lb (40,000 kg); maximum take-off about 184,965 lb (83,900 kg)
Dimensions: wing span 77 ft 11 in (23.75 m); length 132 ft 11.7 in (40.53 m) excluding probe; height 35 ft 0 in (10.67 m)
Armament: one 23 mm (0.905 in) Nudel'man-Rikhter NR-23 cannon, plus up to 22,046 lb (10,000 kg) of ordnance

cross-section for penetration of enemy air defences. In the USSR it was felt that there was little need for impairment of overall capabilities for reasons of economy, and the Tu-160 programme therefore remained committed to both low-level penetration at transonic speed and high-level penetration at a speed of about Mach 1.9.

VARIABLE GEOMETRY WING

The combination of a variable-geometry wing planform and extensive high-lift devices was employed to provide good low-speed handling and therefore the required field performance with the wing in the minimum-sweep position of 20º, excellent payload/range performance with the wing in the intermediate-sweep position of 35º, and very high speed with the wing in the maximum-sweep position of 65º. The wing sweep angle is selected manually, and the high-lift devices include full-span slats on the leading edges and double-slotted flaps on the trailing edges. The trailing edge of the inboard flap sections, which are immobilised when the wings are swept back, has no slot in the fuselage into which it can retract when the wing is swept, and instead folds upward parallel to the aeroplane's centre-line and thus serves as a fence. Some aircraft have a double-jointed folding section which permits a fold to create a fence at either 35º or 65º.

The Tu-160 has a crew of four seated in tandem side-by-side pairs on Zvezda K-36D ejection seats on the enclosed flightdeck, which is entered via a ladder in the rear part of the bay for the two-wheel nosewheel unit of the tricycle landing gear whose main units each carry a six-wheel bogie that turns through 90º to lie parallel with the relevant leg as the main units retract rearward into the thickest parts of the wing. The pilot and co-pilot operate the aeroplane by means of fighter-type control columns for inputs to the fly-by-wire control system, but all the cockpit instrumentation is of the analogue type with no MFDs, CRTs or HUDs. In front of the cockpit is the long pointed radome for the terrain-following and attack radar, with a fairing below it for the forward-looking TV camera used for visual weapon aiming. Inter-continental range is assured by the provision of a fully retractable inflight-refuelling probe. The warload is carried in a tandem arrangement of two weapons bays, each 42 ft 0 in (12.80 m) long and located in the lower fuselage. Each of these bays is normally equipped with a rotary launcher which can carry either six Kh-55M (AS-15 'Kent') cruise missiles or 12 Kh-15P (AS-16 'Kickback') 'SRAMski' defence-suppression missiles.

ABOVE: The Rockwell (now Boeing) B-1B Lancer was designed for penetration of defended airspace under the radar screen for the release of bombs or missiles.

TU-160 DELIVERIES

The development of the Tu-160 to production status was extremely protracted, and at least one prototype is believed to have been lost. Production was undertaken at Kazan and continued until January 1992, when President Boris Yeltsin announced that no further strategic bombers would be built. It was later thought that limited production might be reinstated, primarily to replace the aircraft seized by the Ukraine on the dissolution of the USSR, but this is now considered to be unlikely for financial reasons even though the division of the available force left neither Russia nor the Ukraine with a truly viable number of these advanced bombers. Even after aircraft were delivered to the 184th Heavy Bomber Regiment from May 1987, the Tu-160 continued to suffer major difficulties that severely restricted operations: shortage of basic flying equipment was a major irritation to air crews; lack of ear protectors and anti-vibration boots for ground crew caused deafness in some men; ejection seat difficulties meant that seats could not be adjusted to individual crew members; and reliability of the aeroplane, engines and systems was dismally poor. Operations had therefore to be supported by teams from the Kazan factory as well as the Tupolev design bureau, and aircraft deliveries continued despite the fact that no full production standard had yet been agreed. As a result span, equipment fit, and inlet configuration differ from aeroplane to aeroplane.

Nineteen of the Tu-160 bombers were delivered to the two squadrons of the 184th Regiment at the Priluki air base in the Ukraine where they remained under Ukrainian control after the collapse of the USSR. The Ukraine could not maintain the aircraft, whose transfer to Russia was later agreed. The last 12 aircraft were delivered to Russian operators including the 1st Heavy Bomber Regiment (five aircraft) that is the sole Russian operating unit with the other seven allocated to various test duties. This regiment is located at Engels air base in the Saratov region of Russia, which had originally been intended as the first Tu-160 base, even though Priluki came to enjoy this privilege pending the completion of work at Engels.

THE STEALTH BOMBER

The B-2 Spirit flying wing was designed and developed under conditions of the greatest possible secrecy as a 'stealthy' (low-observability and thus radar and IR sensor-evading) strategic bomber for the 'Cold War' task of attacking major Soviet targets with nuclear bombs and stand-off weapons. The B-2 began as a 'black' programme, which was known in its first stages as 'Project Senior C.J.' and later as the Advanced Technology Bomber (ATB). During the first stages of the programme the most senior officers of the US Air Force believed that the service's first priority in this field should be the B-1B supersonic bomber, so only a very small number of officers even knew of the B-2 project for a subsonic penetration bomber. To the latter, therefore, the B-1B was an 'interim' type to be built and deployed pending the availability of the B-2, and at the height of the 'Cold War' the USAF expected to procure no fewer than 132 of this vastly expensive but undoubtedly capable type. For the design of the new bomber Northrop (now Northrop Grumman) drew heavily on its previous experience with flying wing aircraft, but even so was considerably aided by Boeing, Vought and General Electric. The design team used a 3D computer-aided design and manufacturing system to create the B-2's unique 'blended wing/double-W' planform shape, and more than 100,000 radar cross-section images of B-2 models and components were analysed for assessment of their 'stealth' properties before a combination of scaled-down and full-sized components were used in some 550,000 hours of wind tunnel testing. Some 900 specialised manufacturing processes had to be developed for the programme, these processes including the creation of composite materials able to withstand considerable heat without loss of strength, ultrasonic cutting machinery, automated tooling via the 3D database, and laser sheraography inspection.

Manufacture of the aeroplane is a collaborative effort with Northrop responsible for the forward sections and the cockpit, Boeing for the aft centre and outboard sections, and Vought for the mid-fuselage sections and aluminium, titanium and composite parts, with final assembly undertaken by Northrop Grumman. Graphite/epoxy composites are extensively used on the B-2 as the primary material for the honeycomb material that absorbs rather than reflects electromagnetic energy, and to reduce the IR signature of the powerplant, the four General Electric F118-GE-110 turbofan engines exhaust through Vee-shaped outlets set back and above the trailing edges to hide these heat sources from the ground, while visual observability is reduced by the injection of chloro-fluorosulphonic acid into the exhaust plume to suppress the formation of contrails. The combination of the B-2's 33º swept leading edges and sawtoothed trailing edges help to trap rather than reflect radar energy. Further low-observability measures on the aircraft include S-shaped engine inlets and 'stealthy' dielectric panels: these latter hide the antenna for the Hughes APQ-181 radar from hostile radar waves while allowing it to function normally.

THE B-2'S ELECTRONIC SUITE

The radar has features in common with the APG-70 used in the McDonnell

Rockwell B-1B Lancer

Type: long-range strategic bomber and missile-launch platform
Country of origin: USA
Powerplant: four 30,780-lb st (136.92-kN) General Electric F101-GE-102 turbofan engines
Performance: maximum level speed about 823 mph (1324 km/h) or Mach 1.25 at high altitude; service ceiling more than 50,000 ft (15,240 m); maximum range about 7455 miles (12,000 km) with standard fuel
Weights: empty 192,000 lb (87,091 kg); maximum take-off 477,000 lb (216,365 kg)
Dimensions: wing span 136 ft 8.5 in (41.67 m) spread and 78 ft 2.5 in (23.84 m) swept; length 147 ft 0 in (44.81 m); height 34 ft 10 in (10.36 m)
Armament: typical maximum of 75,000 lb (34,020 kg) ordnance

Douglas F-15C/D/E Eagle, and is a synthetic-aperture type with 21 operational modes including coherent mapping. The B-2 briefly turns on its APQ-181 radar, spotlighting only a small area, to verify the position of targets immediately before any attack. Since 1987 this radar has been under test in a specially modified Boeing C-135, and although radar was installed on some of the prototype B-2 bombers, all radar testing has been done on the C-135.

The B-2's electronic warfare system comprises the Loral Federal Systems APR-50 (ZSR-62) RWR and the highly classified Northrop Grumman ZSR-63 defensive aids system. The cockpit is equipped for operation by a standard complement of two, with upward-firing McDonnell Douglas/Weber ACES II zero/zero ejection seats and a control column for each person, although there is room for a third crew member. The pilot in the port seat has charge of the mission computer, which handles target tasking (or inflight retasking), while navigation and weapons delivery are the responsibility of the weapons system operator/mission commander in the starboard seat. The two primary positions each have four multi-function coloured displays, and all flight, powerplant, sensor and systems information is presented on a nine-tube EFIS (Electronic Flight Instrumentation System) display. The aeroplane has a quadruplex digital fly-by-wire system actuating movable surfaces on the wing trailing edges, which combine aileron, elevator and flap functions and occupy 15 per cent of the wing area. A beaver tail acts as a pitch-axis trimming surface and, along with the elevons, helps in gust alleviation. The moving surfaces on the trailing edge comprise elevons for pitch and roll control, and 'differential drag' surfaces for yaw control.

LACK OF RADAR REFLECTIVITY

Design and manufacturing emphasis were placed on completely smooth surfaces with blended flightdeck and nacelle bulges. As a result, the B-2A's radar reflectivity is very low because of the use of radiation-absorbent materials and a carefully optimised shape (including the shielded upper-surface engine inlets), and a basic head-on radar cross section about one-tenth and one-hundredth of those possessed by the B-1 and B-52 respectively. Although originally envisaged as a high-level penetrator, by the time the design was frozen in 1983, the B-2 had assumed a low-level role. Modifications needed to adapt the original ATB design to this new role included movement of the cockpit and engine inlets, addition of inboard elevons resulting in the distinctive 'double-W' planform, modification of the leading edge, and implementation of substantial internal changes, including the provision of new bulkheads. In a surprise move, the USAF released an artist's impression of the aircraft, which had previously been shrouded in total secrecy, during the course of April 1988. Six prototypes, five of them for the USAF, were funded in 1982, and the first of these machines was rolled out at USAF Plant 42 at Palmdale in California, on 22 November 1988. Northrop carefully managed the ceremony to hide details of the aeroplane's wing design, and the 500 assembled guests had only a limited front view of the B-2 from ground level. Although originally scheduled for 1987, the B-2's first flight took place on 17 July 1990 when the first aeroplane, also known as AV-1 (Air Vehicle no. 1), was delivered to the USAF at Edwards AFB, to begin the type's test programme. The final date had been delayed from 15 July by a fuel system malfunction, and had been preceded by a series of high-speed taxi runs on 13 July, when the nose wheel was lifted briefly. AV-1 was joined by AV-2 on 19 October 1990 and a schedule of 3600 flight hours was started with 16 flights (67 hours) of airworthiness and handling trials. These flights were completed in mid-June 1990 and included the type's first air-to-air refuelling, with a McDonnell Douglas KC-10A Extender, on 8 November 1989. Block 2 testing began in October 1990 for a thorough investigation and assessment of the low-observability features of the real aeroplane. These flights provided the first signs that all was not as advertised with the B-2's 'stealth' features, and

ABOVE: The apogee of Soviet nuclear bomber development, the Tupolev Tu-160 'Blackjack' is a mammoth aircraft. It is currently in service with the Russian air force.

subsequent flights were halted while modifications were carried out on the AV-1. 'Stealth' testing continued into 1993, while the AV-2 was engaged on further performance and load trials. The third aeroplane made its first flight on 18 June 1991 and was the first of the machines to carry the full mission fit of advanced avionics including the APQ-181 LPI (Low Probability of Intercept) radar. The first weapons drop by a B-2 was made by the fourth aeroplane, which first took to the air on April 1992: this machine dropped one 2000 lb (907 kg) inert Mk 84 bomb on 4 September 1992. Earmarked for other weapons, low observability and climatic testing, the fifth aeroplane took to the air on 5 October 1992, followed by the sixth machine on 2 February 1993. By the end of 1993 the programme had achieved 1500 flying hours.

STEALTH PROBLEMS

As noted above, deficiencies of the B-2's 'stealthiness' were revealed from July 1991, and while the Americans have conceded that the aeroplane can be detected by some high-power land-based early warning radars, they have not commented officially on Russian claims that bomber is vulnerable to the CIS's new-generation of SAM systems as typified by the S-300PMU (SA-10A 'Grumble') and S-300V-9M83/82 (SA-12A/B 'Gladiator'/'Giant'). As a result, the USAF is implementing a 'set of treatments' to some parts of the leading edges and flying surfaces to reduce the B-2's signature across a range of frequencies. Problems with the B-2's performance have not helped the type in its battle for production funding. The original target was a fleet of 133 airframes, including the prototype, as carriers for 2000 of the 4845 strategic nuclear weapons in the US Air Force's inventory, but by 1991 this had been cut back to 76 aircraft. After the original six aircraft, ordered in 1982, three more were funded while the B-2 was still a 'black' project. In 1989 funding was allocated for a further three machines followed by that for pairs of aircraft in 1990 and 1991. The Congress then froze acquisition at a mere 16 machines for the USAF, which claimed that it could not offer a genuinely effective operational capability with less than 20 aircraft, and as a result five more aircraft were subsequently approved by 1993. This approval from Congress for the further aircraft came only with the proviso that the type's low observability problems must have been cured before the start of any production.

ABOVE: Currently the last word in bomber capability, the Northrop Grumman B-2A Spirit uses its 'stealthiness' to avoid the attentions of air defence systems.

After the diversion of the first B-2A production warplane, named Spirit of Texas, to Northrop for electromagnetic compatibility and emissions testing, the initial B-2A for the USAF was the eighth aeroplane, named Spirit of Missouri, and this was delivered to the 509th Bomb Wing at Whiteman Air Force Base, Missouri, on 17 December 1993 after taking to the air for its first flight before the seventh aeroplane. Like the other aircraft involved in the flight test programme, the seventh aircraft was delivered to the USAF by 1997. The 509th BW is divided into the 393d and 715th Bomb Squadrons, each operating eight aircraft. The 2nd to 16th aircraft have been completed or upgraded to the B-2A-10 Spirit standard incorporating many of the 'stealth' improvements resulting from the test programme. The 17th to 19th aircraft have been completed to the B-2A-20 Spirit standard that is also being retrofitted to a number of older aircraft, and the same applies to the B-2A-30 Spirit, which comprises the 20th

and 21st aircraft as well as a number of retrofitted machines.

THE B-2'S ARMAMENT

The B-2A is built around a side-by-side pair of weapons bays in its lower centrebody, and in front of each bay are small spoiler panels which drop down to produce the vortices that ensure clean weapons release. Rotary launchers in bath bomb bays can accommodate a theoretical load of 75,000 lb (34,020 kg) and more practical load of 40,000 lb (18,144 kg) but, under the US national war-fighting Single Integrated Operational Plan (SIOP), any nuclear load would be limited to 20,000 lb (9072 kg) in the form of 16 AGM-129 Advanced Cruise Missiles, or 16 B61 operational/strategic or B83 strategic free-fall nuclear bombs carried as eight weapons on each of the two rotary launchers, which can each carry eight 2000 lb (906 kg) Mk 84 bombs or eight Joint Direct Attack Munitions in the conventional role. When the rotary launchers are not installed, the weapons bays can each be fitted with two bomb rack assemblies for a maximum load of 80 500 lb (227 kg) bombs, or 36 750 lb (340 kg) M117 bombs, or 36 CBU-87, CBU-89, CBU-97 or CBU-98 cluster bombs, or 80 Mk 36 or Mk 62 sea mines. The B-2A is too valuable to be risked as a mere 'bomb truck', however, and the warplane's real strength, in the conventionally armed role, lies in its ability to deliver up to 16 'smart' weapons such as the JDAM over a wide area to an accuracy of 30 ft (9.1 m). The 2nd to 16th production aircraft, together with the five prototypes destined for the USAF, have been completed or upgraded to Block 10 standard, which qualifies them to carry 16 B83 free-fall nuclear bombs, 16 2000 lb (907 kg) Mk 84 conventional bombs, or 16 AGM-129A cruise missiles. From 1996 the aircraft were upgraded to Block 20 standard. This intermediate standard adds capability for up to 16 B61 free fall nuclear bombs or up to 36 CBU-87, CBU-89, CBU-97 and CBU-98 conventional cluster bombs, with a limited capability for conventional precision-guided munitions, retrofitted from 1997 to permit carriage of two new weapons. The first of these is the AGM-137 TSSAM (Tri-Service Stand-off Attack Missile), a 'stealthy' subsonic cruise missile with a range of 375 miles (605 km), and a payload of IR and acoustically guided submunitions: eight AGM-137 weapons can be carried in the form of four on each rotary launcher. The second new weapon is the GPS-aided JDAM (Joint Direct Attack Munition). Fitted to a Mk 82, Mk 84 or BLU-109 weapon, the JDAM package provides highly accurate targeting guidance through the aircraft's navigation system and an onboard INS. Eventually the JDAM will be an all-weather, autonomous weapon with a programmable fuse. The last two B-2A warplanes off the production line will be full Block 30 standard, which will be retrofitted to some early aircraft. These will be fully capable of carrying precision-guided munitions, in addition to 80 500 lb (227 kg) Mk 82 bombs. The B-2A-30 will also possess fully operational offensive and operational avionics, an improved synthetic-aperture radar, a Milstar satellite communications system, and an automated mission planning system.

■ABOVE: The B-2 can deliver conventional as well as nuclear weapons, including bombs fitted with the Global Positioning System, which are capable of extreme accuracy.

In mid-1990 it was revealed that the B-2A warplanes have a secondary maritime surveillance and attack role, carrying weapons such as the AGM-84 Harpoon anti-ship missile. The 'stealth' bomber's ability to fly higher while remaining undetected improves fuel economy (and thus range), and enlarges its 'sensor grazing area'.

As we enter the twenty-first century, the bomber's future is far from certain, with the cost of new aircraft development soaring. Missile systems continue to evolve and improve, and unmanned aerial vehicles are increasingly common. However, with the last B-52 currently scheduled to retire around 2040, it seems likely that manned bombers will be around for some time yet.

Index